Lost Ca

Rachel Lynch grew up in Cumbria and the lakes and fells
are never far away from her. London pulled her away to
teach History and marry an Army Officer, whom she followed
around the globe for thirteen years. A change of career after
children led to personal training and sports therapy, but writing
was always the overwhelming force driving the future. The
human capacity for compassion as well as its descent into the
brutal and murky world of crime are fundamental to her work.

Also by Rachel Lynch

Detective Kelly Porter

Dark Game
Deep Fear
Dead End
Bitter Edge
Bold Lies
Blood Rites
Little Doubt
Lost Cause

LOST CAUSE

RACHEL LYNCH

CANELOCRIME

First published in the the United Kingdom in 2020 by Canelo

This edition published in the United Kingdom in 2020 by Canelo

Canelo Digital Publishing Limited
31 Helen Road
Oxford OX2 0DF
United Kingdom

A CIP catalogue record for this book is available from the British Library.

Print ISBN 978 1 78863 816 6
Ebook ISBN 978 1 78863 758 9

Look for more great books at www.canelo.co

Printed and bound in Great Britain by Clays Ltd, Elcograf S.p.A.

Chapter 1

A waste removal lorry crawled along at a plodding pace. It was unhurried. Rubbish collection rounds in the Lake District were protracted affairs. Nonchalant sheep, devoted walkers, map-wielding tourists, overladen caravans and the odd eighty-tonne vehicle delivering building supplies to a cul-de-sac, all got in the way.

The men were chirpy – it was still a man's job – and swapped jokes as they waved at patiently waiting car drivers and caught up on gossip from the *Daily Mail*. It was particularly difficult work at this time of year, when winter gripped the National Park and covered her with a blanket of white for a couple of months, and slowed everything down. The men were used to it and wore thick gloves, woollen hats and undergarments. Their breath billowed in clouds in front of them every time they spoke. In years gone by, the vapour would have been made up of cigarette smoke from fags hanging from the side of every worker's mouth, but not in today's health-conscious society: it was banned on the job, and the smokers had to wait until they got back to the depot to stand in the designated smoking area, just outside of the back gate.

Someone beeped a horn.

One of the men, dragging two heavy purple waste wheelie bins, looked up at where the noise had come from and scowled.

'How long you gonna be, mate?' asked a man with his head stuck out of the driver's-side window of a new silver Mercedes.

'As long as it takes. Mate,' the worker replied, turning round and putting his back to the stranger. The others smirked and carried on with their tasks. There was no time to give everyone an explanation of their progress. Especially a fancy Merc driver who thought himself a cut above. They worked against a tight timeline, each worker an automaton, dragging, pushing, locking, changing, emptying and lining up. It was like watching a production line. It was a far cry from the days when burly, statuesque men carried tin bins on their shoulders and emptied them by hand. Now, the scrawniest teenager could get a job dragging a plastic tub to a machine that did all the work.

The Mercedes driver shook his head and banged his steering wheel. He was going to be late.

Despite snow piled up on the sides of the road, the sky was bright blue and every now and again a bin worker stopped to remove a hat, or his high-visibility orange jacket, throwing it into the cabin, where the driver was warm and dry.

He'd watched from the high vantage point of the lorry's cab as the exchange with the silver Merc took place, and slowed down a little to further frustrate the guy driving. It was a regular pastime to make the job more interesting. He manoeuvred the vehicle deftly round a parked car, taking care to avoid the dry-stone wall on the other side. They were halfway along a narrow road, which was inhabited by possibly five residents, as well as one at the very end, before it opened up and split into two. Why the Merc was using this route was baffling, unless he wasn't local and didn't know either the waste disposal days or the tightness of this route. Or maybe he was one of the residents, though the workers recognised most of the homeowners on their rounds, and they didn't think he was.

'Jesus!' One of the men tasked with lining the bins up bent over and vomit spewed out of his mouth.

'Jim! You all right, mate?' one of his colleagues asked.

The Merc driver rolled his eyes. A milk delivery van was behind him, and then two more vehicles behind that. They all came to a grinding halt. A sheep bleated from behind a stone wall in the distance.

'That fucking stinks.' Jim pointed to a wheelie bin.

His fellow worker was puzzled: they came across foul-smelling waste all day long, and he was at a loss to see what Jim could have found so repulsive. The lad was obviously ill.

Then he smelled it. He covered his mouth and backed away. He stepped from behind the lorry and beckoned to the driver in his cab to wait before he moved off. The driver gave him a thumbs up, which was acknowledged through the reflection in the wing mirror.

'Fucking hell.'

An older guy, seasoned by years of malodorous fumes, stepped forward and walked past Jim and his colleague. A car door slammed and the Merc owner joined them.

'What's the hold-up? Christ! That reeks!' He also covered his mouth and watched as the one worker seemingly immune to noxious, foetid fumes approached the offending wheelie bin and opened the lid. He peered in, and the others were satisfied to see that even he covered his mouth. He continued to look inside the receptacle and then slammed the lid and backed away. He walked towards them, the colour drained away from his face.

'What is it?' they all asked in unison.

'It's a fucking arm,' he said, as he bent over and retched on the side of the road, wasting this morning's fine cup of tea and thick bacon sandwich slathered in brown sauce. The spew steamed, and he could smell the vinegar of the sauce, and the smoke of the bacon.

Chapter 2

Kelly Porter ran along the Ullswater Road, flanked by grey dry-stone walls on one side and the beautiful lake on the other. From Pooley Bridge, where she lived in a small cottage overlooking the River Eamont, towards Aira Force, the traffic was minimal at this time of the year, especially this early in the morning, and she only saw the odd car speeding towards her. She was a confident runner and made her presence known on the road, though anyone who cared for her would have covered their eyes, trying not to wince at the risks she took. Especially with the thick piles of snow shovelled to the sides of the road. But a local was used to it.

She wore thick black Nike leggings, emblazoned with the logo in neon green along the length of her leg. A bright orange sweater made her stand out among the drab, brown stains on the road and the lifeless trees. A snood wrapped round her chin and her long auburn hair was tied tightly behind her head. She was not yet forty; her cheekbones were still high and her eyes bright. Her cheeks were flushed with new life inside her and she pounded the road at a steady rhythm. She could have been mistaken for a runner in her twenties, and vans beeped their appreciation as they passed her, making her smile and wave. Occasionally, if she wasn't in such a good mood, they'd get a middle finger.

To Kelly, running along the main road wasn't a risk. She knew it with her eyes closed and instinctively judged the terrain before her, around every bend and dip in the road. Her breath came in great pillows of vapour and her lungs worked hard to keep the rhythm. There was nothing wrong with keeping up strenuous exercise when pregnant, so her doctor had told her, and she hadn't noticed much of a difference. But then she was only eight weeks gone. Her abdomen didn't look any different and no one, except Johnny, knew that there was another human being growing inside her: a person who she had yet to decide if she wanted to meet or not.

Johnny was adamant: they should raise the child. But Kelly was concerned. Actually, she was terrified. For a start, Johnny had screwed up his first marriage and missed out on the rearing of his only child, Josie. They'd only rekindled their relationship very recently. What if it happened again? No, Johnny was a good man. It wouldn't happen again. He wasn't that soldier any more, and he wanted this child.

Then there was Rob Shawcross. Detective Constable Rob Shawcross, rising star of her department, new father, and showing the signs of what a little person could do to an adult person. It was pure torture. Rob came in to work at Eden House in Penrith, where Kelly ran the serious crime unit for the North Lakes, haggard, sleep-deprived, badly dressed and disoriented. It wasn't a pretty sight. Kelly watched as the man she'd known as the ultimate vision of fitness and strength crumbled in the wake of a swaddled invader. His once-muscular frame was hunched over, his eyes were haunted and wrinkled and he rushed around, forgetting and dropping things, when once he'd exuded the essence of control and poise.

His baby was adorable, there was no dispute about that, but he'd decided to keep his parents up for most of the night every night, and catch up on sleep during the day. The dark circles under Rob's eyes were the colour of the granite fells surrounding the lakes nearby, and they were growing darker by the day. Johnny was turning fifty this year and she would be forty: did they have the energy?

She pounded the tarmac of the road and wondered if she could give up her life for the sake of what was growing inside her. She took a keen interest in any debates on TV or radio that discussed abortion and the rights of the unborn foetus, and she lacked focus at work, reflecting instead on her own quandary. Johnny said it was her choice, but deep inside she knew that she couldn't just go ahead and take such a big step alone; she needed his support. She'd never faced a question of this magnitude before, in her personal life at least. She touched her stomach absent-mindedly.

The only change to her body was a touch of fatigue in the afternoon. It told her to take a nap around three o'clock and she struggled to stay awake. She avoided late briefings at Eden House and opted to stay at her desk, rearranging such activities for morning slots. It was easy to pull off; after all, she was the gaffer. Like today. It was a quiet Monday morning and she'd make her way to the office after she'd made some calls from home.

But, apart from the physical question of whether she could cope with a screaming baby, there was the moral dilemma that raged in her head. In her line of work, seeing the batshit-crazy stuff people do to one another... why the hell would anyone want to bring another life onto the planet?

–

The lake was like glass and, at this time of the morning, there were no boats, steamers, dinghies or even paddleboards to be seen. Snow burdened the evergreen foliage of the trees and mist settled in clumps around the inlets of the lake shore. January in the Lakes was about as peaceful as it got. The post-Christmas lull in the tourist trade came as a welcome break for those who lived there, though the small businesses would always welcome trade. Snow was at its deepest; up on the fells it was as thick as a double-decker bus, and treacherous, making it Johnny's busiest time of year. He was a mountain rescue volunteer and the winter months took him out on the fells in the most extreme conditions. Gullies, cliff edges and changes in terrain were all buried out of sight and caught the unprepared traveller unaware. It was also difficult getting the chopper to the more remote areas and poor visibility made it even worse.

But it was good that he was so busy. They both needed distraction. Long evenings in front of the fire had become the norm and, usually, before they could discuss their options – or her options – she'd be asleep. They had both agreed to share their dilemma with somebody else but neither could decide who. Out of Kelly's colleagues, the best person would probably be DS Umshaw. Kate had three daughters and there was nothing she didn't know about raising kids. However, should Kelly decide not to go ahead with the pregnancy, Kate may possibly judge her harshly and that would make work uncomfortable. One could never guess what people's views were. Johnny had thought about talking to Ted Wallis, the coroner, but he happened also to be Kelly's father and so was involved already. Kelly knew that Ted longed to be a grandparent, so he couldn't exactly be trusted to be impartial. It would also make work more difficult if every time she had to deal with the senior coroner she was reminded of her emotional state.

Johnny would go crazy should he find out she was running alone, in such icy conditions, and along a main road, but at least she'd left her headphones at home. After the murder of a female jogger in a park in Penrith last year, who was approached unawares with her music blaring, Kelly had promised him she wouldn't use them. But she missed them. Music when she ran was like a dramatic context in which to think. Without the pounding of loud beats, running lost its lustre and seemed more taxing. Maybe she'd use them but not tell him. The area had almost got over the paranoia since the murder, as the perpetrators had been caught, thanks to Kelly. Surely it was a one-off, and safe now?

She grew warm and took off her gloves, stuffing them into her pockets. The snood round her neck suddenly felt claustrophobic and her hat made her head itch. She had an overwhelming desire for ice cream. As a police officer, she never left home without her debit card. Johnny called it 'fighting order', a phrase he had used in his army days when he and his fellow soldiers would go out armed with only their cash card, a cigarette lighter and a condom.

The nearest ice cream shop was in Glenridding, which was probably another twenty minutes' running. Pooley Bridge was forty minutes behind her. She decided to carry on to the small village, which was a well-used base for climbing Helvellyn, as well having the best views over the lake and being a popular place to get married. Maybe she'd call Johnny for a lift when she got there. Rummaging around her pockets, trying to zip away her gloves, she realised that she had her wireless headphones with her after all, and she plugged them in. The sound was welcome and made her smile as she faced the last leg of her run. Johnny needn't know.

Her worries cleared and her thoughts turned to her work – or, more specifically, the disappearance of a woman from Ambleside close to the lovely village of Grasmere, last week after the bank holiday Monday for New Year, which had fallen on the weekend. Lisa Lau had been reported missing by her employer, a guest-house owner in Glenridding. All the preliminary enquiries had been carried out by uniforms over a huge area: the woman's background, last known movements, any sightings of her and witness statements. The Chinese embassy was informed by the Foreign Office, because the woman was a Chinese national with a work permit. There was a rumour that she had been pursuing some after-dark activities in areas known for soliciting, such as nearby Bowness, and even as far south as Barrow-in-Furness, but none of that had been substantiated. Sex work went on in every corner of the UK – of that there was no doubt – but proving it was an entirely different matter. There were also plenty of Chinese nationals with work permits in Cumbria, working in restaurants and hotels; Lisa wouldn't stand out for her looks.

The case had put her back in touch with DI Craig Lockwood, the head of serious crime for the South Lakes, which had been a happy reintroduction. She'd worked with him on several occasions and enjoyed the way his mind worked. They were similar. More than similar: they *got* each other. It had been a pleasing reunion, but they both agreed, after a sighting of the woman at Preston train station, that Miss Lau had more than likely taken off to better job opportunities, and the case was transferred to Lancashire Police. The witness had seemed credible, though CCTV was slow in coming through to confirm. Still, there was no evidence of any concerns for her welfare. The woman was, after all, twenty-three years of age; she could do whatever she liked, as long as she didn't outstay her work permit. Kelly had made a note of its expiry, which was this coming weekend, and moved on; but occasionally, like now, she found herself wondering if she and Craig had done everything.

The woman was probably safe and sound in a new job in Preston, she thought. The boss who'd reported her missing was frank about his low opinion of her work ethic: she wasn't missed. The parting wasn't unexpected.

–

By the time Kelly rounded the corner and entered the outskirts of the town, she'd begun to tremble slightly thanks to low blood sugar, and she knew the colour would have drained out of her. It was happening a lot lately and was another indicator of her changing body. She walked to her favourite ice cream parlour with her hands on her hips, trying to settle her breathing. It was inside the tourist information office and so opened earlier in the year than all the others. The quality of its product didn't hurt either. Early-morning walkers stopped there before heading out onto the hills.

Once inside, she ordered a double chocolate and mint cone and watched the woman serving her, checking she was getting her money's worth. Recently she'd begun to understand cravings and how they really felt. It wasn't just a desire, it was a mad obsession that would not abate until satiated. She reckoned it was how murderers felt.

Once outside, she bit into the ice cream and gulped it down. A couple walked past her and stared but Kelly kept chomping, dribbling stray drips down her running top, which she wiped with her hand and sucked too. When she reached the cone, she kept going and crunched the thing down in one. When she'd finished she stared at her hand as if surprised that there was none left. She turned round and went back inside to order another cone, this time with strawberries and caramel.

The woman smiled at her.

'Hungry?'

'Starving. I've run from Pooley Bridge, and I'm…' She didn't finish the sentence, deciding not to share her news with a complete stranger before her own family knew.

'Bloody hell, love, this one's on the house. Local?'

'Yes, I live there.'

'I know you from somewhere. You're that detective, aren't you? I've seen you on the telly. You keep us all safe, you do.'

The woman beamed as she handed Kelly her second feast. Kelly smiled and said thank you. She didn't know what else to say. It wasn't every day that a copper got congratulated by a member of the general public. She walked out of the shop and began devouring her second sweet treat. When she'd finished, she'd already walked a good ten minutes back in the direction of Pooley Bridge, and she felt her blood sugar equalise. She decided to run all the way back home after all.

She was recharged and rejuvenated. It set her mind thinking about another case that had been transferred to Lancashire Police in October of last year. She hadn't given it another thought until now. A woman called Dorinne Callaghan had been reported missing by a youth hostel in Ambleside. She was behind on her accommodation fees and they wanted the room emptied of her belongings. Lisa Lau had also resided at a youth hostel in Ambleside, a different one, but nonetheless only a stone's throw away. She'd been over the details of both cases a hundred times with Craig and nothing had come of it.

Her phone ringing jolted her back to the present. It seemed her run would be cut short after all. It was the office at Eden House in Penrith, telling her about a body in a wheelie bin. She called Johnny for a lift home.

Chapter 3

By the time Kelly was showered, changed and ready to attend the scene of the dead body, forensics had already made their way there and uniforms had sealed off the area. She'd had the obligatory chat with Johnny about personal safety. He was definitely more cautious these days. When they'd first met, it had been a frivolous and charged affair, kept secret initially because she'd lived with her sick mother at the time and hadn't known what the future might hold. He'd been something for her to enjoy without her mother or sister getting in the way. They'd realised pretty rapidly that there was no time at their ages to waste on swooning, tactics and testing. They'd fallen in love quickly, and she'd wanted to keep it the one thing that was hers and only hers. Everything else in her life seemed to be run and dictated by other people: her mother's illness and subsequent death, her sister's constant blame and judgement, and her job, and psychos hell-bent on causing harm in disgusting ways... It all was better put into little boxes to be dealt with when she was ready, or had the energy. Johnny was elevated above all of the other crap, and she didn't want that box tainting.

Now, though, with her mother gone and her sister Nikki staying out of the way, as well as her being three years into her new job, her life had found some kind of rhythm.

Then this.

'You need to be careful.' Johnny was talking to her and following her around as she packed her bags for what could be a very long day. She kissed him. It didn't matter what season it was; he wore the same: shorts, T-shirt and flip-flops. His hair was becoming heavily streaked with grey and she liked it. His skin always seemed to be tanned, like all the mountain rescue volunteers, who all went the colour of mahogany in summer. His blue eyes were serious, but she smiled and pretended to concentrate on what he was saying. She could smell him (another heightened sense thanks to pregnancy): Mont Blanc Legend. That was the smell that had enticed her to his bed in the first place.

'I am careful. I can't stop everyday life. I just went for a run. Then devoured two massive ice creams.'

'Two?'

'The place in Glenridding. She gave me the second on the house. I had mint and choc chip first and then strawberry caramel. Oh my God, they were divine. She recognised me. I'm famous.'

He shook his head and smiled. At almost fifty, his eyes were framed by laughter lines and so much time on the fells had carved deep lines along his forehead. His arms were muscular and he was built like a mountain man, even though he wasn't raised here. Kelly tried to change the subject; pregnancy was making her feel rampant and frankly it was the last thing she had time for.

'Is that officially a craving?' she asked.

'As far as I remember. It's been fifteen years. I was in Northern Ireland and Bosnia for the most of it.' He was referring to his ex-wife being pregnant with the now sixteen-year-old Josie.

'Do you fancy being a stay-at-home dad?'

'I've already told you I do. You can go back to work as soon as you want to and I'll be here, looking after him.'

'Or her,' Kelly said.

'Or her. Another teenaged daughter in the making? Christ, boys are simpler. No mood swings, make-up, hang-ups and needing to talk about endless emotions.'

She fake-punched him. 'I think you get off lightly with Josie. She's an amazing girl. When should we tell her?'

'Have you made your mind up then?' he asked.

Kelly saw tears at the corners of his blue eyes and she didn't know what to say. She went to him and he held her close. She felt guilty for poking fun at him and making him wait; she hadn't understood until now how much it meant to him. There really was no other end to this. She couldn't make love to this man, then ignore what came from that: they'd created a child. She had to let it sink in, though. He held her. She smelled his neck and exhaled. It was like an acceptance of what might come next.

'I need to go.'

'Don't get too close. And wear a mask.' He was talking about the body.

'I never take chances at a crime scene, you know that. Besides, I'm pregnant, not ill.'

'Of course you don't. Sorry. So is it a crime, then?' he asked.

Kelly had been told few details about the scene, just that a binman on shift had noticed a disgusting smell, opened the bin and found a human arm. It had since been confirmed by a forensic officer on site that the arm was attached to a female torso, which had an intact head, but there were no legs.

'There's no doubt that it's homicide, unless she chopped off her own legs and dragged herself into the bin by her hands.'

'Not likely, then. Grisly.'

'Exactly. It takes a lot to butcher a body. Not just a strong stomach, but determination and detachment. It's chilling. I can't help wondering if that Chinese woman actually left the Lake District or not.'

'It's not her then?'

'No, the woman in the bin is Caucasian.'

He kissed the top of her head and she put her forehead on his chest and smelled him again.

'I'm on duty today, and if yesterday was anything to go by, we'll be busy too.'

She reluctantly went downstairs and put on her coat, shouting goodbye to him as she left.

14

She drove to where the forensics team had erected a tent over the wheelie bin. It was the other end of Ullswater, and not far from where Lisa Lau had disappeared, but for now she had to push thoughts of the woman from her mind, and concentrate on this new case, where they had tangible evidence to work with. Disappearances were always so vague.

Her first job would be to study the scene and see what forensics had found, then she'd get back to the office and start a new case file while they waited for an identity. The team's recent work on Lisa Lau had already brought missing persons in Cumbria to their attention, but without a timeline based on the time of death, or facial recognition, Kelly wasn't in a position to make any guesses yet.

The drive to Patterdale, at the southern tip of Ullswater, was just as beautiful as her run had been earlier this morning. Patterdale was a gorgeous tiny village where people parked up to start their walks either up the Helvellyn range or opposite, up Place Fell. The fell always gave her slight shivers, since she'd investigated a case there a couple of years back. But it hadn't shaken her passion for the straightforward, if steep, hike. She'd been up there with Johnny on countless occasions. The view from the top was breathtaking and took in the whole of Ullswater snaking away to the north-east, like a great silver serpent.

She turned off at the White Lion pub and it only took her a minute to find the correct street. It was well sheltered and not obvious, meaning that whoever dumped the body parts probably knew that. Kelly had never driven down it before and she paid attention to the display of affluence. Uniforms had already established that none of the residents on the street had claimed to own the bin, a point that had yet to be verified: only a thorough forensic tracing of the bin would establish if one of them was lying. The remains as well as the bin in its entirety would be transported to the mortuary for examination.

The street was dark because the ancient trees provided so much shade, but through the canopy Kelly could still see the blue sky. Here, away from the main roads, the snow was shovelled up the sides of the road in high piles, turning grey from the few cars that used the route.

She drove to the police tape and parked, not needing to show her identity badge because she was well known across the force. The uniform nodded in greeting. 'Ma'am.'

Kelly went to where the white tent had been erected and paused to look around. She wasn't surprised that there were no CCTV cameras along the street, but that didn't mean that some of the wealthy owners of the large detached houses didn't have their own. There was a slim chance of witnesses too. The waste removal lorry had been allowed to progress with its duties after statements had been taken. Some of the drivers waiting behind the lorry at the time had also been interviewed and then allowed to get on with their day.

She looked up and down the street, deciding that to know how perfect a dump site this would be would take local knowledge and a few reconnaissance missions. Either that or the person who disposed of the body lived here. Uniforms were in the process of going door to door (not that there were many) and at this time of the morning most residents were home and able to talk. Each had displayed horror at what had been discovered on their doorstep and a few local journalists had turned up, hanging around addresses, hoping for soundbites. A body in a wheelie bin would be a huge story. Kelly had certainly never heard of anything like this before in the Lakes. There was the head found in Wast Water years ago and never identified, but this was proper tabloid stuff.

Kelly looked along the ground, all thoughts of cravings and nausea forgotten for the time being; she had her detective head on as she tried to imagine the sheer audacity required to drive a wheelie bin to this remote spot, park up and place it along with the others, knowing when collection day was. They'd need some kind of van. At least this was the theory emerging in Kelly's head. To drag it here through the streets would be too risky. She called Kate at Eden House and asked her to start a search for CCTV footage in the area, specifically looking for vans, at least as large as a Transit.

She pulled her coat around her against the wind that had whipped up and shivered with the lack of direct sun in this dark spot. Beyond the end of the road, it would be business as usual. The White Lion pub would open and serve bar meals, the public car park would fill up with walkers eager to get up the on fells early, and the corner shop would sell the best pasties in the Lakes. That thought caused Kelly to feel a flicker of need to bite into the buttery, crumbly pastry and the rich gravy within.

She pushed it to one side and entered the tent. Two forensic officers were processing the scene. They both greeted the senior investigating officer.

Straight away the smell assaulted her, and she retched. She couldn't help it. The officers, having been in this situation scores of times before, looked at her oddly.

'Sorry,' she said and reversed, desperately rooting in her pockets for the perfume she'd brought with her but forgotten to smear along her top lip under her nose. She'd purchased a small dispenser online, and she found that it delivered the perfect amount of liquid to smudge under her nose. That was better. Her eyes watered and she wiped them with the back of her hand, gloving up as she did so. One of the officers passed her a mask and she took it gratefully, tying it behind her hair. If nothing else it meant that they couldn't see her face when she next got a mouthful of foetid air.

She approached the bin and peered inside. She knew that entomological activity would be slow at this time of the year because of the temperature, but she also knew that the smell indicated that it had indeed started. The question was: had it begun before she was put into the bin? They'd ascertained the gender of the corpse and one of the officers was processing his photographs and checking them before submitting them to Kelly. She'd been wrapped in black bags, which had been gently opened by the officers. The binman who'd had the bad luck to take the first look inside had just seen her arm sticking out.

'It's impossible to know how long she's been in there.'

'Bin in there...'

The two officers laughed together and Kelly rolled her eyes. She was used to the gallows humour.

'A wheelie long time...'

Kelly waited for them to exhaust their armoury of wheelie bin jokes.

'She's in a pretty bad state but it looks to me like most of that was caused ante-mortem; she looks malnourished, beaten up and neglected.' The officer was serious again.

'Torture?' Kelly said. The two officers nodded. There were certain tell-tale signs associated with every death by unnatural causes, which presented quite obviously to someone with experience of them. They discussed them now.

'Her neck has bruising consistent with asphyxiation. Her fingers are raw, as if she's clawed something. Her skin is greasy and grimy, and the same can be said for her hair, which has been pulled out in clumps, perhaps by herself or perhaps someone else. We don't know what else is going on down there because pathology want the receptacle intact. But what we have been able to see is that her legs are missing.'

Kelly nodded and stared at the woman. She was reminded of prisoners in Belsen concentration camp. The images beamed around the world, as the British liberated the camp, were burned on the memories of everyone who had seen them in a history lesson. The woman had the same desperately futile stare too. It was like looking at somebody who'd suffered so much that death had actually come as a release. Kelly shivered again, although she wasn't cold.

'Thanks,' she said and went to find whoever was taking statements from the local residents. The uniform guarding the tape directed her to a driveway behind them.

'They're in there, ma'am.'

She walked around the trees lining each side of the gravel path. The house was charming and sat prettily surrounded by mature bushes and trees: a haven of tranquillity. It was a far cry from the apartment blocks of Penrith, and the terraced housing of every urban area in Britain. Life in the sticks was different; it was slow, courtly, gentle and private. But it could still be shattered.

The woman in the bin without her legs was naked and wore no jewellery and Kelly wondered how long it had taken for her to become invisible.

Chapter 4

He couldn't understand why they always tried to scream.

Didn't they know it was pointless? He studied her face. That was his favourite part: the vision of a face contorted thus. He'd yet to find the right term, he just knew that he craved it. Her expression suggested that she was in the middle of some kind of panic attack, like the ones he'd heard about on the radio: apparently schoolgirls have them. Women gossiped about anxiety and the fear it propagated. He eavesdropped on conversations in shops. Though he enjoyed the expression, it always surprised him. Her face had gone from concentration and sexual arousal to this look very quickly, and they hadn't been here long. He'd picked her up in the Scrag End pub, which wasn't a place to take a lady, but she didn't seem to mind.

And she wasn't a lady.

She'd been excited and turned on by the thought of stopping at the graveyard first. He'd taken her on a stone tomb. She'd looked at him in *that* way and told him that he could have whatever he wanted. For fifty pounds. The price suited him. It was fairly top-end for these parts, around Ambleside and the like, but she was very nice-looking, and they were to spend the night together after all. He liked them to offer rather than the other way round. It meant they were willing, and less likely to expect what he really wanted. His performance in the cemetery lowered her guard.

He continued to squeeze her throat. She looked quite beautiful, but that was the thing: they never stayed like that. They always got whiney, needy and bossy. This way he could remember her as she was when she did as she was told. This way, she would always do as she was told, and he wouldn't need to pay.

The woman's naked body went limp. That would do for now, he thought. He rubbed his hands, needing a break, and sat looking at her a while; her eyes goggled about in her eye sockets, and then she was still. His fingers burned. No matter how much he exercised them, there was always room for improving his stamina. She was laid on a peach-coloured silk throw that he'd placed lovingly on his bed. The room was decorated sparsely but it was warm, cosy and decent enough for a whore.

She didn't seem to be stirring, and he panicked: maybe he'd gone too far?

He got up and went to the bathroom to fill a cup with cold water and came back to find her chest going up and down. He drank the water himself and smiled: he hadn't done it wrong after all. He sat beside her and watched her face, which was peaceful now. He was naked also and he noticed that he was chilly. Had he forgotten to put on the heating? It was the middle of winter and the house was cold. They'd kept warm on this bed, but now he shivered. He'd managed to asphyxiate her three times now, which equalled his personal best. He looked at his watch: he'd been going for thirty-two minutes. Funny how he found it hard to ejaculate when he made regular love to a woman, but now, as she slumbered before him, only slightly labouring for breath, his arousal was almost complete. Now she was weak, he could guarantee that during the final climax, she would submit completely due to fatigue – or what he could only describe from examining her face as fear. She was also growing weak.

When he'd finished, he took his hand off her mouth and lifted her gently off the bed and carried her downstairs, through the kitchen, kicking a door open as he went. The staircase to the lower cellar was narrow, and he manoeuvred the woman over his shoulder in a fireman's lift. Air escaped from her throat and she groaned with each step. He reached the bottom and opened a further door, kneeling down in the dark. The cellar was warm, because he used a heater for them, and was only lit with a dim orange glow from a small bulb suspended from a hook. He already had the keys ready in his hand and, coming to an empty cage, he expertly deposited her to the floor and forced her inside, clicking the lock shut behind her. Inside was a dog mattress, a bottle of water and a blanket – nothing else. He watched for a while as she regained consciousness. He remained on all fours, fully naked still.

Her eyes flickered and settled on him, trying to focus, and she started to try to scream again, but no noise came out. He smiled.

'That's better,' he soothed. Her mouth opened and shut like some great grouper seeking smaller fish to consume. Her eyes were just as wide as the ugly sea creature too.

He'd seen the look in her eyes many times before: it was the type of look that children had when on a scary fairground ride. It was also the look of a man who he'd once seen fall off the platform at Grange-Over-Sands train station, moments before the train arrived and sliced him in two.

It was this look that he sought, and he smiled again. She was going to bring him a lot of pleasure. Still on all fours, he backed away slowly the way he'd come, never taking his eyes off her.

The woman looked around her, desperately trying to force her pupils to adjust to the lighting.

He anticipated her reaction and smiled. Images crept out of the darkness and, one by one, she recognised what they were. Frantically she shook the cage and beat it with her fists. She was a live one. But then she slumped back and closed her eyes, then formed herself into a ball underneath the blanket, and her limbs went flaccid once more. He cast his eye upon the other cages in the cellar, from where no noise emerged, but he wasn't worried about any sound because of the remoteness of his house. Even if there were passers-by who might get close enough, the women

22

who shared his home with him quickly lost both their ability and urgency to scream.

He stood up now, and took a key from a hook on the wall, locking the cellar door behind him. Turning, he went back up the stairs to find his clothes. Back in his bedroom, he gathered hers up first, putting them into a black plastic bag, throwing it into his wardrobe; then he gathered his own things off the floor, quickly getting dressed. He shivered and went to the cupboard on the landing, opening it and adjusting the heating dial. He spent a fortune on heating this time of year. That's what had led to the mistake: he'd left the body in a room with the heating up full. He'd drunk too many glasses of red wine and fallen asleep, forgetting that the thermostat had been put up. By the time he'd gone back in the room the next day, she'd already begun to decompose slightly. It was why he'd rushed to get rid of her and now it was all over the news: the body in the bin. He smiled to himself as he grabbed his coat and van keys. It was time to go to work.

Chapter 5

'That poor boy.'

It was a regular comment from Maureen Johnson when she went to the local grocery store to gossip at the post office counter. The woman behind the counter nodded. The boy in question, who was in fact a grown man of nineteen, had just left the shop and closed the door behind him, having bought a Snickers bar and a bottle of Coke.

'All those E-numbers,' Maureen added, as if she were a nutritional expert. She put most things down to the availability of junk food, from single mothers to the rise of measles. She shuffled her folded arms underneath her generous bosom. Her mouth was set in a downturn and she rolled her eyes often. Her grey hair was set in the same style that she'd had for forty years and her cheeks were rouged with the same Estée Lauder palette she'd used since she was a girl.

The village of Grasmere boasted a population of under 1,000 souls, and Maureen Johnson knew every one of them, or anyway thought she did. The hamlet nestled within a natural cradle of surrounding mountains, flanked by the quiet lake of the same name. Visitors to the peaceful town found themselves hastily corrected should they call it Grasmere Lake, for there was only one true lake in the National Park and that was Bassenthwaite Lake. All the others were Waters, Meres or reservoirs.

Grasmere, and its humble yet delightful neighbour, Rydal Water, were favourites of Wordsworth, and the epitome of Lakeland charm. Life rumbled there slowly, belying the gigantic commercial operation of churning millions of visitors through its tiny streets, edged with grey slate walls, season after season. The centre, apart from a Co-op, a garden centre, and enough pubs for a much larger town, boasted countless artisan shops, which all did well enough during the summer to see them through the bleak winter.

Situated to the north of the main drag, Marvin's newsagent's and post office was a shorter walk for Maureen. It sold all the staples, such as milk, eggs, local butter and cheese, as well as having space for tinned food, crisps and medicines. The small post office counter had been threatened with closure several times, but the local residents, rallied by Maureen, had fought it off. She'd mustered local residents together to post letters, tape up posters and lobby their local MP, and she'd got a name for herself. Today, she had an Amazon parcel to collect, a host of letters to send, and she also fancied a packet of biscuits to dip into her tea this afternoon, when she hosted the knitting circle, like she did every first Monday of the month. Last Monday had been the bank holiday and so the knitting circle hadn't gone ahead. It was still early and the small shop was busy with winter walkers stocking up on snacks and sending postcards.

The owner of Marvin's, of the same name, was now seventy-three, but he still manned the counter and ran a tight ship. He had employed a long list of workers over the years, from young paperboys to the women behind the post office counter who loved to gossip with Maureen. In times of hardship, Maureen herself had done stints stacking shelves and taking stock counts. Marvin Burns was a kind man with a big heart. He was a full five foot seven inches and his girth had grown to an impressive size in the past ten years. He always stroked his bald head nonchalantly when he listened to the ladies chattering. He wore beige slacks and a blue shirt, over which today he'd pulled a knitted tank top.

Marvin's wife Lorna was a city girl, from Liverpool, a hard-nosed woman twenty years his junior, not given to pleasantries. Maureen had to admit that if it wasn't for her ruthless business mind Marvin's would have folded by now; his wife had modernised their services and moved with the times, bringing in enough tourist trade for them to weather the economic storms. Lorna was shrewd, quick-witted and sharp-tongued, but she sniffed money out when others went bankrupt, and Marvin's had endured crisis after crisis, emerging victorious on the other side. It was a mainstay of the area, where most of the boarding lodges and holiday lets advertised package deals and walking holidays to the heart of the Lake District. From Grasmere, one could tackle the Lion & the Lamb, Loughrigg, and the western approach of Helvellyn, to name but a few. Lorna had even monopolised the innovative trade of ferrying tourists to and from walking start and end points: an idea she'd had way back when somebody had asked if she could call them a cab. Maureen had to hand it to her – the woman knew how to make money.

A cab in the Lake District was like a fell herd in Manchester: a little inappropriate. So Lorna had saved up and bought a minibus. Now her blossoming tourist business owned three, and laid claim to a steady stream of visitors wanting shuttling around like VIPs. It was a stroke of genius – and it led to tailor-made holidays. TripAdvisor had awarded them five stars for 2018. They'd also branched out into property and ran several guest houses in the area. Meanwhile, Marvin ran the shop and it suited him. Lorna was rarely to be seen, which suited Maureen and her hen pack. The regular gathering of local women in the shop who came to swap tittle-tattle was not to Lorna's taste at all. When she was around, she gave Maureen long disapproving stares from behind her immaculately made-up face. Maureen stood her ground, because she knew that a woman with an elderly adoring husband who takes herself off to Manchester to shop for clothes, and carries expensive handbags with labels Maureen knew from celebrities on TV, is up to one thing and one thing only: an affair.

'Poor boy,' she repeated. Marvin nodded.

'Odd, that 'un.' It was an average response from Marvin, who'd seen the lad move into the area with his even stranger mother and father four years ago. He was a clumsy lump and what might have been described in Marvin's day as the village idiot, or a pillock.

'Not his fault, though.'

They agreed. The mother was to blame; everyone knew it. Maureen kept Marvin talking as she watched the woman behind the counter sponge her stamps to letters. She didn't like licking stamps and she thought little of the new sticky ones, so she relied on the postal workers to attach them for her. She supposed that everything moved on eventually, but some things were better left as they were. She was sending her customary thank-you cards after the Christmas season, acknowledging parcels and gifts from various grandchildren and relatives across the globe. Maureen, from an Ambleside family (Grasmere's elder cousin, down the road), was the only one who'd stayed in the area. The rest had fled the nest, settling as near as Grange-Over-Sands and as far away as New Zealand. It was a yearly ritual, keeping in touch. One of those relatives was Alice Callaghan, who'd moved to Wigan for a man years ago.

'My poor niece, Alice. She's had the worst Christmas of her life, not knowing where Dorinne is.'

The woman behind the counter joined in with Marvin to bestow sympathy appropriate for such sombre circumstances.

'Good job they lost the second baby, I say.' Then she changed the subject and returned to their discussion of the poor boy and his family, the Flints, hoping to distract Maureen, who'd wallowed in the disappearance of her great-niece for months.

'What a thing to say!' Marvin exclaimed, but with his tongue in his cheek, because he agreed. So did Maureen, happy to have more gossip to distract her from her woes.

'That house is better off with only one of the little buggers. God save his soul. Should they have had more, only He knows what might have come to pass. At least with one, he can be watched. I saw the father falling about drunk the other night, coming home from the Goat and Ladder, tripping over, and mumbling to himself and all that,' Maureen said.

'I'd be pissed as a newt all the time if I was married to her,' Marvin said.

'Marvin Burns!' Maureen feigned horror but blushed and smiled. They were conspirators, assessing the locals from above, giving their expert opinions, satisfying folklore and hearsay. Though sadness marred her glee as she compared Patty Flint to the woman Marvin was married to. Which was worse? A raving lunatic or a scheming cheat?

'I'm easily offended, Maureen Johnson, so I am. I'm a sensitive chap.' Marvin chuckled.

'My arse,' Maureen retorted. She lowered her voice. 'I hear they, you know – the ma and the boy – they have it off.'

'Never! You don't say?' The woman behind the counter set her face in horror but leant in for more, opening her hatch.

'That's why he got let go early from school, back in Lancaster, and they moved here; he was fiddling with himself under the desks, unable to keep his hands busy. Sex-mad, they say, and all taught by her.'

Marvin stopped unpacking a box and shook his head.

'Maybe that's why his pa's always drunk as a skunk. Nowt so funny as folk around here.'

'It's the dark nights: enough to send anyone stir-crazy under these hills.'

Marvin rolled his eyes. 'They're probably inbred. 'Tis a lot of it about and Lancaster's not immune, I tell you. All the families around here have the same uncles, sisters and aunts, so they do, going all the way back when.'

'That include yours, Marvin?'

Maureen laughed along with the other woman.

'All right, have your fun. Mine as well.'

All three of them laughed.

'Aye, they took what they could get. Even in the grand old grounds of that ancient Lancaster castle!'

The doorbell rang as the door opened and an enthusiastic pair of walkers came in. They smiled broadly, satiated with

Lakes air, and Marvin greeted them. Maureen eyed the woman up and down, thinking that her city get-up was probably worth as much as Marvin's car. But it was folk like this who kept the businesses going. Behind them, Harry came in, laden with boxes and parcels on his trolley.

'Morning all,' Harry said jovially. His cheeks were ruddy from the fresh winter air and the exertion of his job. Marvin checked everything off the list Harry gave him and Harry accepted a free bottle of Coke from Maureen, who treated the place like her own. Marvin didn't mind; the driver had become a close friend and, between the three of them, they pretty much had the comings and goings of the local folk covered, even though Harry had only moved back to the area last year after working in Manchester for years. Harry could tell you instantly who lived where and what they ordered from Ann Summers (via Amazon) and they spent many a winter day like this one swapping tales that Maureen said would make a sailor blush.

Chapter 6

Ted Wallis, the senior coroner for the north-west of England and chief medical examiner, stared at his hands. They'd been shaking of late. It all started when he'd been discharged from hospital following him being brutally pushed to the ground during the riots in Penrith before Christmas.

He hadn't fully recovered. He was a physician, and he knew these things, though he might not care to admit them.

This would be his first autopsy of the year, but then it was only the ninth of January. What a way to greet a new week. He no longer dwelled on the fact that he and Kelly saw more of each other in the mortuary than anywhere else, even though they tried to catch up every week outside of such circumstances. It was still a novelty for them both after learning so late in Ted's life that a brief affair with Wendy Porter meant he was a father to Kelly as well as two daughters from his marriage. She'd rekindled the relationship with Wendy, though sadly too late due to Wendy's poor health. But getting to know Kelly as his daughter had been a source of joy for Ted. She'd been acting oddly lately, as if distracted, and he wondered if everything was all right between her and Johnny. He worried about them not making it – most relationships didn't these days. He'd miss the rugged mountain rescue man with his quick wit and caring nature; but more than that, his granddaughter in everything but name: Josie. She was intelligent, sharp, funny and kind. She made time for him and they went for walks together. She told him about her boyfriend, Callum. Now there was a relationship that showed signs of lasting the distance. He saw so many youngsters now with their lives revolving around instant gratification from social media posts, but Josie and Callum were a strong item. They laughed a lot together and Ted reckoned that's what the secret was. When Wendy had still been alive, and they were enjoying their final few months together, they'd laughed daily. Until the very end, when they'd realised what fools they'd been to miss out on so much. Finding out that Kelly was his biological daughter was one of the most wonderful moments of his life. He was no fool; he knew that his spoiling Josie was time that he should have had with Kelly.

He washed his hands thoroughly, not for the protection of the corpse, just out of habit. He liked to be clean when he worked. He hadn't seen the corpse yet but Kelly had told him over the phone that she was in a pretty bad way; but then, dead bodies usually were. He'd seen limbs in bags, heads in suitcases, children in carpets and body parts in socks, but he'd never examined a body inside a waste bin before. It was the purple one too, used for food, so it would stink anyway. Not that the aroma of a dead body offended him: if that had been the case then he'd have been in the wrong trade for forty years. It was more that it would present as quite a challenge to gather all of the available information satisfactorily, and it would take time to sort the waste from evidence of the crime. The bin had wheels, which was good, because wherever it had been dragged to and from would still be adhering on them in some form, perhaps mud, grass, carpet or wood, all of which might point to an area or areas of Cumbria where the bin had been. Doctor Edmond Locard's principle of exchange, that two bodies cannot ever come into contact without transference of matter, was every coroner's cornerstone truth.

'Hi, Dad,' Kelly said breezily as she entered his private office. She looked tired.

He dried his hands and went to her and gave her a large, warm hug and kissed her cheeks, which were freezing from the icy outside air. He was taller than his daughter by quite a bit and, despite being almost seventy, still erect in his posture. He leant over her.

'It's lovely to see you, but not quite so happy for it to be over an autopsy.'

'I get my kicks where I can,' she said.

'What do I need to know?' he asked, even though he'd been sent a report from the forensics team. It was always best to have it spelled out face to face. She brought him up to speed.

'So her legs aren't in there? Are you sure? They could be under her.'

'Yes, that's what the report said but we took the decision not to move her.'

'Good. Right, let's have a look, then.'

—

It was getting late. Kelly had spent most of the day creating a new case file for the body in the bin. There was a definite set of procedures that had to be followed for a homicide investigation, and it was well under way, but they were running out of daylight hours fast. The first forty-eight hours were crucial for any murder investigation and she was doing all she could to tick off and document everything in a newly opened report. She also kept a running checklist longhand in a notebook; she was just comfortable with it that way. She was the self-appointed senior investigating officer and her first job was nailing down a timeline working backwards from the moment the body was found to establish a time of death, of which Ted Wallis was a master. They were both old-school, and though computer software had its place, she preferred to use traditional detective work, and the mainstay of that was her notepad, affectionately known as the Murder Book. She kept it with her at all times, jotting down ideas and comments as they jumped out, like some macabre novelist sculpting plots.

They went next door to the mortuary lab and Kelly – just starting to warm up from the chilly outdoors – felt the cold air keenly. Of course, autopsies had to be performed under controlled conditions, and temperature was vital. It had to be kept low. It matched the bitter air outside and Kelly had kept her coat on for this very reason. She wore gloves and a woolly hat, and, this time, she'd remembered to spritz her finger with perfume and rub it under her nose. She spotted the bin and saw that the lid was closed. An assistant moved around, preparing the workspace for Ted. He nodded to her. Lab assistants were skilled in the dissection of human bodies and their knowledge, after years of helping the pathologist remove, weigh, section and log organs and bits of flesh, was sometimes almost as impressive as that of the surgeons themselves.

Ted trained his assistants superbly, and always spoke constantly into his mic about what he was doing and why. Anyone keen to learn the trade would do no better than to just listen to this master at work. She could tell straight away that the assistant was keen: it was the greeting, the enthusiasm and the preparedness that gave it away. Ted briefed them both on how the next few hours would play out. Kelly steeled herself. She'd eaten almost a full packet of ginger biscuits before coming in, in an attempt to keep any cravings at bay and to stabilise her stomach acid with the delicate spice.

'How are Johnny and Josie?'

'Good, thanks. Actually, Dad, I'll let you in on a little secret of ours.'

He looked at her and waited, tying his mask and checking his mic. 'Come on, then, I'm intrigued now.'

'We're going to move in together. At mine probably.'

'Kelly, that's wonderful news!' He beamed. Kelly thought she saw dampness at the corners of his eyes and smiled at him. Ted coughed and carried on arranging the tools of dismemberment, perhaps similarly to how the perpetrator of this crime had in his garage, or workshop, or shed?

Ted wore gloves to protect himself from unknown pathogens that might be still alive on a dead body, and he'd wear one made of chainmail later when he used the saw. His assistant wheeled the bin into position and Ted opened the top. No one said anything at first, until Ted began to speak into his mic. He detailed everything, beginning with what he saw. He clasped his hands together and made observations. He repeated what the forensic officer had said about the victim's neck and noted what Kelly had spotted: the staring eyes. He took tweezers and slowly and methodically went through the woman's hair. He picked something out and asked for a slide. He retrieved the item and placed it gently on the small piece of plastic presented to him by his assistant. Kelly listened.

'Looks synthetic. Bears no resemblance to hair roots of animals: more likely to be from a tight-weave carpet or even something plastic. There are more. They're white and she has no white hairs.' He flicked one with his thumb as it sat between his tweezers.

'It's robust.'

Kelly found a lab stool and sat on it: she felt a little sleepy, but remained alert, unable to put aside the nature of what she was witnessing. Her stomach rumbled and she apologised.

'If you go into my fridge, I've got some After Eights in there for emergencies,' Ted said, looking up at her. She did so and he stared after her, noting that he rarely saw her eat chocolate.

Distracted, distant, tired, sweet tooth, moving in together... He smiled to himself.

A camera clicked. Kelly could still hear Ted's dialogue from her position by the fridge. She found the dark green box and took five little black envelopes of sweetness from it, popping the first into her mouth, where it melted and satisfied her. She went back to her seat. Ted had delved deeper into the bin and brought out a fingernail that had come away easily. 'Malnutrition. Unless she had underlying thyroid or endocrine issues. The nail bed isn't thick, like you would expect with a fungal infection, so I think it's straightforward neglect.'

Kelly's phone buzzed and she noticed that she had a notification from DS Umshaw back at Eden House. Kate Umshaw was Kelly's number two and utterly dependable. She opened the email. It read simply: *Guv: see attached potential ID.* She clicked to open it and was faced with a photograph of a woman. She was called Dorinne Callaghan and had gone missing three months ago. Like many missing person cases, the trail for Dorinne had gone cold after a sighting outside of the county, in Lancaster, by a member of the public. It's always a tough decision to actively stop looking for somebody, but often it's about resources. When active crime is on the increase, such as burglaries, domestics and assaults, it's hard to justify spending hours on a Jane Doe who simply vanished. As the days and weeks tick by, with all leads exhausted, it's sometimes prudent to assume that person doesn't want to be found.

But. Kelly studied what Kate had sent and she couldn't tear her eyes away from the picture. It was a world away from the reality of what she knew was in the bin in front of her, but deep down in her gut, she knew she saw a resemblance.

'Ted,' she said, 'look at this.'

Ted stopped working and looked at Kelly's phone.

'Pretty convincing,' he said. In both their lines of work, they had become familiar with what makes a face memorable: it was in the bone structure, the jut (or lack of) of the chin, the hairline; but most of all, in the eyes. The eyes of the dead woman were hauntingly cold but, even after life had departed, they still cradled a sniff of the character of their owner. They were also a distinctive shade of hazel. Kelly enlarged one eye on her screen. Around the dark, cavernous pupil, there was a bright ring of amber honey, which flashed out like a sun flare. Then, beyond that, was a glimmer of grass green, finally tapering off, to the edge of the iris, as a pale gold.

Ted leant over the lip of the bin and shone a torch at the face of their victim. Kelly held her phone close to him to compare. He examined the right eye first and referred back to the enlarged photo several times, then he studied the left.

'No two irises are ever the same. While DNA ultimately sets their colour and structure, the furrows, rifts and random pits develop in the womb and are never the same, not even between left and right. It's called chaotic morphogenesis, if you're interested. Not even identical twins have matching irises because they're muscles, and babies flex their muscles inside the womb in a pattern that is 100 per cent unique to them.'

The assistant looked up, as if memorising what he was saying. 'It's her,' Ted stated.

Kelly went back to her seat to let him work. She replied to Kate, then read the file on Dorinne Callaghan. She was reminded of her run along the Ullswater Road, and how she'd mulled over the case of Lisa Lau. A knot sat in her stomach and threatened to make her feel nauseous.

A different team had worked on the case at the time, as it had been deemed a minor incident. Missing persons aren't passed to serious crime unless it is a minor who's gone missing, or a proven crime. Neither was the case for Dorinne Callaghan, just as neither was the case for Lisa Lau. Now, though, a hunch settled under her ribs. There'd been plenty of women gone missing in the Lake District over the last ten years: thousands of them; but the vast majority of them were either found or had moved to another county. The few remaining were eventually forgotten.

Especially the ones who led 'at-risk' lifestyles. Kelly read that it had been discovered that Dorinne took payment for sexual services. Many witness statements placed her in known areas for soliciting, as well as giving direct references to being picked up in pubs and clubs. She was known to move regularly, usually when she found herself in trouble for soliciting and other petty crimes such as shoplifting. As such, they had her fingerprints and DNA on file. Ted would perform the tests and a lab could confirm if this was Dorinne conclusively. Kelly read that the last recorded sighting of Dorinne, inside the National Park, was at a club in Ambleside, but after that the case had dried up. She had been living in digs at a hostel at the time, but was behind with rent and considered a nuisance.

It rang alarm bells for Kelly, because people thought the same about Lisa Lau: she was disliked by her employer for being unreliable and stroppy, and some witnesses said that she worked in the sex trade. It was so difficult to prove, though, because it wasn't as if she filled out a tax return for it every year, or had a business account where clients paid by cheque.

Dorinne had been twenty-five years old and had been reported missing by the hostel in Ambleside last October. They had wanted to rent the room, but it was still full of Dorinne's stuff. But then the sighting in Lancaster had changed everything.

She focused on what Ted was saying and came back to the present, shivering slightly. He asked for assistance in getting the body out of the wheelie bin but he called for another lab technician, not expecting Kelly to help out. She didn't offer either.

It had to be a delicate business, because they needed to be careful to catch whatever fell out alongside what was left of Dorinne. Three extra technicians came to help and they carefully tipped the bin on its side, picked it up and placed the contents on the slab. The torso settled awkwardly alongside a foul liquid, which pooled in a little moat specially designed for the job. Another thud accompanied a second bag, which was still sealed. Ted approached and first examined Dorinne's torso. He spoke rhythmically and detailed the poor quality of her skin. It was one of the most detailed autopsies Kelly had ever observed. Quite quickly after death, she learned, cells in tissues begin to break down, releasing hydrolytic enzymes, loosening the top layer of skin in a process of what those in the know called slippage. It's one of the first steps in the long journey to Mother Nature cleaning up, which ends with a mere pile of bones. Severe blood pooling indicated that Dorinne had already gone through algor and rigor mortis, and she'd begun to bloat with gases excreted from the gut as her body consumed itself.

'Her lower abdomen is distinctly green, consistent with a short post-mortem interval of a couple of days. The bin was presumably closed and she was wrapped in plastic bags, and it's my estimate that this was done quickly after expiry, but the level of putrefaction also indicates that she was then left for a couple of days, before discovery. Insect activity already present inside the receptacle no doubt encouraged bacteriological activity inside the gut.'

Kelly knew that after death, not everything inside the body died too, such as the billions of bacteria alive in the gut; and they proceed to have the feast of their lives. It looked like whoever dumped Dorinne had to think about it for a while and that wasn't tidy. It was remiss. Or indicative of a loss of courage.

'Testing for putrescine and cadaverine in the blood, though I can smell it already. There's my first maggot,' Ted said.

Kelly looked up from reading and watched as he placed a couple of them inside a tube and screwed on the lid.

'Not many yet, which is consistent with my theory that she was left for a short while before being wrapped, then they did their work inside the bin.'

Kelly also knew that one single blowfly could lay three hundred eggs, which would hatch within a day, and the resulting maggots would feed for a week before becoming new blowfly and the process would repeat.

'No live flies. Just maggots – here's another one,' he said, pulling one from the nose.

'Dismemberment – likely defensive to dispose of rather than offensive to cause death – consistent with crude surgical knowledge. The legs were removed at the hip joint and they've been hacked a few times, indicating poor anatomical training. The femurs were removed by pulling and tearing, after a sharp knife or saw was used to get through the mass of muscle structure surrounding the pubic bone, ilium and femurs. Femoral artery is sliced through but blood still present in mass host suggestive of post-mortem injury.' He looked at Kelly. 'She was dismembered for business, not pleasure.'

'Small mercies,' she said.

He examined the other hip joint. 'Swabbing vagina for DNA, though it's severely degraded, you never know, we might get lucky,' he said. He put his swab into a screw-top jar and took a couple more from different angles. It is a sorry fact that abductors and torturers are usually motivated by sexual thrill; if Dorinne had been recently sexually active, then they might find some foreign DNA to work with.

He then focused on her head. He opened her mouth. 'Either she had terrible oral hygiene or several of her teeth have recently been cracked. We should get the X-rays back this afternoon, as I'm guessing that if this is recent trauma, her jaw might be broken too.'

'She has a pretty standard set of gnashers in her photographs,' Kelly said, looking at the image of Dorinne Callaghan on her phone again.

Satisfied with the search for clues as to her time of death, Ted got on with his examination of her terrible wounds that seemed to have been inflicted ante-mortem. More nails came away from her fingers and he pointed to where photographs should be taken of her neck and eyes. The sclera of the eyes were cloudy around the edges because they too were being eaten by microorganisms; however, it was the burst blood vessels around those beautiful irises that caught his attention.

'Bruises also visible consistent with manual strangulation.'

Kelly looked up again. 'No ligature?' she asked.

'No, the bruises are too wide and irregular. Either it was a large inflated inner tube or a hand. Or pair of hands. There's a distinct thumbprint by her clavicle — look, it matches mine,' he said, placing his thumb close to the wound. Kelly agreed. 'Wait, that's a unique lesion there,' he added.

'What?' Kelly asked, moving closer.

'Look, if I put my hands round her neck like this, that pressure point matches perfectly with where a ring on my finger would be, and it's a specific size for such a developed bruise. There are other smaller ones close by as if he changed the position of his hands.'

'The killer wears a ring?'

'Looks like it,' Ted confirmed. 'And they also strangle more than once.' He turned to her hands.

'Deep cuts and severe grazing of the fingers. Some are healed and others fresh. I'd say she tried to escape from something, by climbing over a rough surface like a brick wall or floor.' He bent over further and took his tweezers again, removing a tiny piece of metal from the end of one of Dorinne's thumbs.

'It's twisted over, like barbed wire but without the barbs.' He looked up at Kelly. 'Cage?'

'Oh Christ.' She shook her head and made a note. Ted would send her a full report and, no doubt, they'd mull it over a pint at some point, away from anyone else in their family, who wouldn't understand why they chose their respective careers.

As Ted worked on Dorinne's torso, reaching for his saw to break through her sternum so he could begin work on her major organs, a technician opened the other black bag, gathering samples of the tape used to seal it and swabbing the whole surface, looking also for prints.

Inside were two legs, bent over and broken to lessen their mass. It was a shocking sight and Kelly winced.

'Leave them,' Ted said to the assistant. 'Help me get these ribs off.'

Chapter 7

After two and a half hours, Ted was ready to take a break and allow his assistants to finish up. Kelly noticed that he'd delegated quite a lot during today's operation and she was glad. Ted turned seventy this year. He wasn't old, or slow, or lacking vitality, but he deserved to take his foot off the pedal. It was somebody else's turn. He needed to enjoy his retirement – if he ever stopped work at all. Secretly, she had been planning with Amber and June for months a birthday party for him at the Peaks Bay Hotel on Ullswater. Ted had taken Wendy there. The ashes of John Porter, Kelly's nominal father, were also scattered there, underneath a rhododendron bush that bloomed more than the others around it, from springtime all the way to late summer.

She and Ted arranged to meet in the staff canteen upstairs and she left him to clean himself up. Kelly relished the warmth of the corridor outside and thanked the NHS for their faithful old radiators that never stopped working, and which they all hated in the summer. She made a call to Johnny to check in and found he was on his way up Stybarrow Dodd, in failing light, to rescue a party of five schoolchildren with their teacher who'd got lost. Kelly looked out of the window and stared at the darkening sky, and mused at how easy it was for a group of walkers to get lost in this weather: it changed so quickly out there. The teacher had admitted to forgetting to bring a map.

The stories from mountain rescue never failed to raise an eyebrow. She knew that Johnny would have them safe in no time at all.

'I promised Josie I'd take her to the climbing wall tonight.'

'That's great.'

And it was. Josie had witnessed a horrific climbing accident last year and was still receiving therapy. To be willing to even visit the climbing wall was considerable progress. They hung up, having agreed that it was probably pointless making arrangements to see each other that evening; she no doubt faced a long arduous day, and he should concentrate on Josie.

She took a tray from the pile and perused the cake display. She ordered tea.

She turned to see Ted coming into the canteen. He looked so different away from the mortuary slab. He looked like a visitor, perhaps dropping in to see a poorly friend and having a welcome pot of tea to refresh afterwards. He reached into his pocket, ready to show his card to the staff so he'd collect a discount. Ted was a frugal chap with the little things in life, but hugely generous with his family. He joined her at the counter.

'Johnny is taking Josie to the climbing wall tonight,' she told him.

'Well, that's incredible news! What a brave thing to do. I knew she'd give it a go again; she's made of strong stuff.'

'I wonder who she gets that from,' Kelly said.

'Indeed,' Ted agreed. He chatted away as he pointed out a potted shrimp salad. The little glass jar, full of pink mushy stuff, reminded Kelly of organs in formaldehyde in a museum. She supposed that all surgeons must have this gift that lets them switch off to the visions of flesh they face during their everyday work. He told her of his plans to decorate his kitchen. He lived in a lovely stone cottage in Keswick, and he had plans to renovate. He'd recently seen a picture in a magazine of an open-plan space and he thought it would accommodate the family better.

'I'm waiting for building permission.'

'Crikey, Dad, that was quick. You don't hang around, do you?' The cottage was lovely, but he had a point; when they all assembled there, it was a squeeze. The house had bags of charm with three rooms downstairs and three bedrooms upstairs, as well as a converted loft. The view out of the back window was up onto Grisedale Pike and Grasmoor. The front was close to the main road, but there was so little traffic that it didn't bother him.

He put the briefcase that he carried everywhere down on a nearby seat and rifled around, pulling out architect's plans, showing her. His excitement was infectious and she knew this was the right time to tell him her own news. The CAD drawings were in colour and she was impressed with their scale: it looked beautiful – open and fresh. He put the drawings back into his bag as they neared the cash desk, but carried on talking about it. A member of staff was ready to serve them and Kelly ordered three slices of a variety of cakes. Ted ordered the shrimp and a side of hot toast.

'They're moving the stairs?' she asked as she stared at the sugar-laden treats with enthusiasm. He nodded. She could tell that he was excited and she felt it too. 'Can I help with the accessorising when it's done? That's my favourite bit.'

'Of course! I think I need to start over again. What colour scheme?' he asked.

'Whatever you want to live with. I like greys and greens. You should have a look at all the home magazines, they give you incredible ideas and examples.'

'I've been buying them. I'm subscribed to three of them that come every month. I've been stockpiling them. I love the layout of your place, and I want the family over more.'

'On that note, there's something I want to tell you. Let's sit down.'

He paid. Kelly had tried to argue with him in the past about paying her own way but she'd never won and had given up.

They took their trays to the table where Ted had left his briefcase and set down their plates, drinks and cutlery.

'Should I be worried?' he asked.

Music played gently in the background. It was the hospital radio channel, and it was quite good.

'Something's eating away at you, isn't it? Is it a case?' he asked. 'Is it the autopsy today?'

'No. It's something about me. Well, it affects more than me.' She tucked into her first cake and Ted stared at her as she licked her fingers.

She looked up at him and he stopped staring as he sipped his cup of tea and started slathering his toast with piles of shrimp that looked like tiny brains. He had a gentle face. When they'd initially met over Kelly's very first case for Cumbria Constabulary, she'd mistrusted him, seeing him as part of the same ageing white male institutional bullshit she'd come to expect from the force. However, after getting to know him, and seeing him work, she'd grown very fond of him.

Then came the bombshell. Her mother's affair, over forty years ago, with a dashingly handsome pathologist, resulting in a pregnancy she passed off as being with her husband: John Porter. The man Kelly had thought was her father for most of her life. Ted put his cup down and reached out to hold her hand. She'd seen his hands contribute to cracking so many of her cases; they were strong, lean and warm. His nails were trimmed and scrupulously clean. She looked at his large, open face and his white hair framing it.

'I'm pregnant.'

He said nothing. She took a slice of lemon cake with her free hand and stuffed it into her mouth, relishing the sweet sharpness and the creamy butter. She closed her eyes.

'Nine months of eating like this and I'll barely roll up Cat Bells.'

He held on to her hand and the corners of his eyes went glassy.

'How long?' he asked. His voice had broken and she squeezed his hand, then released it so that she could wipe her mouth.

'About eight weeks.'

'Early days. It's marvellous, I'm thrilled for you both. I wondered why you were telling me that you were moving in together. I couldn't have wished for a more wonderful reason.'

She stopped eating and took a gulp of tea. 'I'm scared.'

It was a small, quiet thing to say, and she couldn't remember the last time she'd felt more exposed.

'If there's one thing that old age teaches you, it's to not be scared any more. Time is so short. I spent my life worrying about the girls, about Mary, about my job, the bills… anything. Now, I take joy wherever I can get it, because life isn't for ever. I was too scared to leave Mary and tell your mother how I truly feel about her, and I missed so much of your life. Don't be scared. You'll both do an excellent job.'

'I knew you'd calm me down.' She smiled broadly.

'You know, I did my share of changing nappies in the middle of the night and pushing the pram around to get the girls to sleep. It's not the end of the world, it's just a new chapter. Your life won't end, it will just change. I like Johnny. He's a good man. And a sister or brother for Josie!'

'And another grandchild for you. Johnny's a bit nervous too. He's scared that because he screwed up when Josie was little, he'll do it again. But he still wants to give it a go.'

'Really? But he's not in the army now, and you're not his wife. You have a life here, together, you can make it work.'

'What about my job?'

'What about it? You'll have maternity leave then flexible hours and there are things called nurseries, you know. Besides, has it crossed your mind that Johnny comes and goes as he pleases? I would have loved to have been a stay-at-home dad.'

'That's all he ever talks about. I don't think I'll have any choice in going back to work, but that's not really what I meant. I mean the nature of my job: bringing a child into this…'

'There's no certainty in anything, and you have me, and Amber and June. We'll all help. I could retire and look after the baby now and again. Seventy is too old to be rushing around examining bodies when I could be enjoying my family. I've been thinking about it for some time.'

She looked at him. 'I can't imagine you not working.'

'Well, babies are hard work.'

'Don't say that, you'll put me off!'

'You know, time stops for no man – or woman – and I often find myself thinking what life would have been like without children. I always come up with the same answer: dull and two-dimensional. Children bring an element of unpredictability that gives our lives richness. Maybe you should order another slice of cake,' he said. 'You're going to need it.'

Chapter 8

Kevin Flint walked above the treeline, taking in the icy air in huge gulps. His exertions made his body strong and he smiled to himself, not knowing why, looking out for his footing in his great heavy boots. There was no one about as he trod over ferns and rocks, hidden under snow. He knew the paths so well that he didn't even check what was hiding underneath the thick fluffy blanket, untouched by any other human since falling from the sky.

His regular walks took him to the very edges of the National Park and, over the past four years since moving here – when he'd begun walking and cycling seriously, as a pastime, more to get him out of the house than for enjoyment – he'd learned the area as well as anyone could. He'd found that, if he stayed trapped in the home that had become his prison, he'd become enraged and in need of inflicting harm on somebody. Anybody would do, just to rid himself of the overwhelming desire to lash out and hurt another living thing. Usually he felt like harming his mother. But he never hurt her; he couldn't bring himself to, and so he hurt animals, or boys at school.

He didn't like it.

It made him feel like a coward.

The disgust was something that he wished to rid himself of, and he knew that the only way to do that was to come out here and walk it off. Now, he spent most of his days wandering around, finding new routes, exploring new hidden paths and being free from the toxic threat of people. He didn't much like people. They were all like his mother and father:

47

always shouting, conflicting, making noise, snarling, jibing and uncaring.

Out here, no one gave him grief. He saw the odd deer or squirrel, who stopped to sniff, and work out who'd entered their territory and then, once happy, would scoot off and get on with their business. There was no violence, no rage, and no hollering. Just silence.

He liked hush. He found words jarring. They harassed his peace of mind and shattered his inner stillness. Hush calmed him. He could sit for hours watching a lake or tracking a lone bird, sip from a mute stream, or watch a leaf falling from a grand tree. All done quietly. At this time of the day, in winter, the park was indulgently quiet, and it was his favourite time to get out.

The minute he got home, all that was gone. Sometimes he made it to his room without his mother noticing that he'd returned. Those days were good days. He only went home to sleep, or, occasionally, eat; but most of his food was wild and foraged. He trapped game, caught fish, gathered herbs, shoots and berries, and ate them in nature's restaurant, surrounded by the grandest designs seen anywhere in the swankiest eateries: rock, lake and sky. He'd learned to make fire years ago and cooked on home-made pots and pans, formed from odds and sods found in his pa's shed, no longer used by the man who spent all his waking time drunk. No wonder. She was a tyrant to both of them. Kevin now carried everything he needed in a backpack.

His belly was full. He made his way across the scar underneath Gowbarrow Fell, overlooking Ullswater. He couldn't see the road below, hidden by the trees surrounding Aira Force, only sky and lake. Not a vehicle disturbed the surface of the serpentine lake. It was about as perfect as one could wish for. Through the darkening sky, he couldn't quite see Glenridding, which sat quietly to the east, but he could just about make out the majestic peaks of the Helvellyn range to the south-east. Kevin could name every one of them, and he was mesmerised by the pure white snow sitting on top like icing dripping down a cake. Only a lone figure running along the shore of Ullswater caught his attention. He couldn't make out whether it was a man or a woman, but it didn't matter: whoever it was had found a way to get outdoors and be part of the beauty of nature. He appreciated that and felt connected to the stranger.

The colours of winter were extraordinary. The flat light created a new visionary canvas upon which to set one's eyes, and he stood staring at the panorama in front of and below him.

But today, folk jumped into his head uninvited.

They thought he was stupid.

They felt sorry for him.

But they could think what they wanted to. The gossipmongers in the village made up their stories regardless of any roots in truth. What was real and not didn't matter, only the story. He kept himself to himself and did his chores, aware that a regular job might not be a possibility for him due to his unique limitations. But still they laughed behind his back, as if it were his fault.

He couldn't read or write when he left school but he'd taught himself by listening to tutorials online, in the privacy of his room, hour after endless hour; he'd progressed to reading short stories, then full books. He'd joined the local library and hadn't told his mother. It was a cheap way to enjoy the freedom he couldn't buy from a working wage. He'd tried labouring and building work but it was too noisy. He'd snapped, lashing out at another young apprentice.

That was the end of another job.

He'd tried waiting in the restaurant of a hotel in Glenridding, but he couldn't remember how to work the till, and customers laughed at him when his massive fingers pressed too many buttons at once. He'd tried being a deckhand for the Ullswater steamers but people asked him long questions and made him feel like he wanted to jump over the side and swim away. He shoved a passenger roughly when she demanded he seat her under cover from the rain, despite there being no seating room left.

That didn't last long either. They said he didn't know his own strength, and that his size intimidated passengers.

–

The fells and lakes brought him solace, and by the time he descended and returned to his bicycle, left chained to a tree at Aira Force upper car park, the light was already beginning to fade and he knew he'd have to be careful on his way home. This time of year, the day ended by three o'clock on dull days. Grasmere was a long cycle ride away and he'd been picked up by the police countless times for not having any lights on. They knew him, though, and always gave him a lift, warning him to be more careful in future. He promised he would be and accepted the lifts gratefully.

Coppers weren't noisy.

Chapter 9

'You know it's a knocking shop?' Maureen dropped it into the conversation casually. She didn't look up from her knitting.

'Maureen!' another woman exclaimed.

'It's true, I've seen perverts going in and out of there.' Maureen's lips were terse: she couldn't help herself. The poignancy of the topic wasn't lost on the other women; there was gossip that Maureen's missing great-niece, Dorinne, had worked in the sex industry, but it was something they never discussed.

'You haven't!'

'So I have. I swear on my mother's life.' Now she looked up.

'Maureen, you are the biggest gossip when you're bored.' Another member of the knitting circle stated fact.

'We're not called "stitch and bitch" for nothing,' Maureen quipped. The statement was edged with disgust and they fell silent.

It was indisputable that Maureen loved to generate scandal. Now and again she was proved right, like the time when Kevin Flint had been caught masturbating in the churchyard. The experience had traumatised the local woman who saw him, to the extent that she spent a few nights in the Penrith and Lakes hospital, where she received treatment for shock. The lad was strange; everyone agreed. Why anyone would go to a place of worship and do that was shocking and bordering on the deranged.

It had been at St Oswald's, a church dating back to the thirteenth century. William and Dorothy Wordsworth were buried there. It was a tiny structure but still operating, under the diocese of Carlisle. Its Gothic style and medieval roots gave it a sinister flavour after dark, but during daylight hours it was a pretty tourist attraction. Christmas was always a highlight of the calendar and Maureen attended the carol services, checking out the local turnout and surveying the state of people's marriages. Talk about the incident involving Kevin had rumbled on for weeks after and attendance at the church had taken an upturn.

However, afterwards, Maureen had regretted making a meal out of the whole affair, because Kevin had walked around with bruises for a good while. Inflicted by his mother, or so everyone surmised. Maureen had reached out to the lad, asking him if he was all right and if she could do something to help his dad. Apart from buy him a bottle of brandy, that was. Kevin had ignored her and Maureen had taken renewed umbrage, seeing it as reason to criticise the family even further.

She relived the whole episode now.

'It wouldn't surprise me if Kevin Flint used the place.'

'Maureen! He's only a boy,' one of the women said.

'No he's not, he's a man. He's nineteen! I've seen the way he looks at the young backpackers coming and going, up and down the fells with their tight shorts and big smiles.'

The table fell silent. It was a serious accusation and not one many were willing to follow through. Also, none of the women were happy to venture into the murky details of how Dorinne had disappeared. Maureen was unpredictable and was clearly in a bad mood today.

'We don't hear about that missing Chinese woman no more, or my Dorinne,' Maureen said.

'She took herself off to the bright lights,' somebody else suggested gently.

'Preston? Do me a favour.' They'd all read about the police investigation in the local paper: it was perfect discussion material for the knitting circle.

'Are you saying that Kevin Flint had something to do with her going missing?' the same woman asked.

'It's not for me to point the finger. It's not right going round accusing people. But he hangs around those graveyards and he's got nothing to do. The devil makes work…'

'Oh for goodness' sake, Maureen! Stop with your tittle-tattle. The poor boy has enough on his plate with his pathetic excuse for a father and a monster for a mother. In days gone by, she'd have been dragged away to the infirmary and locked up.' The woman defended the young man and showed her impatience with Maureen, who looked horrified.

'Or burned as a witch.' Another wasn't so kind, but it dissolved the tension.

'No one knows what he's endured, leave the lad alone,' another chipped in.

With that, the subject was closed, and they moved on to matters of afternoon tea. A certain leeway had been afforded Maureen since the disappearance of her great-niece, but enough was enough. The members discussed their reasons for settling in Grasmere, and they got on with their knitting. However, the subject of a suggested brothel in the sleepy village never quite left the conversation. Next door, Ambleside was one of Cumbria's oldest villages and had turned into a great tourist hub, full of gastropubs and restaurants, complete with walking shops, as well as trinket and gift offerings. The allure for foreign workers was massive, and keeping a check on them was a huge task, one entrusted to the Home Office but woefully undertaken. There in the sticks, things went unnoticed and unchallenged. As a result, the black market thrived in the Lakes, from booze and cigarettes to OxyContin and sex.

–

Ambleside was Grasmere's older sibling, and boasted the same slate and stone walls, drawing in thousands just to pose next to the Bridge House. Traffic and noise were more noticeable, and a young scene had developed, with foreign workers and travellers demanding nightclubs and trendy watering holes. Grasmere, by comparison, had stayed quaint. But gossip that there was a brothel there in full working order had raised eyebrows more than once, and when the police came to ask questions about the missing Chinese woman, several of Grasmere's residents had flagged it up. No one really knew the exact address, but people were sure it existed. Maureen was convinced that Kevin Flint was a regular.

Maureen had been the one to call the police and lend her theory as well as giving them an address. They'd come and asked questions and even investigated the possibility of the running of a brothel in the town. They hadn't seemed that interested and it infuriated Maureen. No one seemed to care. Dorinne's involvement in sex work – and no one in her family denied it – had made her vulnerable and the police less inclined to investigate properly. Or that was what she suspected. Of course, the cops had got off scot-free because of the supposed sighting of Dorinne in Lancaster and the Chinese girl in Preston. But Maureen wasn't buying it. What if they had never left the Lakes, despite what the police would happily have them believe? She couldn't let it go.

The proposition had since gone down in urban myth and the police had found nothing (maybe they never looked), stalling the investigation until they all presumed it was shelved, but Maureen tried to keep it alive. Many cars containing one male driver, alone, passed through on the route to Ambleside, and Marvin agreed with her that these men must be getting their kicks somewhere. Maureen had even once propositioned Marvin to take a drive with her, to watch the debauchery unfold in the central square in Ambleside, but they'd chosen the worst night of the year to go and observe the underbelly of Cumbria's culture: Halloween. They hadn't even realised the date, with trick or treating and dressing up decades behind them both. On that evening, anything goes and the police weren't interested. Characters from books, films, stage and fantasy graced the streets, and Maureen and Marvin found themselves immersed in a confusion of ages. They'd given up and gone home, exhausted.

—

'Poor lad,' someone said.

Maureen got up to answer the phone. She still used her landline but only a few relatives, and cold callers, used it. She looked at the little window underneath the receiver and recognised the number. It wasn't a cold caller; it was her niece, Alice, calling from Wigan. She picked it up and the women around her table stopped what they were doing and looked at her, just as the receiver fell out of her hand and Maureen's knees gave way. As she went down, she hit her head on the fireplace and grunted. The women rushed to her aid. One called 999.

Chapter 10

Kelly arrived at Eden House well after dark, and greeted the uniforms behind the reception desk. The mood was sombre, as it was when any news of a homicide hit the team. It created a sense of urgency and seriousness. The press department at HQ would be busy. She had other work to be getting on with: a conversation with DI Craig Lockwood, some cold cases to trawl through and filling the hole left by DC Rob Shawcross's paternity leave. But none of that would be a priority for what was left of the working day; in fact it would all be shelved, except perhaps for the conversation with Craig about the missing woman, Lisa Lau.

Dorinne's case was playing on everyone's mind; they'd been happily getting on with their workload while a woman who'd gone missing on their patch was being tortured and abused in unimaginably agonising scenarios. It had happened under their noses and they'd been none the wiser, content that Dorinne had taken off to Lancaster. This briefing would be tough. It had certainly been a relief to get out of the office, she reflected, even if it was for an autopsy.

The only silver lining this morning had been a visit from Rob Shawcross, who'd been coming into the office sporadically over the last couple of weeks, and had admitted that it was more to get a break from Mia and the baby, rather than get any work done. It was good to see his face. They all poked fun, especially Kate, who'd raised three daughters and had the grey hair and the lungs of a heavy smoker to prove it. They'd gathered around him and asked questions. He'd showed photos and told stories of midnight feeds and sleep deprivation.

No one had noticed Kelly leave the conversation early to go back to her office. No one had noticed her wince at the mention of the hardships inherent to parenthood. She'd held her flat belly absent-mindedly and walked away from intense conversation involving feeding, sleeping, cleaning, reading nursery rhymes and the examination of bodily fluids. It all sounded like an alien world, where a little monster clung for its very life, sucking vitality from every pore. She shivered, despite the radiators blasting out furnace-level heat.

She'd sat behind her desk, the door to her office shut, brooding on the sick mind she faced battle with. Never one to shy away from a challenge, Kelly vowed to find whoever did this to Dorinne. She concentrated on the job of reactivating the case file. They had three months of information to sift through, having lost any chance of getting back the first forty-eight hours, known as the Golden Hour. Time put distance between the police and the perps, and working in those early hours of opportunity benefited cases enormously and Dorinne had gone missing back in October. However, they did have one huge advantage: she hadn't been killed until this week. Ted had demonstrated that clearly. There was always a possibility that a person had been frozen or somehow preserved after death for a period; a killer might like to keep trophies around him. But Ted emphatically ruled that out. Frozen tissue, when it defrosts, is shattered by the process and it's very obvious at autopsy.

It was a glimmer of good news: a body was always the prize piece of evidence on a murder case, not just because it proved they were dead, but because of the immense amount of information always left behind by the murderer. She'd once asked Ted why he went into pathology and eventually performing autopsies and he'd said that it enabled him to speak for the dead. An autopsy was the victim's last chance at telling their story. A skilled pathologist could look inside a body, and indeed at the surface of it, and create a timeline and a visual of what the injured party had endured.

She logged on to her computer and read an email from Craig Lockwood. He had some news about Lisa Lau.

She'd first met DI Craig Lockwood when she'd had to travel to Barrow to investigate a missing person case over three years ago. The mother of the ten-year-old victim had lived in Amble-side, and Kelly, keen to impress her new superiors at Cumbria Constabulary, jumped in her car and drove the thirty miles to one of the loveliest villages in the whole of the district. In the end, it was the victim's uncle who proved pivotal to the case, and he lived on Walney Island, near Barrow. It was thanks to Craig, head of the serious crime unit for the Southern Lakes, that the joint operation ran so smoothly, and they eventually cracked the case and brought closure for the mother, though Kelly doubted that the horror of losing a child in that manner would ever diminish: another reason not to have kids in the first place. She pushed the visions of brutalised children from her head. They were more likely to get run over on their way to school, she told herself. Not that that was a comforting thought either. There were so many risks involved.

There was a knock on her door and Kate appeared with a steaming mug of coffee, which she set down on the desk for her boss. Inwardly, Kelly gagged. She was finding the smell of coffee, cigarettes and fish repulsive at the moment.

'Thanks, Kate.' A lone Christmas card sat untouched on Kelly's desk and Kate turned it round. They chatted about the festive season, which was still fresh in everyone's minds. The holidays had been a welcome reprieve for the whole team. It had been a rough year. Kelly reflected on the gaping hole left by DS Will Phillips, and felt a twinge of regret and melancholy every time she walked past his desk. She hadn't seen it coming; no one had. They'd been a tight unit for over three years and Kelly had reckoned she trusted all of them with her life, until things began to unravel and Will's past caught up with him.

DC Emma Hide felt it the keenest. Kelly caught the young detective often, looking over to where Will had sat day in day out. They'd all shared laughs, stories and memorable moments with him and he was sorely missed. Kelly was torn between blaming him for allowing himself to become a pawn of the superintendent and understanding how he had, ultimately, no choice in the matter.

After Kate left her office, Kelly stared at her coffee. She got up and moved it to the windowsill, behind a curtain, so she couldn't smell it. There was a row of them.

Back at her desk, she picked up her phone and dialled Craig's office number. His department was situated in the centre of the large town of Barrow, at the tip of the Furness peninsula, and was housed in a beautiful red sandstone building similar to Eden House. They'd been built back in the days of Empire, when governments had money to spend on their public sectors. Barrow had been at the centre of the iron industry and rich pickings were to be had by entrepreneurs, who grew fat and wealthy, leaving civic and architectural reminders of themselves in the form of statues and buildings. The police station in Barrow used to belong to the Hematite Steel Company: the biggest in the world at the time.

Craig picked up straight away and Kelly figured that his team was enjoying some post-Christmas downtime too. Though, she was in no doubt, news of the body in the bin would have reached them by now. Crime generally spiked around the festive season, simply because people who are drunk are arseholes. Fights, domestics, dares, drugs, love rivalries and old wounds flare up when people are brought together and have time off, and too much booze.

Barrow had a larger percentage of such alcohol-related incidents than anywhere else in Cumbria, and it kept Craig busy. The main drag of nightclubs and bars was affectionately known as the Gaza Strip, and Black Marias waited in their dozens along the adjacent roads on a Friday and Saturday night. Craig wasn't usually involved in the niff-naff and trivia of booking pissheads, but occasionally his cases took him down to the streets. Such as in the case of Lisa Lau.

Craig was an old-fashioned copper, and as they spoke Kelly pictured his broad shoulders and warm eyes. Not that she needed the protection of a male hero; she'd proven that very quickly in London, but it was good when Craig Lockwood had your back. Even over the phone, the security of his physique shone through in his gravelly voice, indicative of years on the force and putting bad guys away where they belonged. Craig had the nose for the job.

'Kelly, how are you?'

He always wanted to chat, and Kelly found it soothing. He wasn't all about work. The first time they'd met and he'd taken her for breakfast, he wanted to get to know her better, not just as a copper, but as a person. It was refreshing and she applied it to her own team. She believed that they bonded together at Eden House because they didn't just co-exist as automatons, they actually got on. No one had to share private information, it was simply a way to connect, and when they felt part of an alliance, they worked better.

'I'm good,' she lied. She felt nauseous and tired. 'How about you? How's Barrow in the snow? I presume you've heard about our body in the bin?'

'It's always pretty in the snow: it covers everything, and if I look up towards Black Combe, I can almost see you. Yep, we heard.'

'How are your boys?' She always asked after them, though they were men now.

'I hardly see them: two at uni and one studying for his final A level exams. They're good kids.'

'What's it like, though, worrying all the time, wondering if they're going to turn out okay?' It was out before she could stop herself and there was a pause on the other end of the phone. 'I mean…' She attempted to backtrack, but she didn't need to.

'Good question. It's a rollercoaster ride, that's for sure. But nothing is guaranteed in life, is it? I could get run over by a bus tomorrow, or they could. Why fixate on that when I can just enjoy them?'

'Have they got girlfriends?'

'Two have. My eldest is gay and has a partner.'

'I'm sorry, I didn't mean to imply they should be straight. God, what an idiot.'

'Don't worry, Kelly, you know me. He was terrified of telling me, in fact he only told me at Christmas. He actually had his partner in the car waiting for me to lose it, so he could hop in and drive straight back to uni. He thought I'd go mad.'

'What did you say?'

'Nothing. I just hugged him and asked when we could meet. He brought him in from the car – lovely chap, a bit older than him. Anyway, what about you? How's life treating you? Christmas must have been tough, a year anniversary?'

Craig knew that she'd lost her mother just after last Christmas. It had been a shock and Kelly fancied herself too young to be without the woman who'd raised her – rightly or wrongly – to be the person she was today. There'd been a polite phone call with her sister, Nikki, who still didn't know they were only half-sisters and that Ted was Kelly's real father. It was time to tell her, really. Maybe at the same time she could tell her that she was going to be an auntie.

Kelly had no idea why she wanted to share her paternity with her half-sibling. Her and Nikki's relationship had been tumultuous to say the least, not because they hated one another, just because they were so different. They rubbed each other the wrong way. And poor Mum had seen the worst of it. They'd bickered over her in hospital like two toddlers and now Kelly felt shame when she remembered. They could argue all day long about whose fault it was. Nikki accused Kelly of lording it over their mother, returning from London as the prodigal daughter, lapping up the attention. For her part, Kelly saw

Nikki as someone stuck in time who'd never really grown up. She had three kids, who Kelly rarely saw. Maybe a new baby in the family would change that? It made her remember the patience of her mother. Wendy would have been over the moon at her news. Another grandchild to spoil. Nikki's kids were growing up and had become stroppy prepubescents. A baby was a joy. Though, she didn't get that impression from Rob Shawcross.

Christ, she was getting soft. She'd noticed that decisions that used to be clear-cut now presented her with emotional dilemmas. Johnny had said, in his infinite wisdom, that it was her mothering hormones kicking in: from now on, she'd be more compassionate, sensitive and intuitive. It hadn't gone down well.

At least she had Ted, and his daughters: her other half-sisters, June and Amber. There'd be no shortage of people willing to help. She wondered how Josie might take it when they told her. Would she love the idea or hate it? Would it be embarrassing to know that her fifty-year-old father was still having sex, never mind fathering more children? She did a quick calculation and realised that when their baby was twenty, Johnny would be seventy. She got to the point.

'I read your email,' she said. He waited.

She'd read in Craig's email that a reliable witness from Barrow had gone on record to say that a friend of his had regularly travelled to Bowness and Ambleside to sleep with women for money, and his favourite was a young Chinese girl called Lisa.

'Who's the friend?' Kelly asked.

'We've checked him out. He's married and keen to keep it quiet. He's called David Martin.'

'Aren't they all keen to keep it quiet?' she said.

'He gave a positive ID from a photograph. I don't think the friendship with our witness will last, though. His alibi for the second of January checked out. He says the last time he saw Lisa was a couple of days before New Year, but he did give us a few addresses where they used to meet. You might want to check them out, as some of them are in Ambleside and Grasmere. He agreed for me to swab him for DNA and I've sent the sample off to the lab. Was the pathologist able to get a DNA profile from your murder victim?'

'We won't know until the results come back. Our coroner wasn't sure there was enough genetic material in the sample he swabbed, there was so much blood around the site where her legs had been hacked off, but he tried his best. She was a sex worker too. She was called Dorinne Callaghan, twenty-five years of age, reported missing in October from a hostel in Ambleside, which is where I'm heading today. She was behind on her rent and last seen in an Ambleside club.'

'What was the name of the club?' Craig asked.

'Heaven, why?'

'That's where our friend, Mr Martin, met Lisa Lau.'

Both detectives were acutely aware that people of all ages, genders, backgrounds and inclinations go missing all the time. However, two known prostitutes going missing in close proximity, potentially frequenting similar hostels, bars and casual places of work, was something that they hadn't seen in the Lakes before. Not since the colossal trafficking ring of the infamous Tombday case three years ago had the sex trade reared its head in any fashion at all. The fact sat between them in a silence that lasted a second or so.

They both knew that Bowness was a hub of sexual deviance, be it nightclubbers swimming Windermere naked and stoned, or nude bathers hooking up along the many pretty islands along the lake made famous by Beatrix Potter. But hard-core crime was fairly rare. Even prostitution didn't attract significant resources, even though it was widely known it went on there. Committing valuable funds wasn't worth a few soliciting charges. It was always notoriously difficult to get reliable witness testimony and prove money had been exchanged. Neither party was ever willing to talk to the cops. But Kelly couldn't help asking herself the question: what if they were on the cusp of unearthing something?

She broke the silence first.

'I'll send a photo of Dorinne through to you. Can you get David Martin in and ask him if he knew her too? I can't justify giving as much legwork to Lisa Lau without more evidence, although we haven't even had it confirmed that she left the county yet.'

'What? I thought she was seen in Preston.'

'Yes, and we had a sighting of Dorinne Callaghan in Lancaster too.'

'Right, you have my attention. Where was she found?'

'Patterdale. But she lived in a hostel in Ambleside.'

'The same one as Lisa Lau?'

'No, a different one, but they must have crossed paths. The seasonal worker sector in Ambleside itself is relatively small and they all socialise in the same places. The hookers all know one another, maybe that's why no one's talking.'

'Has there been a post-mortem yet?'

'Yes, I've just come from the hospital now. She was tortured and abused for a long period – possibly weeks or even longer – before she was finally manually strangled to death. The coroner has ruled this as cause of death but also indicated sub-causation as malnourishment and general neglect. In my head, if I'm honest, she was kept somewhere, we think possibly a cage – at least it was something metal because she managed to embed some of it into her thumbs where we think she'd tried to get out. She had cracked teeth, evidential of gnawing something hard.'

Craig exhaled loudly. Details such as these didn't come as a surprise to coppers, they just made them even more weary about the human race and its capacity for inflicting pain.

'David Martin doesn't strike me as the type, but it's the quiet ones who always surprise you. I'll interview him and use some body language techniques,' Craig said.

The study of body language, as well as voice markers and psychological tools, was often vital in assessing whether a witness or suspect was telling the truth. The methods had cracked many high-profile cases, such as the Soham murders.

Kelly knew that most of Craig's budget was used up on drugs raids and the constant ferrying of drunken yobs to cells to sober up over the weekend. As well as the usual burglaries and domestics. In Penrith, she faced a slightly different dynamic. Closer to the M6, the ports of Workington and Scotland, it provided a haven where criminals could hide misdeeds and try to get away with it. The northern lakes were also better to hide geographically. Cumbria was essentially one big mountain with impossible rock dividing the two halves of the county. There was literally a physical barrier denoting her and Craig's worlds. But sometimes they collided and they had to find ways around the giant obstacle. Now was one of those times.

'We need to review the CCTV footage of the sighting of Lisa Lau at Preston train station,' he said.

'I agree, have you seen it?' she asked.

'No, I thought you had.'

This was the only drawback of joint investigations: things got missed. Even with the HOLMES dynamic reasoning software that did the job of a hundred officers and never went wrong because it wasn't fallible like humans, it still relied on human fingers to input data.

'It was sent to Preston directly. Didn't anyone there review it?'

'There's only one way to find out. Look, you've got your hands full with this new case. Let me chase the CCTV.'

'Thanks, Craig.' They said their goodbyes and agreed to keep in touch.

Kelly got up from her desk and went to the ladies' toilet across the hall.

She refreshed her face with water, held tissues up to her eyes and breathed. Whenever she got a quiet moment, images of babies flooded her head. In Penrith town, she saw teenagers pushing prams everywhere. Only the grandmothers looked around Kelly's age. She couldn't ever remember hearing children the way she did now. To her, they sounded constantly annoying. They never shut up, shattering any hope of ever enjoying peace again.

Memories of herself and Johnny reading on the terrace on a Sunday afternoon, with a blanket and a glass of red wine, sailing up and down Ullswater or Derwentwater on the *Wendy*, mooring up and making love, and swimming in hidden tarns and rock pools, not caring about another soul—

Stop!

Not telling anyone in her office made her feel claustrophobic; not telling anyone *at all* made her feel trapped. Telling Ted had been a revelation, and they'd tell Josie soon. If only Wendy was alive. What would she say?

Kelly knew full well what her mother would have said.

You will learn patience, kindness and selflessness all in good time. It is the most natural thing in the world…

She stared into the mirror. The door opened and Kate came in behind her. Kelly made herself busy washing her hands.

'All right, boss?' Kate asked. She smelled of her last cigarette, and Kelly put her hand over her mouth.

'The cleaner just cleared the cups off your windowsill,' Kate added.

'Thanks. I, erm, forgot about them.' Kelly spoke through her fingers as she fought the nausea.

'Full coffee cups,' Kate stated.

She was rumbled.

'Is it true?' Kate asked.

Kelly nodded and looked down at her shoes.

'I'd hug you but I'm guessing that, judging by the coffee mug situation and your face, you're at the coffee and fags make you sick stage? I'll try and cut down, boss. It will pass. It's bloody fantastic news!'

Kelly didn't say anything.

'What's up? Are you sure you're all right?' Kate asked again.

Kelly had never confided so personally in a work colleague before and it felt odd, but when she looked into Kate's eyes she knew that she must take the leap of faith for her sanity. Kate was a good person, and she knew everything there was to know about kids.

'I think I'm too old.'

'Old! You're just about to turn forty! I'd say that was pretty good. You've lived, you know how shit works, you're wise and experienced. So is…' Kate's voice tapered off.

'Yes, it's Johnny's.' They both laughed.

'Just checking,' Kate said.

Kelly relaxed a little and even smiled. 'You're the only person who knows, apart from Johnny of course. And my dad.'

'Well I'm privileged then. Don't look so scared. You'll be an incredible mother, DI Porter.' Kate winked. 'I'm desperate for a piss, but I promise to only bring you water from now on, or herbal tea? Ginger biscuits…'

Kate disappeared into the cubicle and Kelly wished that she didn't hate the smell of smoke right now because she really could do with that hug.

Chapter 11

Once Kelly had composed herself, she checked her preparation for the first brief on the murder of Dorinne Callaghan. She thought about the woman whose life had ended so horrifically. From her file, Kelly knew that she had family. Albeit not a close one; but she was still a daughter, a sister and an auntie. Dorinne had no children and that was a blessing. Kelly knew that her mother lived in Wigan and was only in her forties herself, and she worked in Asda. Dorinne's father worked as a labourer on building sites, carrying bricks and putting up scaffold. They had a dog. It was a boxer called Lady.

All this information had been processed as standard, back in October. Paperwork had been filled in, witness statements collated from friends, co-workers, and the guy she topped her gas meter up with at the local post office in Ambleside. Every human was at the centre of a vast community made up of hundreds of lives: some important and impactful, others not so much. The network of exposure to any one of these networks could hold the key to how Dorinne had found herself at the mercy of a killer: did she know him? Where had she been kept? Did she try to escape? Did anyone hear her cries, thinking it was the wind, or a fox in the middle of the night?

Was more than one person responsible?

She walked into the incident room and twenty people stared at her. As well as her close-knit team, they had all sorts of police staff available when investigating a murder: uniforms ready to do the legwork, from newly qualified bobbies to senior sergeants used to working such cases and knowing, without having to be told, which questions to ask and how to ask them to get the best results.

Kelly loved being in the community, chasing leads and filling gaps, interviewing people who she thought important enough to keep an eye on. She was also a realist. She knew that she couldn't chase everyone. If she did that, she'd make mistakes. She had capable and trustworthy staff to send the length and breadth of the Lakes should she need to, and she had a hunch that, if Lisa Lau had met the same fate, and had not been on that platform in Preston, a joint inquiry with Craig was the only way they could cover the whole county. It was looking more and more likely that Ambleside and the surrounding areas was somehow at the centre, and that was slap bang in between hers and Craig's patches.

It was a good job they liked each other.

'What we know,' she began.

The room was darkened and the projector screen filled with the familiar mind map of HOLMES. Dorinne Callaghan's picture was at the centre: her beautiful hazel eyes stared back at them.

'Twenty-five years old. She worked as a cleaner for various agencies – and fell out with several of them, seemingly carrying on as an independent. This meant she went into lots of homes in the Ambleside and Grasmere area. Many of them were traced when she was reported missing. Dorinne also worked as a prostitute when she needed extra cash. We had a few willing witnesses give us information about clients, habits and routine, all of them checked out, and none of them were investigated further. Her room-mate at the hostel was also helpful. We spent fifty police hours on this, and then we received the sighting in Lancaster, out of county and far enough away to presume she'd moved.'

Lancaster was thirty miles beyond the Cumbrian border and almost an hour from Ambleside.

People took notes, and some shuffled paper. No one talked. Everyone listened.

'We're behind the power curve because we now know that Dorinne never left the county. I know it's been a long day, guys. Spend a couple of hours on it and we'll pick up tomorrow. Our priorities going forward are twofold: firstly, we review the information gathered during the missing person case from October, and that'll take a lot of boots on the ground. We need to concentrate on who she was with in the days before her disappearance. The file is large. Secondly, working on tracing that wheelie bin and catching this bastard when we do. Forensically, we've got an abundance of evidence to process and it's going to take time to work through it all and wait for the results, so in the meantime, most of you will be chasing the original leads from before the case was transferred to Lancaster.'

Kelly turned to the projector screen and pressed some buttons on her remote.

'We have an MO that is seriously disturbing. I spent three hours with the coroner this afternoon, and I stood in on Dorinne's autopsy. There is no doubt that Dorinne died recently. There is also no doubt that she was tortured for a long period of time. I don't need to remind you that sex workers take risks, and when we've had cases of murder among that population, it is almost always as a result of being exposed to strangers in the line of work. So it seems likely that we're looking for a predator who picks up sex workers locally. This is the photograph of the dump scene.'

Everybody watched as Kelly talked them through the remoteness, darkness and security of the road where the wheelie bin was left.

'All the residents have been interviewed. Each one has denied owning the bin, and they all come over as fairly trustworthy.' The nose of the interviewer was always taken into account when piecing together suspects. The first impressions of the officers on the ground were invaluable and they were trained to pick up signs that made them suspect if a character should be looked at further. Body language, speech, eye contact were all ways to do this.

'The bin has been sent to a lab, now the coroner has finished with it, and we're going to get samples sent from the wheels: soil, organic matter and then, on the inside, the bags and the tape that were used to wrap the body. The victim was dissected, with the legs in a separate bag.'

Kelly changed the slide. A table appeared with various time frames and figures on it. 'This is the entomological evidence.' She explained how the coroner thought that the victim had remained in a warm place after death, and then was wrapped and disposed of.

'Perhaps a blip in confidence, or a mistake? Maybe the killer didn't expect her to begin to decompose so quickly?'

The next slide was a map of Ambleside and the surrounding area. It showed where witnesses had spotted Dorinne, as well as where she lived and where she was known to have picked up clients.

'It's worth mentioning here that I've got DI Lockwood, who is in charge of Barrow, looking at the CCTV footage of Lisa Lau at Preston station. There's a question mark over whether she left the county and DI Lockwood has just informed me that a witness met Lisa at the same club where Dorinne was last seen. Now, while I appreciate not jumping to conclusions, it's not insignificant information and I'm waiting to hear from DI Lockwood. Some of you who I tasked with looking into the report of Lisa Lau will spot similar patterns here on the map, for example where she lived, travelled and met clients. DI Lockwood is checking out her movements, not least because there's been no activity on her bank account. I'm not ruling anything out. When I go down to Ambleside tomorrow, I'll take the opportunity to check out a few details regarding Lisa too. Her work permit also runs out this weekend.'

She clicked on the last slide, which summarised everything she'd said, and then a final slide with jobs indicated for those in the room. A lot of the tasks centred on Ambleside and the weather forecast wasn't good. A fresh dump of snow was expected overnight. It would make moving around the locations central to their inquiries difficult, but all they could do was try their best. Interviews were always more desirable face to face, but telephones weren't the end of the world.

Kelly dismissed the room and went to her office, shutting the door behind her. She opened her drawer and got out a packet of ginger biscuits. She was exhausted and it wasn't even six o'clock. It was fully dark outside and it made her job more onerous. It felt as though all their opportunities went away in the dark and only tomorrow would they have a proper chance at chasing leads. That wasn't true of course, people could be interviewed in the night, but it *felt* harder.

She was glad that Josie and Johnny were busy tonight. She wanted to concentrate on what faced her, right here, right now. The task that she'd given herself was to make sure that HOLMES was bang up to date, and go over Dorinne's case from scratch, in the peace and quiet of her office, armed with biscuits and tea, and to look with fresh eyes and see if anything stood out to her. It's human nature, but even detectives notice different things when reading about a disappearance that was now a murder.

Chapter 12

Night-time came to the Lakes quickly in January, despite the winter solstice having been and gone. No one seemed to notice the days getting longer, simply because they didn't seem to. The heavy winter light prevented the sun from bursting through the sky, and shadows covered the land by four o'clock.

St Oswald's wasn't the only ancient church in Grasmere, but not many knew about the even older Saxon structure, hidden behind dense forest, just off the road to Ambleside. It wasn't easy to get to but there was a select group of people who headed there, after dark, to pursue their particular interests. Kevin Flint was one of them.

The church had once been a glorious example of Celtic crosses and architecture, but had been surpassed by the position of St Oswald's in the centre of Grasmere as the main attraction, especially since the Wordsworths were buried there. The church, called St Brigid's, had fallen into disrepair after the Second World War, when austerity kicked in and the Anglican Church chose St Oswald's to make the main pen for the flock of the surrounding hills. What was the point of up keeping two old churches, when one would do? Besides, St Brigid's was in an awkward position and, by the time it closed its doors in 1949, had only one regular attendee. The church didn't even bother selling the building, they just left it to go to ruin. It was indeed a handsome relic, and attracted all manner of wildlife that had set up home there among the gravestones, which were left to crumble and moss over. The relatives of those consecrated underneath were long gone, and all that was left were overgrown thorns and ivy, which strangled the epithets and messages of love. The cemetery told a story of the wealth and stature of the area, and the great mausoleums and statues represented centuries of money from slate and lead mining.

Kevin took the road south out of Grasmere, and cycled in the direction of Ambleside. The residents of Grasmere were tucked up inside their cocoons, warm in front of their orange fires and happy with their family tales and goings-on.

All he could hear in his head was his mother berating him for something he'd done, and he couldn't even remember what it was now. She never needed any excuse; she'd make stuff up if she had to, all so she could torture him and make him feel less than a man. She would have him stay a child for the rest of his life. He didn't know what day, or month, or year, he'd realised that he hated his mother; it had just occurred. There was nothing he could do about it. She'd made sure of that, by crippling his confidence and stunting his development when he was a child. He didn't do the stuff other kids did, like run, jump, cycle and play. He stayed indoors, in servitude to the woman he thought was protecting him. All the while his father sat in an alcoholic stupor, fit for nothing but demanding another drink when he woke from his latest blackout. He'd forgotten the faces of all his classmates now. No doubt they'd have jobs, children and lives.

He was stuck here, with her, nurturing his rage.

The place to which he headed on his bike was thankfully one of his releases from the loathing that he possessed for himself and his parents. For a few hours he could forget the shame, and the crushing knowledge that he was different.

He was caught once, by the village gossip no less, playing with himself in the graveyard of St Oswald's. The humiliation was total. But he hadn't known what else to do. When the urge came, he had no choice but to find solace. How was he to know the difference between normal behaviour and not? He'd told the police that he thought it was all right because he was alone.

74

He was warned that his behaviour was lewd, whatever that meant, though he knew it was bad, and he was let off. Even the police felt pity towards him. It intensified the self-flagellation and the need to find privacy. That's how he'd found St Brigid's. He'd been reading a book in the library, where he was a regular. The local community library in Grasmere was quiet and safe, and the old ladies there didn't give him judging looks; they let him be. He had two passions – walking and reading. Cycling was a means to link the two. St Brigid's satisfied both. He'd learned that two lovers, like the Abelard and Heloise story he'd read, had come here to make love, even after being forbidden by both of their families. Background and upbringing disallowed their union – one was a Celt and the other Norman – but they couldn't abandon their love. When their enraged parents discovered their secret trysts, they were tortured and banished for ever, but legend had it that they both found their way back and died holding on to one another, in the graveyard in some macabre embrace, and entered the afterlife together. A monolith had stood in St Brigid's burial ground for eight hundred years, or at least that's what the book said.

Kevin had sought the legend out and found it to be real. The first time he'd discovered the site, he'd stared in amazement at the weathered stone and sat for a long time on a grave, immersing himself in the peace and quiet. But he wasn't the only one who'd found the decrepit gem.

As he pedalled around Rydal Water, he could see why tourists got confused and thought it an extension of Grasmere: the two stretches of water looked as one, with a small narrowing in the middle. They were two of the district's most peaceful lakes and Kevin knew every route around them. He'd once applied for a job as a tour guide but hadn't been taken on because they said he wouldn't be any good at talking to guests. Why anyone would want to talk when walking around the lakes was a puzzle to him. He'd simply wanted to point out the most interesting features, like the coffin trail and the Rydal caves.

He'd applied for the mountain rescue too, but been turned down for his lack of empathy towards victims. He knew the area well, so could be sure to find lost people, but when asked what he'd do first upon locating a casualty, he'd replied that he'd warm himself up with a flask of tea as he waited for the chopper. Apparently that had been wrong, and he should have said he would talk to them and make them comfortable. It was baffling.

Past the turning for Rydal Mount, where William and Dorothy Wordsworth lived at the height of the poet's success, he turned down a narrow lane and went as far as he could, crossing a cattle grid and finding another, even narrower track, leading to a field. It was where he always left his bike, taking his backpack containing a torch, a flask of tea and a towel to sit on. As well as tissues.

He walked towards a stile and climbed across it, jumping down the other side. He could hear the rush of water, from the beck underneath the bridge, but didn't flick on his torch; it was only for emergencies. Anyone blind to the hidden beauty behind the wall covered in thick foliage would walk straight past the iron gate, but Kevin turned in, and felt at peace when he saw the old remains. He smiled as he went to find a place to settle for the next few hours. From his vantage point, he watched the clouds turn even darker, from purple-grey to oily black. He didn't mind the cold. The snow was at its thickest off the beaten track and he simply wiped away a space to sit. The crystals glinted in the moonlight and gave him great comfort.

–

He was almost ready to go home for the evening when he heard a car. Sure enough, it stopped and then he heard a woman's voice. She was laughing. She sounded drunk. He didn't have to wait long for a couple to come into the graveyard, and for the woman to be given a brief history lesson about the place. There wasn't much room, but Kevin sat undetected in the shadows and watched the drama unfold.

Even by the light of the moon, he could tell the woman was definitely drunk. She staggered about, held up by the man. Kevin had seen him before from a distance, several times in fact, and he knew what was about to happen. He couldn't believe his luck. He sat transfixed by the couple.

'It's wet!' she said.

'That's why I gave you my boots!' The man laughed and calmed her.

'You are a pervert!' she slurred.

'You want me to be,' he replied.

It was always the same rig. Kevin watched his favourite actor play out his fantasies and held his breath, as the woman figured out if she was going to play along.

She did.

Steadied by the man, she opened her coat and lifted her dress. Kevin could hardly contain himself as he watched them embrace. Kevin watched in silence as the man undid his trousers and then unzipped the woman's dress. The man leant her back on a gravestone and took off his coat, laying it down for her. She lay back and he took her legs in the air. She wore no underwear and Kevin's world stood still for a moment as he took in her perfection. The colour of her skin, the way her hair touched the wet stone, the length of her neck as she bent backwards, and how wide her legs could spread. The man worked expertly, as Kevin had seen him perform before, and the woman's flesh wobbled around as she was held down and thrust upon. Their breaths came in steam clouds and the moonlight made the vision eerie and captivating, as if an angel had wafted in here to make love to God. The ice twinkled and fell to the floor as the woman tried to hold on and the man neared his climax. But suddenly, he stopped, as Kevin knew he would. The woman looked up, panting and wanting more, but the man took his hands off her jelly-like breasts and put them onto her throat. She leant her head back and allowed him to squeeze – not too much but just enough for her to gag. Kevin could hardly breathe as he watched her breasts bouncing up and down as she pleaded for him to stop. He did so and carried on with his mission, allowing her to breathe as he neared his end. Kevin had no idea when his hand had gone down his own trousers, but it was working furiously and he came at the same time as his hero.

The woman panted and the man pulled out, leaving her prone and suddenly ugly. Kevin found a tissue and cleaned himself up.

'I need a drink,' she said.

'Of course you do, my darling,' the man said. It was the same every time. He helped her off the grave and she quickly covered up.

'Come on, let's go and get warm.'

As they left, Kevin watched them and wondered when the man would return with a new woman. He felt almost bereft that it was over and he sat staring at the couple's backs as they made their way to the old gate. But before they exited through the dense trees and bushes, the man turned and looked directly at Kevin – or where he was hidden – and smiled.

It couldn't be. Kevin questioned his eyesight. He tried to make the conflicting images fit. Had he seen the man's face before?

Chapter 13

Kevin opened the door quietly lest his mother hear him. His heart fluttered with trepidation because he never knew what he'd find inside the house where he'd spent the past four years of his life. A lot had happened in those four years. Most males became men between fifteen and nineteen, but he'd regressed back to the boy he was when he lay awake at night, waiting for his mother's gentle footsteps, stopping outside his door. When she didn't lie with him, he couldn't sleep and the nightmares came. She was the only one who protected him from the drunken rages of his father, who ranted and threatened until he passed out. All Kevin wanted to do was please her, and when he didn't she could be a bigger monster than Tommy Flint ever was. His father now spent his waking hours at the pub, picking up women, and his hours of stupor on the floor or sofa of anyone who'd have him. He'd ceased being Kevin's tormentor years ago. Now it was her. He wasn't as stupid as they all said: he knew she'd planned this tyranny all along. The guise of maternity had been used to make him weak. She'd groomed him to obey. And he did, because it was the only place he felt safe, even if it was merely to be molested and even if he hated himself for admitting it. She'd nurtured inside him a kind of evil dependence, where he detested her presence but relied on it. It was all he knew and there was no way out. In his darkest moments, when he was truly alone, sometimes up on the fells, watching rabbits screwing, he also knew that he could never leave her. They'd run from social services, to different counties, so many times he'd stopped counting. He'd never needed those institutions to save him, and hope was a thing of the past.

Until now.

Watching the stranger at the graveyard made him feel alive. It was something he'd never felt with his mother. It had planted a seed inside of him: one that he'd begun to believe in.

He'd always wanted a friend. A girlfriend especially, but he'd been painfully awkward at school and hadn't known how to get one. He watched in envy as girls threw flirtatious gazes at his classmates but never him. He was seen as a '*neek*' (a cross between a nerd and a geek, though he was neither) and somebody to avoid. But the urge to be near girls was overwhelming and he ended up scaring them half to death, or so his teachers said. He had been permanently excluded from seven schools by the time they left Lancaster.

He hadn't meant to worry anyone or come across as creepy (another accusation that hurt so bad it felt like a knife); he just wanted to make friends. Now he knew for certain that he couldn't do that. His was a solitary world where he played out the minutes, hours and days alone, trapped inside his own head, or here in this house, with his mother. His father, when he was there, rarely made it to the kitchen for food before staggering back to bed again, then occasionally getting dressed to go out, remaining absent for days on end.

Mother was his only companion, or at least the only person who knew him properly, or had a conversation with him. People in the village said hello, or talked about the weather, but he had no clue what to say back, so he didn't. They looked at him as if they wanted to help him, but he didn't understand their sympathetic faces. They looked upon him like they would victims of accidents, or mentally retarded people, and it puzzled him as to why they saw him as someone who suffered from an illness or bad luck. But after a while, people stopped talking to him and just looked at him funny, like Mrs Johnson at the post office. It was her who'd caught him at St Oswald's and the shame was etched into his cheeks for ever. He couldn't look at her and her eyes bored into his back when he stopped at Marvin's to buy a Coke and a packet of crisps.

–

There was a light on upstairs and he closed the door and hung up his jacket. The thoughts of the woman on the gravestone hadn't left his head the whole way back: her flesh, her large wobbly breasts, the smile on her face and the way the man ploughed into her and she seemed to like it. She wasn't rejecting him or repulsed by him. In fact the opposite was true, and Kevin tried to work out why. He memorised the man's clothing – his specific facial features being forgotten – and decided that, tomorrow, he might go shopping. But it was more than the man's appearance that struck Kevin as something that might be considered attractive to all the women he took there: it was the tone of his voice; it was commanding and firm. Kevin's voice was small and quiet, so he didn't use it all that much. But then, with his mother doing all the talking, he had no need for it.

'Where have you been, you dirty little boy?' his mother's voice, as if on cue, hissed from a dark corner.

He froze. The familiar knot in his stomach caused him to feel slightly nauseous, and his pulse quickened. He looked to where her voice came from and began to make out her silhouette, as his eyes adjusted to the lack of light. She smoked a cigarette. Boxes of her anxiety pills were strewn over the table next to her. Even she needed a crutch.

'Where have you been?'

Her voice rose in volume slightly. Kevin's nerves grated.

'Nowhere,' he said, knowing she'd never believe him.

'Come here, let me smell you.' He hung his head and shook it, hoping she wouldn't see. But he did as she asked and went to her.

'Kneel down,' she commanded. He did so. He sat at her feet, where she took his head in her cigarette-free hand and held it steady with his hair. She leant over and sniffed, not that she could smell anything over the tobacco, but she did it anyhow. His stomach flipped over and he remained dead still. He'd learned a long time ago to do exactly as he was told. But tonight he felt resistance. It manifested in a sense of dread and a desire to question her and to push back. But he knew he wouldn't. She was too powerful.

'You need to take a bath and scrub your skin clean, you dirty boy. Have you been visiting whores again?'

His cheeks burned and he closed his eyes to stop the tears from coming: she hated weakness; his lower lip wobbled and he shook his head.

'No.'

'What?' she shouted.

'No! I promise!' He spoke louder and felt sweat gathering on his body underneath the heavy jacket he'd worn to the graveyard. Fat tears spilled down his cheeks. His head thundered with noise and the loathing inside him almost gave him the courage he needed to smash her skull in, but not quite.

'If you're lying to me!'

'I'm not!'

She took his head and forced it into her lap, and began to stroke his hair. Her hand became rougher and rougher and she started to tear at his scalp, making him wince with pain, but still he said nothing. Ash fell onto his neck and she stubbed out her cigarette roughly into the overflowing ashtray on the table. The pulling turned to grabbing and she swung her hand up suddenly and brought it down on his head. The ringing in his ears was normal. The blows came swiftly and adeptly, making perfect contact each time.

She never hit his face; she was cleverer than that. She stood up, making him fall to the side, and he stayed there on the floor, his heart beating furiously. She kicked his back, as if to tell him to get up, and walked towards the stairs.

'Kevin!'

He daren't breathe. He peered up at her figure in the hallway; he could barely see through his tears. He held back and remained strong, trying to control his sobbing. That was just what she wanted: to hear his cries, so she could punish him and hit him harder. He got up off the floor and took off his jacket. He'd have to have a bath and endure her watching him to make sure he scrubbed his skin until it was raw, to satisfy herself of his cleanliness.

It was a routine they'd followed since he was a little boy. It was what had got him into trouble the first time, and it had been the moment their secret was almost revealed. At a party – in the days when he was still invited to them – he'd tried to get a girl in the bath with him to wash. The mother had screamed and called his father to collect him, but Mother had come, red-faced and seething.

That was when he found out that he shouldn't tell. Since that day, he hadn't told a soul.

The whole incident had been explained as Kevin's peculiar proclivity to be a good boy and keep clean, but from then on, the girls had been terrified of him and called him Water Boy. It led to another house move. Gradually, the towns and villages they moved to became smaller and quieter, leading Kevin to crave company even more.

Grasmere was about as isolated a backwater as you could get, and its sleepy charm and ignorant residents gave an air of respectability and reliability: the perfect place for his mother to be anonymous. She could tell the nosy neighbours anything she pleased. She informed them, when eventually she was asked, that her husband didn't work and her son was a simpleton. Kevin had looked up the word and figured that associated words, like foolish, cretinous and gullible, didn't describe him at all. It was the first time he'd questioned her love. Why would she say that? The locals believed her and to them he became the fool she described. At least he was left alone.

He followed her upstairs to the bathroom and didn't even glance towards his father's room; he'd be passed out by now and dribbling, if he was even home. The booze had finally caught up with Tommy Flint and he'd aged rapidly: his speech was impaired and he was confused most of the time. He was a shadow of Kevin's former tormentor. Mother looked as though she prayed for the day she'd find him dead in his bed. Their lives wouldn't change.

The light from his mother's bedroom illuminated the hallway slightly as she went into the bathroom and began running the bath. She always used bubbles and he found comfort in the familiar smell. Maybe this was the price he had to pay for his visit to the graveyard, and enjoying it. If Mother ever found out, he had no idea what she'd do. The light along the hall was the only way to see the bath as Mother didn't want lights on inside the bathroom. She sat on the edge of the bath, humming a song that he recognised from a long time ago. She always did it and it soothed him further, so he began to undress. She turned to watch him and stirred the running water with her hand as she did so. She even smiled and it made him feel a little wanted. He took off his clothes and laid them across a stool inside the door and stood in front of her, waiting expectantly. He no longer felt the effects of the earlier blows to his head.

She stopped the tap, satisfied with the level of water, and beckoned him to get in. She stood up and he did as he was told, getting into the water and sitting down. He sighed with relief and she sat on the floor next to him as he reclined and fully immersed himself. She handed him a flannel.

It always started like this: in time she'd progress to a loofah and then metal gauze, but there was no rush. It would take time for the lesions to heal, as it always did, but he'd grown accustomed to the sensation of raw skin. Besides, that was part of the ritual: her rubbing soothing cream all over him to aid the process.

Her hand reached out to touch him as he washed all over and he felt his tensions slip away, one by one, stroke by stroke, touch by touch. He lay fully back and exposed himself above the bubble line.

His mother smiled.

'Good boy.'

Chapter 14

Harry drove down a dark lane and parked outside a grand mansion. He knew the drill: he was to buzz the intercom, wait for an answer, then the gates would open and he could drive to the rear entrance and deliver his package. He whistled gently as he waited for the faceless monitor to speak to him. He didn't mind what hours he worked; he lived alone, slept at random hours, and had never been one for routine. He preferred driving around the Lake District when it was hushed. There was something ultimately calming about quiet. He guessed it went back to sometime in his childhood, when characters are made and habits are formed, and he supposed that's why he was a delivery driver. He worked in a tranquil mobile office, going at his own pace, passing pleasantries with only those who were of such inclination, swapping stories with old folk who anticipated his call with joy because he stopped to chat with them about their hip operation or their daughter's prom. He had time for good honest folk who worked hard and were decent. On the other hand, he had no time for spongers and people who tricked the system.

Harry was self-employed for this reason: to be his own boss, and Marvin's was only one of dozens of post office counters he serviced. He had contracts with all the large companies, but on his terms. People willing to deliver to the more remote areas were in high demand and he was reliable, quick and didn't charge stupid money. He kept it fair and hung on to his various commissions, undercutting the larger chains from Penrith, Workington or Kendal who had huge overheads to pay for. Loyal post office proprietors, like Marvin Burns, kept work coming his way, and he was content.

The buzzer sprang to life and he was allowed in. It was jobs like this where he could charge a little more. It was a foolish man who thought that delivery men like him didn't know what was inside a package just because it had no label on. It was easy to scan the barcode and locate the company, product and a photograph from every package he handled. It was kind of a hobby.

The address he was at now ordered some pretty fruity parcels, that was for sure. The same middle-aged woman always answered the door and asked him to leave the boxes in the porch. Harry unloaded them and did as he was bid, smiling at her. She never responded with anything more than a polite thank you. He smiled to himself, smug in his knowledge that the property took regular orders of items one would associate with either a large family's keen interest in group sex, or a knocking shop. Oh, if only he could tell Maureen; she'd have a ball. But his job was too precious to him. He kept his knowledge to himself; the thousands of tubes of lubricative gels, the toys, the disposable sheets, the light fittings, benches, cages and dressing-up clothes. He'd save his chuckles for when he returned to the van, imagining Maureen's face should she ever see what was inside those boxes. The woman passed him an envelope and he knew that it contained his usual fifty-pound tip. He took it and thanked her. She closed the door like some regal lady of a bygone era, handing the servants a gratuity so meagre as to be offensive, and she, all the while, oblivious to her own disdain.

He climbed into the van and pulled away, down the gravel driveway to the open gate. He had three more similar drops to make this evening and he had to avoid the bloody roadblocks put into place by the police stopping everybody, asking about the body in the bin. Whoever owned these places must be making a killing, he thought.

Chapter 15

'Mrs Alice Callaghan?' Kelly asked.

The woman on the other end of the phone was expecting the call. She'd been informed of her daughter's death by local police in Wigan. An informing team, as well as a bereavement team, had already visited her. They'd asked her permission to release the news to the press and she'd given it.

'I'm sorry for your loss, Mrs Callaghan, please accept my deepest sympathy.'

'Go on. I suppose you've got questions, have you?' the woman replied. She sniffed gently down the phone, as if not wanting the policewoman to hear. Kelly didn't judge her hostility. Losing a loved one to murder brought out a whole array of different reactions from people.

'I know you spoke to police before, when Dorinne was reported missing. I don't want to make you repeat yourself, but I wasn't in charge of the missing person case. If you remember, there was a sighting in Lancaster and so they took the case. I wanted to speak to you myself.' It sounded like a lame excuse for not trying harder to find her daughter. Would the same turn out to be true for Lisa Lau?

The woman sighed and blew her nose. It had always been a slightly repulsive noise to Kelly, and it reminded her of a class-mate who was always ill, and had been reprimanded constantly by their teacher for snuffling and snorting his way through the day. In her current condition, it made her stomach turn over.

'She was a lovely girl, really. But she fell in with the wrong crowd when she was fifteen, and there was no controlling her after that. She stole money, stayed out drinking late, bringing fellas back here. We had enough, and told her to leave last year. I knew she'd gone to the Lakes to work, you can get hotel jobs two-a-penny. An auntie of mine lives up there in Grasmere, and she told me she saw our Dorinne one day in Ambleside, she said hello but Dorinne was rude. My auntie said she was dressed like a tramp and she got into a car, like, you know, she was turning tricks.'

'What exactly made your auntie think that?'

'The way she was dressed and the way she acted when she got in the car. She had a lot of make-up on and a short skirt with high boots.'

'That's quite a stereotype. Can I talk to your auntie? I wouldn't want to jump to conclusions.'

'My Auntie Maureen needs no encouragement to chatter. I'll get her to call you.'

'Thank you. When was the last time you saw Dorinne?'

'I went to meet her in Windermere. I took her for tea. She was constantly on her phone. She looked like she was taking no care of herself. She was smoking heavily and irritable. That was the last time I took an interest.

'I was told she was found in a waste bin. Like rubbish. I don't want to know what happened. But I do want to know when you catch him. My husband says you live by the sword you die by the sword, but she used to be a sweet girl. That's what I'll remember.'

'I think that's the best you can do, and it's the way she should be remembered.'

Kelly gave Mrs Callaghan her number. She hadn't dealt with any of the persons of interest in the case back in October, because it was a standard missing person case. Budget constraints meant that senior investigators didn't work on every incident reported; it was physically impossible. But she was fed the details in reports.

She said goodbye to Mrs Callaghan and expressed her sympathy once again. She made a mental note to look up the details of Dorinne's great-aunt Maureen, but the name rang a bell anyway and she knew she'd heard it before. Next she ran Dorinne's number through technical support. They confirmed what she suspected, that it hadn't been done back in October because of the Lancaster sighting and the transfer of the case.

Every mobile phone in the country, when it's switched on, sends a signal to two or three local cells. Triangulation of the signals can trace phones to a geographical location, and by doing so, Kelly would find out where Dorinne's phone was last active, and on what day. Further GPS tracking might be able to pinpoint it exactly, depending on the model of Dorinne's phone. They were facing an uphill climb to find a killer who was actively abducting three months ago, but the chances were, with this sort of MO, he could possibly have done it again already, and might have done it before.

Next, she called an old friend who happened to be the Met's best criminal profiler. Dr Demi Cramer had helped Kelly out on a few occasions and she had a nose for whackos. Demi was a single, childless, workaholic tour de force, who didn't mince her words. Kelly hoped she picked up.

'Kelly Porter! You must have a maniac on the loose. How the hell are you?'

Kelly smiled. 'I'm afraid that's exactly what I have. But it is good to hear your voice. Still at the Met?'

'I'm lecturing full-time now. I'm at the University of Durham.'

'Beautiful city,' Kelly said.

'It is just that. It has the charm of a medieval keep, the history of the venerable Bede, and the self-satisfaction of Hyacinth Bucket. I love it. Of course all of my lectures are in the castle.'

'I wouldn't expect anything less. Do you wear your gown and mortarboard?' Kelly affectionately referred to the shape of the graduation cap resembling the bricklayer's tool.

'Obviously.'

Kelly ran the MO past Dr Cramer and received a flurry of excitement in return. It was a juicy one. She could imagine the expert scrambling for reference books and searching her bookcase for precedents as she waited. She imagined Demi sitting in an old reading room, surrounded by centuries-old oak tables and floor-to-ceiling bookcases made of mahogany or walnut.

'You've got my attention. This is so rare, you know. You'd expect to come across a case like this maybe once in your lifetime. The combination of abduction, captivity, torture and murder, over a long period of time, is… astounding. I've had the honour of actually being involved in something like this before, and we know who that was.'

Demi was talking about a serial killer in the Lake District a couple of years back, who she had gone on to write a book about. They'd both interviewed the monster and delved into the crazy mind that drove them to abuse women over several decades. But this was different. Kelly told her about the metal, the cracked teeth and the length of time Dorinne had been held captive.

Kelly could see another bestseller for Demi. But she deserved it: the woman was brilliant. She might even get a TV deal out of it, like Kelly had seen more of recently on criminal investigation channels. Using experts gave them credibility. Josie loved to watch them, but for Kelly it was a busman's holiday, talking about murder at home. She humoured her stepdaughter and they discussed famous cases. Secretly Kelly enjoyed it: Josie had an inquisitive mind, and she asked intelligent questions. It wouldn't surprise Kelly if Josie went into something investigative in her future. Then, for a moment, she imagined Josie feeding a new baby, and pushing a pram. Everyone would think she was a teenage mum. That thought made her smile. People could think what they liked.

'There are four types of killers: thrill-seekers, mission-oriented, visionaries and control freaks. I would imagine a man like this has a traumatic history of violence, probably at the hands of his mother, or another dominant female. The fact that he kept Dorinne alive for a long time suggests that he was doing something with her that gives him immense pleasure. But that's not what defines thrill-seeking: that refers to enjoying the media attention and toying with police. This is more about control, perhaps a control he lost as a child. He enjoys inflicting pain and watching somebody in extreme discomfort. He will live alone, in a remote location, away from busy urban areas. He likely will use the services of sex workers, because they are easy targets and he can act out fantasies: practise, if you like. You did say that you had another missing woman?' Demi asked.

'I agree,' Kelly said. 'And, yes. Our enquiries are taking us in that direction and we've flagged up known areas that attract sex workers. The other woman, who went missing last week, was living in the same area, but they're like ghosts, these workers – almost impossible to track.'

'That's why he's targeting them,' stated the enthusiastic psychologist.

It was the first time that anyone had put it so bluntly: the glaringly obvious coincidence of Lisa Lau's disappearance. From anyone else, Kelly would have dismissed such a quick assessment on very little information, but Demi knew the human mind like no other. She promised to look at everything Kelly could send her and provide a detailed analysis as soon as she could.

'That's a long time between abductions; have you looked at other missing person files?'

'It's on my list of things to do, but you know what it's like trying to get information about women in that trade.'

'Send them to me,' Demi said. It was an instruction not a request, but Kelly was used to her bluntness.

Kelly opened the Lisa Lau file and saw that no activity had been logged since it passed to Preston police. The CCTV file from the train station hadn't been uploaded yet. She had to leave it to Craig, who she knew would get round to it. The temptation to take everything on at once was overwhelming. She'd already delegated who would do what tomorrow and she was satisfied that she'd get results in good time. She wanted to run the whole affair from Eden House, but it was more important to visit locations to see for herself; that's when she got the best feel for a case.

She sat back in her chair. Her back ached and she felt dog tired. She must have read around two hundred pages of information regarding Dorinne Callaghan. Uniforms had been dispatched to go over information received when Dorinne had been reported missing, back in October. Kelly had chosen which ones to follow up and further investigate but nothing was really jumping out at her. Their key witness so far was Dorinne's room-mate, who'd urged the hostel to report Dorinne missing in the first place. She'd said Dorinne told her that she was meeting a friend at the Scrag End pub in Ambleside. She never came back. Even the room-mate wasn't surprised, though. Dorinne was known for her fickle nature: she followed her nose, living from moment to moment, taking risks, allowing men to pay for food and hotel rooms. The notes said that a squad car had paid the Scrag End pub a visit and the encounter was logged.

Maybe the Scrag End pub was where they should start, now that it was a murder inquiry. But not tonight. For both her and Craig, Ambleside was a good hour away on a good day. She had to call it a day, and so did her team. The night shift would follow leads where they could. After the budget cuts almost a decade ago, lots of Cumbria police stations had been auctioned off, but Windermere was still open. They could send a car from that station to the Scrag End to get things moving, and tomorrow they'd consolidate. She'd spend the whole day in Ambleside tomorrow.

She was expecting a new recruit to start in the morning. What a way to join a team. He was supposed to have turned up today, but there was a problem with his house sale. He was a young DS from Glasgow who'd moved to the area to start afresh. It was a well-travelled journey from the city to the Lake District.

Personnel from huge hubs of crime in cities up and down the country regularly applied for jobs in the sticks after burnout. When Kelly worked in London, they often had ten murder cases running alongside one another: it wasn't for everyone.

Chapter 16

Kelly woke naturally but it'd been an unsettled night. Josie had got halfway up the climbing wall but had frozen, and it had taken Johnny, and an instructor, two hours to get her back down. Johnny had stayed with his daughter through the night and Kelly had tossed and turned in her large bed, missing Johnny's body next to her. She'd tried to vomit first thing but the usual retching had produced nothing. She kept telling herself that by week twelve or thirteen, she'd be all right. Morning sickness was a first-trimester thing for most women. Before now, she'd never heard of a trimester.

She'd forced down some ginger biscuits and some herbal tea and had filled a flask with soup, made from scratch in the blender. It had been a Christmas present from Ted's daughters, June and Amber. A machine with blades so powerful that the friction cooked the soup as it blended. Genius.

Outside, her breath escaped in vapour clouds, billowing into the bitter cold morning air. The temperature was barely above freezing and the forecast predicted snow this afternoon. The remnants of the last covering still lingered at the sides of roads and, of course, on the fells above them. She rubbed her fingers and sat on her hands in the car, as she waited for the heated seat to fire up. Pooley Bridge was still half asleep, and only dog walkers and shop owners were about. The steamers ran a skeleton service in the winter months, and the campsites, dotted along the whole of Ullswater's coastline, were sparsely populated. She cleared her back windscreen of mist and enjoyed the warmth from the heaters as it came through. She switched on the radio and heard the news bulletin about Dorinne. It made for sober listening. They didn't need to draw attention to Dorinne's alleged after-hours work. As the news spread, she knew that sex workers who knew Dorinne would still offer their services, aware there was a predator about, but in desperate need of money. They'd carry on taking risks, thinking it would never happen to them. When the gossip spread to ordinary folk that the victim was a woman of 'low morals', it would bring out a kind of moral hierarchy and enable women who thought themselves above the deceased to assume themselves safe.

But Kelly had seen it before: sex workers being targeted, and women of higher social standing feeling immune; then one day, a well-to-do female goes missing and suddenly society takes note. Murderers don't care about CVs, they just target the most vulnerable. And women are always vulnerable, regardless of their economic status.

The drive east to Penrith was uneventful and she crossed the M6 with ease. Sometimes the junction could be snagged up, but if she timed her journey well, and went into work earlier than nine o'clock, then she was usually all right. It was seven thirty a.m. The office would be quiet and she could plan her day. She yawned. Her restlessness last night had centred round imagining being surrounded by scores of babies, all demanding her attention at once, and her not able to satisfy any of them. It was a bad dream of nappies, bottles, breasts and high-pitched wailing. She'd always assumed that nightmares starred figures who conjured horror in the form of knives, dark alleys and strangulation. No, not so: she'd discovered that terror could come in small packages too.

Penrith was quiet and she parked with ease behind the beautiful red sandstone building of Eden House. Mentally, she was ready for the day ahead, for her team to concentrate all of their efforts on the Dorinne Callaghan case. Nothing prepared her for what she was met with as she stepped foot inside the office: notification that a pod in Kendal had received a 999 call reporting a young mother missing since yesterday afternoon. The small hairs on Kelly's arms stood up and she felt a sense of dread come over her. She remembered Demi's words: 'That's a long time between abductions.'

Adults, and minors, went missing all the time and the vast majority reappeared alive and well within forty-eight hours. Some did not, like Dorinne Callaghan, and look how that ended. This new disappearance had been called in by somebody who was actively concerned for the woman's safety, and had pointed the finger in the direction of a supposedly aggressive partner, who'd been with her the night before. It was what Kelly called a flag: in other words, it was something to remain mindful of. Anyone who goes missing from an unharmonious relationship is always considered fairly high-risk.

Or at least that would have been her reaction if it wasn't for Dorinne's chopped-up body sitting in the mortuary waiting for tests to return from the lab. The woman had gone missing from her home in Glenridding, but the aggressive partner lived in rented accommodation in Grasmere. The village next door to Ambleside.

Kelly thanked the uniform for the information, and frowned. Suddenly one missing person had turned into two, and another one dead. Her police head told her not to jump to conclusions, but instinct and experience told her the opposite. She made her way upstairs to the warm incident room. Downstairs was fairly draughty, as the doors were flung open on a regular basis to allow squads making arrests in, visitors out, or both. The room was empty and she went to her own office and sat down in front of her computer, dreading what she might read on what they knew so far about the woman reported missing this morning. Before Lisa Lau, she might have seen things differently, but now, after yesterday, and Dorinne's murder, everything had changed, and at breakneck speed.

She read the information gathered on the missing woman so far. Her name was Lucinda Dockie and her partner was a British national with a Turkish father: Yus Ali. Then she called Craig Lockwood.

It turned out that Craig knew the boyfriend from a burglary in Bowness. He was bad news. It wasn't a good start; however, the lad had no previous involving violence. The fact that Lisa Lau had worked in Glenridding sat between her and Craig, with them both knowing the implication: another missing woman, linking at least two together. It was where Lucinda Dockie lived.

'My gut is saying treat them as connected,' Craig said.

'Mine too,' she agreed.

'Did you say she was a mother?' Craig asked, referring to Lucinda Dockie.

'Yes, to a toddler. She's three.'

'Who's looking after her?'

'The notes say Lucinda's mother, who lives in Bowness.'

'I can cover that. I can send a car over there if you like?' Craig said.

'Thank you, that'd be a great help.'

'How old is Lucinda?'

Kelly checked her notes. 'She's twenty-four. I'll start a new case file and copy you in as joint SIO, if that's all right. I have a bad feeling about this. I spoke to a criminal psychologist yesterday and she worked on it through the night. I sent her everything we have and I've received a tentative but fascinating profile.'

'That was quick.'

'I've worked with her before; she's a machine. Anyway, she's painted a grim picture of whoever killed Dorinne. Nothing about it is surprising, when you read it, but having her backing gives it credence. Frankly, no SIO wants a character like this on their patch. She said that she'd be very surprised if this killer didn't have previous and I'm looking into other missing person cases.'

'Including Lisa Lau?'

'Exactly. We need to get to the bottom of this as quick as we can. Did you find the CCTV footage of Preston station?'

'Yep. It's on my to-do list today. I'll appoint somebody else to shift my workload and I'll put everything into this.'

'Thanks, Craig. Let's talk soon.'

–

Kelly heard her office come to life and listened as members of her team began arriving and greeting one another. She also heard an unfamiliar voice, and it was Scottish.

'Ma'am.' Kate poked her head around Kelly's door. Kelly raised her eyebrows in question. Kate walked into the office and Kelly could see that a man waited behind her: a young, good-looking man.

'DS Dan Houghton reporting for duty,' Kate said with a grin, introducing their newest recruit. Kelly and he shook hands over her desk and he stood erect and serious.

She fleetingly thought about Will Phillips. She missed him. She missed his Ralph Lauren aftershave first thing in the morning. She'd come to associate it with comfort and familiarity. But that was a closed chapter and she smiled at his replacement. Kate hovered.

'Take a seat. We've just had a missing person case come in – the second in as many weeks, as well as a dead body turning up yesterday – so you've arrived at the perfect time. So, you've come from Glasgow? What brings you here?'

'Just a change, ma'am. I worked Glasgow for ten years and it's time to do something else other than drugs and knives. I also wanted to work for you.'

'Oh, we have our fair share of drugs and knives,' Kate said. Kelly looked at DS Houghton.

'In the office, Dan, you can call me Kelly. Would you like Kate to get you a coffee and we'll have a catch-up?'

Kate looked disappointed at being dismissed, but managed a smile.

Dan nodded. 'If you don't mind, a coffee would be fantastic. I only moved down yesterday and it's a big journey.'

Kate disappeared without asking Kelly if she too fancied a coffee. Kelly had checked: the cups had definitely been removed from the windowsill.

'I've read your service history and it's sterling. You've been promoted quickly. Ambitious?'

'I'd say so.'

'Where do you see yourself in five years?'

'DI, ma'am, I mean, Kelly.'

'So, you're after my job?'

He looked embarrassed.

'I'm toying with you. With cuts as they are, especially in Cumbria, you might have to go elsewhere to chase that promotion, but meanwhile, I'll keep you busy. Fancy getting out of the office? I need someone to visit Ambleside and Grasmere with me, and I don't mean sightseeing, though they are two of the nicest villages in the Lakes.'

'Absolutely! I've heard of them.'

'It's an unfortunate but surprisingly uplifting aspect of our job here: the backdrop is stunningly beautiful. I can point out the sites on the way. Do you know Cumbria well?'

'Not at all, I'm used to the Scottish Highlands for my walking and carry-on.'

'Well, we'll have to convert you, then, won't we?' Kelly smiled conspiratorially and Dan shook his head.

'Not a chance!' he said.

Kate came back in with a mug of coffee and set it down on Kelly's desk, in front of Dan. Kelly got up and walked to the window, looking out of it, peering to the fells. The sky was dreary.

'It's starting to snow so we'll keep an eye on the forecast, aiming to leave about eleven? The pubs open at midday and I want to start with one that's cropped up. Kate, I'm taking DS Houghton to Ambleside. Hold the fort, will you, let me know if any lab results come in from the bin?'

'The bin?' asked the new DS.

'Our body yesterday was found in a wheelie bin. You can read HOLMES on the move.'

'Yes, ma'am.'

Kelly smiled. She could tell that Dan Houghton had been used to working in a formal environment, as she had in London. Her office was more relaxed. He'd get used to it.

'This is proper snow. Finally, after all that indecision; it's here and looks thick too.' She continued to stare out of the window. The delicate fat flakes were mesmerising, like a gracefully over-weight ballerina. Dan Houghton joined her with his coffee. She moved away and began packing a bag.

'When you said you wanted to work for me, why was that?' Kelly asked as she gathered her phone, Toughpad and notebook.

'Your reputation for solving cases: it's way above the average for a small team. You never give up. I get the impression it's not just a job for you. I read all the bulletins and I've followed your cases for a few years. I knew I wanted to join when a transfer vacancy came up.'

'Well, welcome to the team, Dan, I'm sure I'll find lots for you to do.'

She stood behind him and gazed beyond to the grey, thick-ening sky. The snow was beginning to settle on the pavements and roads below.

Chapter 17

In Barrow, DI Craig Lockwood scanned the CCTV footage he'd been sent by Preston police station, taken around the time when the sighting of Lisa Lau had been reported. He'd spent over two hours on it and he hadn't seen Lisa at all. Then, just as he was about to give up, an image caught his eye and he paused the tape, rewinding it.

He stared at the image of the woman on the platform, who appeared to be waiting impatiently for a train. He checked the time and it matched the sighting, give or take half an hour. He zoomed in and took in her body shape, as much as he could of her face and her mannerisms.

The woman was East Asian, but she was not Lisa Lau. Of that he was sure.

He got the file up on his computer system and read the entry from the officer who'd interviewed the witness. There was a marker attached and he opened it.

It read: *Possible sighting at same time in Ambleside?* It was a tag that had been added a week ago, after the case was handed to Preston, but he still hadn't been notified. He read the officer's name and sighed. The guy was experiencing some issues at home and hadn't been on the ball lately. He sat in an adjacent office and Craig went to see if he was on shift. He was.

As soon as Detective Constable Mark Diamond saw Craig's face, he knew that something was up.

'The Lisa Lau case, Mark?' Craig left the implied question in the air.

'Yes, sir? The one that went to Preston?' the junior officer replied.

'Yup, the same. You added a tag last week about another sighting, but this time in Ambleside?'

'Ah, yes, sir. I did,' said DC Diamond, looking relieved to have a ready answer.

'And you didn't think to inform me?'

The DC's face fell as he realised Craig was unimpressed. 'Erm, the case had already been moved, sir. I thought Preston would act upon it.'

Craig stared at him.

'Sorry, sir.'

Craig sighed. 'Do you know any details of the supposed sighting in Ambleside?'

DC Diamond's face went pink. 'No, sir, I...'

'You assumed Preston would act upon it? Christ, if their witness turns out to be unreliable, then we have to have that case back here in South Cumbria.'

The DC looked down and rubbed his eyes. Craig patted him on his shoulder and sighed again.

'Look, don't be leaving loose ends. I know it's tempting, because it gets another case off our hands, but if we miss something, it could mean we ignore an opportunity to find her.'

'I thought she'd gone down south, sir.'

'We only thought that because of that damn sighting at Preston train station, which, I've just discovered, was not her,' Craig said.

The officer opened his mouth.

'Which leaves the question: what if she never left?' Craig added before walking away.

He knew there was no point disciplining the lad harshly; the young DC looked worn out and distracted. Many on the force wore the same look. A lot of them were overworked, and the slightest opportunity to offload work was taken gladly.

Back at his desk, Craig called the missing persons desk in Preston. They told him that no new leads had been forthcoming but the case was still open. He asked about the tag and the officer sighed and rechecked.

'Ah, yes, a woman said she saw her in a bar in Ambleside and she knew her personally, so it's a reliable lead.'

'And you didn't contact me?'

'The officer handling the case makes those decisions. I'm guessing, looking briefly at the notes, that she was sighted in Preston afterwards, so it's not your remit.'

'It wasn't her in Preston. I've reviewed the footage.'

'Oh.'

Missing persons cases could stay open for years. One hundred and eighty thousand people are reported missing in the UK every year, and many are never heard of again; around four thousand of those are in Cumbria. It was widely accepted in the police force that the figure was unsustainable: in other words, the police didn't have the resources to dedicate to so many cases, and errors were inevitable.

Craig was determined that Lisa Lau's disappearance wasn't going to be one of those cases. He asked to get the case transferred back. The Preston desk sergeant sighed down the phone at the extra admin. He was probably thinking how incompetent Cumbria Constabulary was, but Craig didn't have the time or the will to argue. The legwork had been done by uniforms from Barrow to Penrith, and Kelly Porter knew as well as he did that if no one talked to each other, then nobody was actively joining any dots. As soon as the witness statement on the sighting in Preston came in, everything had stopped. Sure, it had taken up until last week to transfer the file, but Preston police had taken over straight away. He scanned HOLMES, looking for evidence that progress had been made.

With the phone under his chin, he scrolled through the file and realised that nothing else had been inputted until his colleague's marker last week, which had obviously fallen through the net. He closed his eyes and rubbed them. The sergeant was banging on about something to do with signatures and senior officers. Craig said all the right things in response, but inside he was seething. Finally, he replaced the phone and went back to the beginning of the report on Lisa Lau. He noticed that the Home Office had sent a letter of information to the Chinese embassy – a detail he already knew – but he decided to read every word of the file. The response had come from the Chinese embassy in London. He read that Lisa Lau was estranged from her family in China, but they were known to be extremely influential and wealthy. The embassy was looking into their own investigation and Craig wondered why he wasn't aware of that. Politics probably. The Chinese embassy had also put a marker on Lisa's passport the day she was reported missing so it would flag up with the police if she left the country. Craig worked out the time frame in his head. Lisa had been reported missing after failing to show up for a shift at the Glenridding guest house where she worked. The proprietor had reported her missing as some kind of revenge act intended to teach her a lesson not to mess him around, as she was allegedly on her last warning. Craig jotted down the name on a fresh piece of paper. She'd worked a shift at a bar in a pub in Patterdale before that, which checked out, so she would not have had time to leave the country.

Patterdale was where the body in the bin had been found.

He carried on reading. Every single statement had been taken by different squads on the ground. Kelly had relied on information from uniforms the whole length of Cumbria. Sometimes it just worked out that way. To be honest, they'd both been relieved when she was sighted in Preston and it added weight to the story that she was an independent, wayward girl, who made her own mind up about where and when she worked. But now, red flags were popping up like apples in a bucket on Halloween.

He began reading every statement and realised that some of them weren't on HOLMES. He hung his head. It was looking like a clusterfuck and Kelly wouldn't be happy when she found out. He had to call her. Between them, they'd relied too heavily on each other to manage the case that spread over both of their remits. Now, Craig realised that neither of them had appointed a duty officer to watch over the case: nobody had been assigned the case because, firstly, adults aren't treated as in danger when they go missing unless there is evidence to the contrary, and secondly, they had both assumed it had been done by the other. After all, Lisa Lau was a foreign national, with a soon-to-expire visa, who by all accounts could look after herself. He questioned whether Kelly was letting her profiler friend lead her to waste valuable resources on a simple case when she had a murder to solve. Perhaps he was being harsh.

They'd discussed it so many times over the phone, and had thrown ideas around as they chewed over the leads and names, but neither of them had got a handle on the case before it was simply whisked away to Preston, where, they assumed, a detective would be given the task of bringing the case together.

Kelly would kick herself, as was he doing now. But he had to tell her. She'd want to investigate herself, he knew that much.

Especially when she found out that the Chinese embassy might beat her to it.

Chapter 18

'The report is straightforward. According to her mother, Lucinda had a volatile relationship with her boyfriend. They'd been arguing a lot recently, so the mother says. She was supposed to babysit but when she got to the house the child was alone. She called Lucinda's work, but she hadn't turned up.' Kelly talked as she drove, and Dan stared out of the window. They were on their way to Ambleside to visit the Scrag End pub. It was a lead on the Dorinne Callaghan case, but it had been picked up by HOLMES that Lucinda Dockie frequented the same joint, according to Dorinne's room-mate. Kelly had left Kate in charge and she tapped the steering wheel lightly, eager to gauge the world graced by Dorinne when she was alive, and perhaps that of other women in the same line of work, including Lisa Lau. Kelly had given a long brief at Eden House and trusted Kate to chase the paper today. It was frankly a dull job, and not the work of a senior investigating officer, but Kate was good at it, and didn't mind being the one left behind in the office. She was a grafter and would flag up any anomalies to Kelly immediately.

'Was she the type of mother to leave her three-year-old child alone in the house?' Dan asked.

'Lucinda's mother said she adored the girl and spent every last penny on her. Quote: "she's the reason she breathed".'

'I wonder if the boyfriend has a key to the house?' Dan said. They drove through Glenridding, where Lucinda Dockie lived with her daughter, but their priority today was tracing Dorinne's last movements. Kelly had made arrangements for

Lucinda Dockie's house to be searched this week. After all, despite the stench created by three women going missing from the same area in as many months, the murder took priority. The common denominator was their chosen line of work. If the three women had been of different ages, socio-economic status, demographic, employment and location, then Kelly wouldn't be letting it play on her mind so much. Granted, Lisa Lau should be making her way back to China sometime soon, but a passport check had revealed no such activity.

'Preliminary door to door revealed pretty frequent arguments and noises of door-slamming etc.' Kelly was familiar with the notes and had gone over the information they had several times, looking for similarities with Dorinne.

'Classic domestic stuff,' Dan said.

'Yep. We need to speak to the three-year-old but that will need setting up with the legal team and child protection. DI Lockwood was sending a car to the mother's home in Bowness last night, is that on HOLMES?' Kelly asked.

He held his iPad as she navigated the snowfall that was steady and unrelenting. She questioned the wisdom of driving deep into the Lakes on a day like this, but pushed it out of her mind.

'Yes, here it is. The statement was taken last night, and is pretty much the same as the prelim questions at the time she reported her daughter missing.' He read on. 'She'd gone to collect the child for the evening as Lucinda was due to work in a local pub diner in Glenridding and found the child home alone. What do we know about the boyfriend?' Dan asked himself as much as Kelly. He was in the zone as he continued reading, and it was a shame because they were travelling through some of the best scenery in the Lakes.

Kelly smiled to herself. He was using the familiar pronoun of a team already and she liked it. She was impressed with his focus. He carried on.

'Here we go. Known to us. DI Lockwood down in Barrow has previous record for a burglary in Bowness. None involving violence but a few warnings for drunk and disorderly.'

'Does he work?' Kelly asked.

'Labouring when he can get it.'

'Did he do time?'

'Six months,' Dan said. 'So we've got prints and DNA.' His mind worked like hers.

Kelly drove around the lake and headed south.

'You've just missed Ullswater but don't worry, Brothers Water is coming up and it's gorgeous. Keep looking behind as we go over the pass, if you can put your iPad down.'

Unforgiving mountains of ancient rock stood between them and their final destination. They could go across to Keswick and then down to the tiny village, or carry on south, via the narrow pass called The Struggle, which was a shortcut from Kirkstone Pass to Ambleside, then double back up to Grasmere to visit Yus Ali and Dorinne's Auntie Maureen. The Helvellyn range was in their way and either route made no odds. Kelly chose to go over Kirkstone Pass and navigate The Struggle across to Ambleside and then on to the short journey to Grasmere.

'I wonder what drew Yus Ali to Grasmere; it's a sleepy little place. Probably cheap accommodation in a guest house is my guess. For a young guy, it's not exactly Ibiza. And it's not exactly a throbbing hub of builders and labourers. Lucinda's mother said that he'd angled to stay with his girlfriend in Glenridding, but she'd resisted the idea because of her young daughter. Another red flag.'

As Kelly navigated around Brothers Water and up to the Pass, Dan went quiet. The mist that usually accompanied heavy snow sat in the valley, between the fells, and it looked magical. She watched him as he took in the scenery. Kelly had been the same when she moved back from London three years ago. The first time she'd driven over Kirkstone Pass since returning to the Lake District had taken her breath away and brought back whole swathes of memory, almost, but not quite, erased, of herself and John Porter hiking up on the contour line. The snow drove at her windshield and made the vision appear ethereal. She drove an Audi four-by-four that could easily cope with the conditions. Besides, they were at the highest point of their journey and it wasn't so bad. The wipers fought against the snow and the heater gave them a sense of security. They drove past an occupied Mini, which seemed to have given up and was parked at the side of the road near to the Kirkstone Inn. The inn would put them up overnight if needs be. They'd get a warm local welcome too and a hearty plate of food.

Kelly always marvelled at the moors around Kirkstone, because they were about as remote as one got in the Lakes. They went on for miles and didn't really attract tourists, who preferred to row on Windermere or walk up Cat Bells. It was what attracted her to them. She itched to get up on the mountainside, to trudge through the snow and ice, making the first prints of the day.

She turned off on the road called The Struggle and they saw Ambleside in the distance.

'Not long to go now,' she said to Dan, who was still quiet.

Arriving in Ambleside, they had to wait to get through traffic that was snarled up due to the weather, as well as navigating around soaking walkers caught in the blizzards over the fells. Sodden hikers trod miserably through the town, but many of them were still jovial, stopping to swap notes with fellow pursuers of the wilderness.

'Ambleside always reminds me of Ardmore,' Kelly said.

'You know the Cairngorms?' Dan was suddenly animated.

'Of course. I used to go up there quite a lot with my hiking club at Lancaster University. We once camped beneath Glencoe, and cleaned up about fifteen whiskies from the top row of the only bar around. It always amazes me how you can find a wee dram, without fail, in the remotest of places.' Kelly used the Scots colloquialism affectionately.

'It's more precious than water,' Dan confirmed.

'We sat up with the mountain rescue team, who got called out around midnight to rescue another group of students without torches or whistles.'

'Numpties,' Dan said. She agreed.

The Scrag End pub was at the end of a lane, in the heart of Ambleside, off Market Cross, surrounded by walking and camping shops, trendy cafés and a market. It had been there, in an old coaching inn's alley, for three hundred years.

Kelly had no idea what the place was like nowadays. She hadn't been in there for twenty years. It used to be on the Ambleside Amble, a pub crawl of twenty-six pubs to denote the miles in a marathon. The Scrag End was last and always the rowdiest. The name apparently came from it doubling as a butcher's shop in Victorian times. The wooden block, various hooks and ancient knives hung on its walls for decoration.

It hadn't taken them long to find a parking space in the centre, with most shoppers being put off by the snow, and the gritters were out already, making the fresh white powder turn to brown sludge. They trod carefully through it towards the long alley. Dan looked around, taking in everything like a good detective.

'What do you think?' she asked.

'It's lovely, so it is. And like Ardmore, but bigger.' His thick accent was peppered with colloquialisms she'd heard from many Scots. His accent wasn't as harsh as she remembered those of most Scottish people from the west coast. To her, the Edinburgh accent was softer, but Dan's Glaswegian accent was smooth and pleasant. He had an air of quiet responsibility about him. She reckoned he kicked ass when he had to, but he was also a gentleman – and easy on the eye. Her time in the car with him had introduced to her part of his personality and she'd sized him up so far as warm, loyal and unequivocal. In fact, he reminded her of a younger Craig Lockwood.

–

The alley was smaller than she remembered and more bland. It had none of the bohemian charm she recalled from her nights out here with mates. Though, the snow did give it a clean blanket under which to hide. No one milled about in the few shops down there, which looked like junk shops and sewing places. There wasn't a café and it all made for quite a let-down for Kelly.

She went into the pub first, followed by Dan, and the entrance split into two: right and left, both leading to bars. She took the right one first. The bar was empty and no one seemed to be serving, so they made their way back and went into the left side. In here, there were a few people sitting alone, and one group of three men. A man in his twenties or early thirties stood drying a glass behind the bar. Everybody in the place stopped what they were dong and looked at them. Kelly ignored them and strode to the bartender, who stopped wiping.

Kelly lifted her neck tag and showed her ID to the man. 'Can I ask you a couple of questions about a woman who used to drink in here?'

Immediately, people stood up and began to leave.

'Hold on, folks, we're not that scary,' she said. Her voice was firm. Some carried on packing up bags and putting on coats; others stopped. 'I'm just asking for information. Maybe some of you can help if you're regulars.'

Three, four, and then all six people got up to leave. Dan squared his shoulders but Kelly got in first.

'Now, hang on just a minute. This is a police investigation and I need your cooperation. I'll only take a minute of your time, so sit yourselves down. Now. Please.'

Dan gave a sideways glance to his new boss. The punters did as they were told.

'You take them, I'll take these,' Kelly said. 'No need to be so nervous around us coppers, if you've got nothing to hide.'

The bartender shrugged. 'People don't like to get involved in trouble, it's quite normal isn't it?' He was a Scot and Dan held out his hand to shake and introduced them both. The man lost some of his edge and took the offered hand.

'What makes you think there's trouble?' Dan asked him.

'I don't think you've come in here to blather.'

Dan began with him and Kelly turned her attention to the group of three men sitting together. She produced a photo of Dorinne Callaghan, receiving blank stares in return. Next she held up a photo of Lisa Lau. More blank stares. A photo of Lucinda Dockie got a different response. One of the men recognised her.

'She drinks in here,' he said. 'I know her fella.'

'Yus Ali?' she asked.

He nodded. 'Piece of shit, don't know what she's doing with him.'

'When did you last see her in here?'

'Can't remember. Last week maybe. Good-looking woman.'

Kelly took their details and said they could leave. She overheard the bartender confirm that he recognised all three of the women, and she cocked her ear.

'It's a small space, you get to know regular faces,' he said.

'How regular?'

'Maybe once a week.'

Kelly turned to a young woman sitting on her own. It was an unusual sight; pubs were normally the domain of single men. Women usually ventured in groups into places like this for a laugh.

She showed her the photos.

'I knew Lisa. So, she never went to Preston then?'

'You followed the story?'

The woman nodded.

'How did you know her? She's still missing, sadly,' Kelly said.

'Yeah, we hung out here and there. She paid for everything because she was sent money by her family. Apparently they're loaded but she hates them.'

'Why?'

'They want her to do as she's told, and Lisa's not like that. She breaks all the rules.'

'Yes, I see that in her too, and I only know her from her profile,' Kelly said gently. 'What's your name?'

'Mandy Williams.'

'Mandy, if she had so much money from her family, why was she working?'

'To annoy them.'

'I'm just going to ask you directly, was she working as a prostitute?' Kelly asked.

Mandy looked at Kelly and her eyes showed fear and indecision. Kelly saw that she didn't want to get her friend into trouble.

'I'm not really interested in if she was or she wasn't, but it could help find her,' Kelly added.

The girl relaxed.

'I think she did. I mean, I know she did. She bragged about what men bought her if she did stuff with them.'

'Where did she go? Hotels? Cars? Flats?'

'She said they took her to nice houses. They were always clean and tidy. She felt safe.'

'Maybe they weren't safe?'

Mandy looked at her hands and didn't answer.

'Why are you in here on your own?'

Panic flashed across Mandy's face again as she stumbled over her reply. 'I'm not, I'm erm, waiting for someone.'

'Who?'

'A friend.'

'Name?'

The young woman's eyes darted about. 'Can I go now?' she said, looking desperate.

'What about your friend?'

Silence sat between them like a fat elephant.

'Did Lisa ever mention someone called Yus Ali to you?'

Mandy shook her head.

'Did she ever tell you any of the names of her clients? Did she have regulars?'

'They never give real names.' Mandy sniggered, as if the detective should already know this. She'd let her guard down.

'How do you know that?'

The woman stood up.

'I'll need your personal details in case I need to speak to you again. How well did you say you knew her?'

'Not really well.'

'And who is the friend you're about to stand up by walking out?'

'Just a friend.'

'Give me a name and you can go.'

Mandy sighed, but then answered, 'Kian Delaney.'

Kelly had got what she needed. She moved on to an elderly man sitting on his own. Mandy Williams left.

'Good afternoon, sir. Are you a regular customer here?'

'I've been coming in here for fifty-odd years, I reckon. I see all the young girls come and go, and I remember the Chinese one because she was always laughing her head off, she was. It warmed the soul. It's cramped in here on a weekend, but you remember the pretty faces.'

'These pretty faces?' She showed him the photos. He acknowledged all three and nodded. 'The other two were more serious, and always alone.'.

'Did you ever see them with partners?' Kelly asked.

'What do you mean by partners?' he asked.

'Somebody they drank with, and had a good time, I guess. We're trying to establish who they came into contact with. It makes a difference.'

'So, all three of them are missing, are they?'

'This one's dead.' She pointed to Dorinne.

'Good heavens. In my day, we took care of our ladies, nowadays they're not treated the same. I saw them with folk all the time. I couldn't tell you who, though.'

'Sir, why do you drink in here if it's full of people who frankly don't sound that pleasant to me?'

'I'm not going to change my local just because of a bunch of young lads looking for trouble. I like coming here.' He looked away and sipped the end of his pint. For the first time, Kelly saw his confidence wane.

'Are you married?' she asked. He blushed.

He looked at her squarely. 'Look, young lady, I might like to look and pretend I'm young again, Lord knows I'm not. There's no crime in it.'

'No, there isn't.' She took his details. He said they called him Old Bobby. She could have sworn that she had seen Mandy Williams at his table when they walked in. He gave his name and address and put on his jacket and flat cap, nodding at her as he left, shouting thank you to the bartender. Kelly turned her attention to Dan again. She overheard the bartender giving him the name of another pub.

'The Gate Inn, in Glenridding.'

Kelly joined them. Between them, they'd spoken to everyone in the place. Last night a squad on night shift from Windermere had done the same and gathered information from several witnesses, all recognising the three women as regulars, and some of them alluding to the fact that they thought they picked men up here. It was useful information but at the same time not, because it told them everything and nothing at the same time. Yes, they were prostitutes; but ask who their clients were and they hit a brick wall.

'Who's your boss?' Kelly asked the bartender.

'The place is owned by someone called Burns. Lorna, I think. It's a private brewery. I don't know her personally, she never comes in here. But she pays my wages.'

'Does she have any other pubs?'

'I just told your colleague that she owns the Gate Inn in Glenridding.'

'Any idea if Dorinne went there too?'

'No idea.' He looked her straight in the eye. She figured that to work the bar in the place like this, a poker face was pretty essential.

'What about Yus Ali? You know him? He drinks in here, right?'

'Yes, everyone knows Yus, he's always looking for a fight. Lucinda doesn't like him telling her what to do. She doesn't come in here with him much, but he turned up recently, and she was with another fella, and he went berserk. I kicked him out, along with a few other lads looking to get involved.'

'What happened to Lucinda and this man?'

'They left.'

'Can you recall what day that was?'

The bartender thought for a while. 'It was last week some-time.'

'Do you know the man?'

'I've seen him about but I don't know his name.'

Typical, and probably a lie. 'Can you describe him?'

'Sure. Middle-aged, chunky, dressed kind of smart, bald, erm, a bit weird.'

'What do you mean a bit weird?'

The bartender laughed. 'Like a peeping Tom.'

Chapter 19

It wasn't long until Kelly and Dan were leaving the circular route around Ambleside, heading north to Grasmere, and Dan checked the address for Yus Ali. A visit to the youth hostel where Dorinne last stayed had proved pointless. It was so long ago she'd been there that half the staff had changed and no one remembered her. She was just another dosser down on her luck, working jobs and living hand to mouth.

'That's Rydal Water.' Kelly pointed to the tiny lake. It was a vision of calm and tranquillity that found its way onto many postcards, tea towels and mugs on offer in the tourist shops.

'It's bonny.'

They rounded the next lake, which Dan thought was another part of Rydal Water.

'No, it's Grasmere,' Kelly corrected him. 'They're two lakes.'

'They're tiny wee things. In Scotland, the lochs are huge.'

'Everything bigger up there?' Kelly asked.

'Aye, the salmon are like marlin.'

Kelly appreciated his quick wit. He was good to be spending a car ride with; it cut the frustration of driving from place to place without getting any answers.

The village of Grasmere appeared deserted. They drove past a shop called Marvin's that promised a post office inside, and fresh ice cream, and Kelly experienced a craving deep within her brain that triggered an obsessive image of her drinking freezing-cold cola, even though it was minus six degrees out. Maybe they'd stop there on the way back.

It didn't take long to find the right street and they parked outside a row of stone terraces. The one rented by Yus Ali advertised vacancies. The snow wasn't letting up and it settled in thick fluffy clouds on the windscreen when Kelly turned off the wipers and parked up. They got out and put on heavy coats, and trod carefully on their way to the door. Dan rang the bell. An intercom sounded and a woman's voice asked what they wanted.

'Police, madam. We're here to see one of your tenants. Mr Ali.'

'Oh, him. What's he done?'

'We just need to ask him some questions.'

'I'm on my way.'

She hung up.

'Here we go: she wants some gossip. She could have let us in but I reckon she wants to rubber-neck,' Kelly said.

A middle-aged woman wearing an oversized cardigan over leggings appeared and unlocked the door. They showed their ID and she let them in. The place stank of cigarette smoke and stale air. Kelly took the landlady's details, which she gave readily, smiling, and they were shown to Mr Ali's room. Once there, the woman knocked on the closed door and then shouted, without waiting for an answer, 'Yus! Police!'

'How do you know he's in?' Kelly asked.

'He's not got work right now. I know when he comes and goes. He came in late afternoon yesterday and he's probably been in his bed ever since.'

'Do you know exactly what time he came in?'

'Yep. It was four o'clock because I had just finished watching *A Place in the Sun*.'

'Thank you, that's very helpful. We'll take it from here,' Kelly said. Lucinda's mother had said that she'd gone to her daughter's house at five p.m. and found no sign of her, and she'd spoken to her around ten o'clock in the morning, so Mr Ali didn't have an alibi. Yet.

The door opened and a man, seemingly in his twenties, rubbed his eyes and stared at them blankly.

'Yus, get some clothes on! It's the coppers, what you been doin'?' his landlady scolded.

'Thank you, if we need you again we'll call.' Kelly stood her ground and the woman sauntered off, offended and disappointed that, for now, her piece of the action was over.

'Can we come in, Yus?' Kelly introduced them both and the man, coming to now, took stock of the situation.

'What's going on?' he asked.

Kelly looked at Dan.

'Mr Ali, your girlfriend, Lucinda Dockie, has been reported missing by her mother and we have reason to believe that you were with her yesterday. We'd like to ask you some questions.'

They waited.

'What? She's missing?' He had a thick northern accent and it made him sound more aggressive than was appropriate.

'Is that a Barrow accent, Yus? What brings you up here?'

'Work.'

Craig had warned Kelly that Yus Ali was adept at manipulating and lying. He was particularly good at stalling for time.

'Her mother reported her missing after finding her young daughter alone at her house. May we come in?' Kelly asked. Ali opened the door and beckoned them inside. It was what one might expect from a twenty-something lad, living on his own, short of cash. He lived in a single room, with a sideboard acting as a kitchen, which was scattered with ready meals, an open microwave and a kettle. His sink – presumably intended for personal ablutions – was full of dirty crockery, and clothes were strewn everywhere. At least the window was open.

'I saw her yesterday morning.' Ali turned his back to them and found a jumper to cover his naked torso. It was a curt, emotionless statement. 'She won't be missing, her mother's a stupid old cow who likes to butt her nose in, and she'll be somewhere.'

It was lame.

'What time yesterday did you see her?' Kelly did the talking and Dan took notes.

'Dunno, about nine. I stayed there Sunday night. She asked me to babysit the little 'un but I couldn't, I had to look for work, so I left.'

Kelly side-glanced Dan: Lucinda's mother had said that she didn't leave the little one with him, because she didn't trust him.

'Why did she want you to babysit? Where was she going?'

'She said she had work.'

'Where?' Kelly asked.

'Dunno,' Ali replied.

Kelly stared at him and he looked away. 'You don't seem too bothered that your girlfriend is missing,' she said.

'We kind of broke up yesterday.'

'Really? Why?'

Ali glared at her. She could tell that he was squirming, but that was exactly what she wanted: if he was uncomfortable then she needed to know why. He placed his hands on his neck and rubbed.

'Do you know where she is?' she pressed on.

'No.'

'Why do you think she would leave her three-year-old alone to go out?'

'To make money, of course, what a stupid question. And you guys think I'm the one who's dumb.'

'There's really no need for that, is there?' Kelly asked. 'How was she making money?'

'I didn't like it but she said she had no choice.'

'Can you be more specific?'

Ali paced up and down, flustered. They waited.

'I caught her with another fella. I reckon he was paying her. She denied it, but I think it's true.'

He looked genuinely pained, but that didn't mean that Lucinda hadn't come to harm at his hands, especially now he had a motive.

'So you were angry with her?'

'I know how this works, you know. I'm not stupid. Am I under arrest?'

'No. But can you give me an alibi for between ten a.m. and four p.m. yesterday?'

'I left her place, and I hitched back to Ambleside: that took me about two hours. Then I went to the pub. I got back late afternoon and went to bed.'

'Which pub?'

'The Scrag End in Ambleside.'

Dan made a note.

'Did you have sexual intercourse with Miss Dockie yesterday?'

'Why the fuck do you need to know that?'

'Routine.'

'Yes.'

'And you have no idea where she was going, to meet other men to perhaps receive money for services, as you've indicated?'

'No. I first saw her with a fella here in Grasmere, she didn't see me, and I confronted her after.'

'When?'

'Last week.'

'Where?'

'Walking arm in arm, towards the bus stop.'

'That's a bit of a risk, considering that you live here,' Kelly put to him.

'I was away working, but I came back early.'

'Did you recognise the man?'

Yus shook his head. 'No.'

'Can you describe him?'

'Erm, oldish. Fifty. Nice clobber. Creepy and small. It was dark. She was dressed like a whore.' The words were venomous.

'Sounds like a peeping Tom, chief,' Dan said.

Yus nodded. 'Yeah, a peeping Tom all right.'

Kelly watched Yus as he hung his head in apparent pain, but only from his wounded ego, not from any concern for his girlfriend.

'Thank you, Mr Ali. We'll be in touch. If Lucinda makes contact or you remember anything else, please do call us.'

They left him in his room and saw themselves out. The landlady appeared and angled for information, but none was forthcoming. They thanked her and walked back to the car.

'Fancy a Coke?' she asked Dan. He looked at her strangely.

'You drink that filth?' he asked. She almost took him seriously, but knew him well enough already to know that he was joking.

'I'll buy you an Irn-Bru,' she said.

She smiled as she accepted that another craving had taken hold of her and she couldn't get Marvin's post office shop out of her head. She began to think about the caramel taste and the coolness of the crisp bubbles. She drove back the way they'd come, found the shop and parked along the street.

'You never know what juicy scandal they'll tell you in these little town shops that've been here for years.'

They got out of the car and went inside the shop, and the bell above the door rang. A plaque on the entrance read: *Est. 1976.* She noted the decor and the feel of the place and figured that Marvin's hadn't changed much over the years. However, there was still a touch of success about it. There were boxes of local farmers' eggs on display, and baskets of locally knitted toys, as well as a book stand.

'Hello there,' a woman said from behind the counter. She eyed them. An elderly man came into the shop from a back room.

'What can I help you folks with? Are you lost?'

'I'm just buying a Coke, actually,' Kelly explained.

'Diet?' asked the man.

'God no, what's the point?'

He laughed. 'Well that's nice to hear, a lady not obsessed by her weight. They're over there in the fridge. And you, young man? We've got fresh pasties and of course there's sticky toffee pudding from Cartmel.'

'I'm good thank you, sir.'

'A Scotsman!' the man exclaimed. 'Welcome to the Lake District! God's country. Not taking away from your lovely land, but there's none like this.' He saw Dan's neck tag sticking out from behind his coat.

'Coppers?'

Kelly nodded. 'The shop has been here a long time?' she asked him.

'I'm Marvin, this is my shop. I bought it forty-four years ago.'

'Pleased to meet you, Marvin. We're not in here for police work, but you're very observant. Yes, we are detectives, just passing through.'

'Detectives just passing through?' sniffed the woman behind the counter. 'Well, maybe you should stop. There's plenty going on around here to keep you busy.'

Kelly noticed the woman had a dressing on her head.

'Now, now, Maureen, there've been rumours, that's all,' Marvin said gently.

'Maureen? What's your surname?' Kelly asked.

'Johnson, why?'

'You're the great-aunt of Dorinne Callaghan?' Kelly asked.

'I am that.' Maureen sniffed while Marvin watched her with a sympathetic look on his face. It was quite obvious to Kelly that the two were friends. Presumably she'd come here for comfort after the terrible news.

'You hurt yourself?' Kelly asked her, gesturing towards the dressing.

'I fainted when I heard the news.'

'I'm so sorry.' Dan echoed the sentiment.

'Her poor mother. God knows what animal did that to her, but I told the police when she went missing about all I knew of what goes on round here,' said Maureen.

'What about?' Kelly asked.

The woman looked at Marvin and then around the shop as if to make sure no one else was about.

'Do you work here?' Kelly asked, changing tack and trying to remain casual as she strode to the fridge to get a Coke from the shelf. It was freezing cold and she took it back to the counter. Her taste buds let her know that they were waiting.

'I've always helped Marvin out. I live just across the road.' Maureen took the bottle from Kelly and scanned the barcode, and Kelly paid by contactless. No sooner was her card back in her wallet than she'd opened the screw top and gulped a mouthful. It was like nectar to a honeybee. She closed her eyes and Maureen and Marvin watched her.

'You in charge?' Maureen asked Dan.

'No, Detective Porter is.'

Maureen turned back to Kelly and waited, watching her slug the drink.

When Kelly had taken her fill she put the cap back on the bottle and tried again. 'So, Maureen, what did you tell the police when Dorinne went missing?'

'I gave your people information on a house in Grasmere that I thought was being used as a brothel. I also told you about a teenager – a man – a local man, who I thought visited it.'

'Ah, yes, I seem to remember that. Officers were sent to investigate,' Kelly said. She knew she'd heard Maureen's name before she spoke to Dorinne's mother. The case file had her name logged. At the time, Maureen was seen as an interfering busybody with little weight behind her story, and her views had been dismissed.

'Pah! A few coppers came and asked questions. The wrong questions. The lad wasn't even touched.'

'Touched? As in, arrested?' Kelly was surprised by the vicious tone, but then, the woman's great-niece had been murdered.

'Yes. Exactly,' Maureen said with a defiant tone.

'I'm afraid we need evidence before we do things like that. I'm not a sheriff who can charge around throwing people in jail.' Kelly kept her tone pleasant, mindful of the woman's loss. 'If you've got anything solid, we can look into it.'

'Well, maybe if you looked a bit harder you'd find some.'

Kelly ignored the dig and pushed a little further. 'Dorinne's mum said you saw her daughter shortly before her disappearance, getting into a car with a man?'

Maureen turned away and busied herself with some items on shelves. She was clearly miffed that she hadn't been taken seriously about the brothel. But she kept talking.

'That Chinese woman who disappeared, she was a prostitute wasn't she?' she said without looking at the detectives.

'There's no evidence of that. Besides, it's not illegal,' Kelly explained.

'Not illegal? What are you talking about?' Now she turned to face them.

'The exchange of sexual services for money is legal. It's soliciting or pimping that isn't,' Dan clarified.

'Same thing,' muttered Marvin, who had been standing quietly until now. 'Isn't a knocking shop a brothel?'

Kelly answered but kept looking at Maureen. 'It would be classed as that, yes, but we haven't found one. That's our problem.'

'Well, it's common knowledge round here. Dorinne could often be found picking up takers in the Scrag End down in Ambleside.' Dan stared at Kelly when Maureen mentioned the pub, but she ignored him. 'Heard of that, haven't you?' Dan's reaction hadn't been lost on Maureen.

'It's an old pub. I grew up here. Yes I've heard of it, it's a memorable name. Are you telling me it's a brothel?' Kelly said.

Maureen had been fiddling with merchandise on the counter but stopped now and folded her arms.

'What have you heard, Marvin?' Kelly turned to the man. The bell above the door rang and a delivery man in a casual uniform, with a cap, came into the shop.

'Morning all,' he said cheerfully. He stopped abruptly as he took in the iciness of the atmosphere. 'Bad timing?' he asked.

'Come in, Harry. These police officers were just asking questions about Maureen's great-niece, God rest her soul.' Marvin made the sign of the cross over his chest, though he only went to St Oswald's on Christmas Eve. Maureen looked stern and Harry looked awkward.

'Shall I come back for my parcels, Marvin?' the delivery driver asked.

'Know the area well, then, in your line of work?' Kelly asked him.

'No one better,' Marvin answered for him.

'Maureen, what was that address you said was being used as a knocking shop?' Kelly asked, but kept her eyes on the driver.

Dan had to stifle a smile hearing his new boss use the old-fashioned term. In Glasgow, they called them 'hoor hooses'. Maureen said the address and Kelly looked at Harry the delivery man, who shrugged his shoulders. 'I don't do a lot local, I go to remote houses that the big vans can't get to, or aren't worth the while of the massive companies. I've only delivered to a handful of addresses in Grasmere itself. What sort of thing would I be looking for?'

'Regular deliveries from companies renowned for sex equipment, and I know you delivery boys know exactly what's in every box,' Kelly said. It wasn't an accusation, just a little carrot.

'Those days have gone I'm afraid. It's a breach of data protection.'

'Unusual activity, people – mainly men – coming and going, who don't look like members of the same family, not staying for long periods of time, or deliveries accepted by the same person over and over again, with little attempt to engage personally. Any of that sound familiar?' Kelly wasn't going to let this chance pass.

Dan had plenty of experience with brothel raids in Glasgow; it had been estimated that every neighbourhood there had one. He chipped in. 'Or newly purchased properties but no removal vans, with regular exchange of owners, indicating a "pop-up" type arrangement. Maybe advertising massages or spas, or perhaps looking as though no one actually lives there. Multiple different vehicles visiting the property at one time.'

Kelly was impressed. They waited. Harry looked a little overwhelmed. The poor bloke had walked into a post office to pick up deliveries and had been bombarded by questions about illegal sex. She gave him a small smile before speaking again.

'Sorry, Harry was it? There's always gossip about such things in small Lakes towns. It's the perfect place to hide them, isn't it? Behind holiday lets and the thousands of pubs and digs. They've always been around.'

'And you people tried to clear them many a time, but now I think there's no care for it, is there?' Maureen butted in again. 'You're off dealing with violence and kids taking drugs, who cares about a few houses servicing a few desperate old guys?'

'We do care, and the sex trade is increasingly linked to other trades now, like drugs and money-laundering. The days of independent brothels run by Granny with a blue rinse have gone,' Kelly said.

Maureen touched her perm.

'Besides, if it's happening in pubs, the landlords must know. So, what's the lad's name again, Maureen?' Kelly asked. 'The one you accuse of visiting establishments for sex.'

Maureen glanced at Marvin. 'Kevin Flint. He lives just down the road. His mother, Patty, is always at home, hiding away with shame. The father, Tommy, is always pissed up at the Scrag End, and Kevin's usually up to no good.'

'Do any of them work?' Kelly asked.

'Don't be daft. They get state handouts. The boy has "special needs". You know: good for nothing.' Kelly winced. 'They get money to take care of him and Tommy's disabled. Disabled my arse, he just can't walk because of the drink.'

'Are you saying that Kevin Flint is a minor?' Kelly sought clarification.

'No, he's nineteen, but soft in the head. He may as well be a child.'

Kelly now took a pad and pen out of her pocket and made a note of the names and the address that Maureen readily supplied. Maureen unfolded her arms and gave her more addresses.

'Wait, can you just slow down a bit?' Kelly tried to keep up.

'Maureen, that's one of ours,' said Marvin. Harry and Maureen stared at him. Kelly looked up from her pad and Dan folded his arms.

Marvin looked from detective to detective, and to Maureen and Harry.

'What?' Maureen asked.

'What?' echoed Kelly and Dan.

'My wife runs a holiday cottage business. It's a small place in Grasmere that is let to tourists. It couldn't be used regularly because it's rented by the week.'

'Okay, well I'm sure you wouldn't mind me talking to your wife about it. Every lead needs following up. Do either of you know Lucinda Dockie?'

Maureen and Marvin exchanged a look again, and Harry looked nonplussed. Maureen answered for both.

'The one shacked up with that Turkish bloke?' she said.

'Who might that be?' Kelly asked.

'He's got digs here in Grasmere. The people who take in labourers have thrown the town under the bus. Most of them are immigrants and up to no good. All of them are drunks. He's called Yus Ali. I know Lucinda, she always said he'd be the end of her. What's he done?'

'Nothing.'

'What?' Maureen asked, surprised.

'How do you know Lucinda? Are you close?'

'Her grandmother is part of my knitting circle. Why?'

'Maybe you should give her a call; her granddaughter's missing.'

'Oh my God!' Maureen put her hand over her mouth. 'It *has* to be Yus, the bastard,' she said angrily. 'Dear God, not another one. When will you people do something?'

The 'has' was emphatic and immediately aroused suspicion. Sometimes the saying 'there's no smoke without fire' rang true, but rarely in police investigations; in fact quite the opposite was true and part of Kelly's job was not jumping recklessly to conclusions. The facts usually came as a surprise in the end.

'Marvin, I need to go and call her.' Maureen made her exit politely, and they were left with Marvin and Harry, both looking baffled and bewildered. Marvin ran his hand through his hair.

'So, this property, Marvin. Do you have authority to enter at any time?'

'My wife does.'

'Can you call her?'

'Yes.'

'Before you do that, could I ask if you two agree with everything that Maureen has just told us?'

Marvin faltered. Harry looked at him but said nothing.

'She likes her gossip, like most of the women who grew up here. My shop has always been the hub of it really, it seems like that's what people come in for,' Marvin said.

'And they get Maureen embroidering quite the picture, do they?' Kelly probed.

Marvin sighed. 'Harry, I'll get your parcels and then I'll call my wife. Come on.' Harry followed Marvin out back and Dan turned to Kelly.

'What d'you think, guv?' Dan asked.

'I think we've struck something here. This letter on the counter, look. It's addressed to Marvin Burns. I wonder if they're the same Burnses who own the Scrag End. And I wonder if Marvin's wife is called Lorna. Did you notice Marvin shrinking into the background while we asked our questions? He was happy for Maureen to have the entire conversation to herself.'

Chapter 20

'Kevin!' Patty Flint hollered.

'Kevin!' she repeated. He was nowhere to be found. She roamed, fuming, from room to room, even getting down on her hands and knees to look for him, with no luck. Tommy was out as usual, and she had no one to berate for her increasing anxiety. She'd already taken the maximum four propranolol; what would another couple hurt? She popped them into her mouth and washed them down with the contents of the nearest bottle. The gut-wrenching feeling of agitation was borne not of a clinical diagnosis but from the fear that her son would finally leave her.

The snow was getting thicker outside. Maybe he was stuck somewhere.

Everybody gossiped about them. Patty knew it. All three of them. In fact it was probably Tommy who got off lightest, for simply being a drunk. People seemed to like it when they could label you. That was the problem: no one knew how to take her and her son. Everywhere they went, people always ended up making their stories up. And they ended up running away.

It was her fault. She'd dropped him as a baby and he'd turned out simple. The truth was she couldn't remember if that was true or not, or if it was just to do with Tommy's good-for-nothing family, why Kevin had turned out so dumb. She couldn't remember *actually* dropping him. He'd been different as a baby, and a toddler, and then he'd turned into a teenager, all gangly arms and hormones. She caught him doing despicable things with animals and they'd got rid of their dog, King. One night, Tommy took King down to a local reservoir and beat him with a rock, then weighted his body and threw him in the water. Tommy never cared much for King anyway. But Kevin did and he was distraught. It had been her job to appease him and it was the first night he'd ejaculated into her nightie. That marked the step from manipulating a little boy to controlling a man.

She sat heavily on the couch and lit a cigarette. She was losing her grip over him. She'd have to go out; it was her last one and she couldn't go an hour without them. She sucked in the smoke and exhaled loudly to perhaps expunge some of her anger. She'd been angry her whole life. Angry about her bastard dad, angry about perverted teachers, angry about never amounting to nothing, and angry about how much it hurt giving birth to Kevin. The second child she carried died inside her and she was angry about that too.

Now, when the house was quiet, and she was alone with herself, the voices started and didn't stop. They hounded her and told her that she was bad, she was rubbish: a fragment on a dump of other scraps, deserving of nothing and a waste of life.

She had no mirrors in the house. Her youth, along with her hope, had died many, many years ago and was not coming back. She was ugly, she knew that much, but Tommy wasn't picky. He couldn't see straight half the time anyway.

She began rocking to and fro in an attempt to still her self-contempt. She knew it was there but, surrounded by noise and with Kevin by her side, she didn't stop much to listen. Even Tommy, raging and falling about, was preferable to being alone with just herself and the inside of her head.

She'd plucked up enough courage to visit her GP in Amble-side, who'd given her antidepressants and the propranolol for anxiety. Both seemed to help. Those, and thirty or forty fags a day. She didn't notice the thick fog inside the house and nobody visited to tell her. Only Kevin commented on it occasionally, but received a whack across the head for his insolence. It was only recently that she'd begun to realise how big a man he was physically. She'd never really noticed before. Something about him had changed.

She heard a noise and looked up to the ceiling. Surely Kevin wasn't inside the house? She got up slowly and went to the door, stubbing her cigarette out. She opened the door and went into the hallway and towards the stairs. She didn't hear anything.

'Tommy?'

Nothing.

She went quietly up the stairs and her anxiety bubbled up. She felt in her pocket and took out another strip of propranolol, popping two out of the silver foil and slipping them, one by one, into her mouth. She looked about for something to drink, but found nothing and swallowed them without. Instantly, the fear radiating through her body stilled a little, and she carried on.

At the top of the stairs, she turned around the landing and came to Kevin's door.

'Kevin?' She knocked and still there was no answer. She put her hands on the handle and curled her hand around the metal, pushing down slowly, and opened the door. She was faced with a waft of stale air. Her eyes adjusted to the dark and she went to pull the curtains back. The sunlight made her squint. She stood in the middle of the room and looked about it. It reminded her more of a cave. Clothes hung everywhere, stuff covered every surface, but that didn't bother her so much; after all, her house wasn't exactly tidy. Mess was normal. It was more the emptiness of the space in terms of feeling. The walls were bare, the carpet was covered, the bed was unmade and the colours drab. It was like a hostel room and she sat on his bed glumly.

She took a cigarette out and lit it with a lighter. She sucked on it then placed it in a used cup on the windowsill and closed her eyes. A familiar feeling filled her body and she began to shake with anger. It was his fault that she was nothing. His fault that she was stuck. His fault that she would forever have to mother him. And his fault that everybody hated them.

She felt the need to go to the bathroom but, instead of walking next door to the toilet, she allowed it to flow out of her onto his bed. She smiled to herself as the hot liquid left her body and soaked into his bed. It empowered her.

She got up and opened some of his drawers, dark urine dripping down her legs onto the carpet. It smelled strong, and she remembered she hadn't been to the toilet in hours. Tommy wasn't the only one who drank away his sorrows, but Patty held it together better. She didn't rush, she sipped over the course of the day. Her piss was the colour of cheap brandy.

She found a magazine and she knew what was inside. He watched most of his filth online now, as all men do, including Tommy. Her father had only had magazines, because that's all that was available. He kept them under his bed and her mother knew they were there. She knew because she had to enact what was inside them, whether the kids were watching and listening or not.

She didn't want to look at what was inside but she couldn't help herself. She opened the flimsy, well-thumbed production randomly, and was faced with a close-up of a woman's vagina, with something sticking out of it. She closed the page and flicked to another, looking away in disgust but glued to the thing. Some of the pages were faded but she could still make out the images clearly. She wondered how old the rag was and who still stocked top-shelf mags. Marvin probably did.

Another image of two men doing things to a woman held her gaze.

She threw it roughly across the room and went to her son's wardrobe, slamming the doors open. She took his hoodies, one by one, and with an almighty superhuman strength ripped the hoods off. She tore his trousers and pulled apart boxer shorts. She spat on his shoes and stamped on teddy bears thrown to the back in an attempt to put away childish things.

By the time she breathed again, she was spent of her rage and her chest heaved up and down. Her legs felt sticky and she realised that she still hadn't cleaned up the piss. She left the room and went to the bathroom and closed the door.

Chapter 21

Kelly and Dan followed Marvin to the address of the holiday let that he owned with his wife in Grasmere. It wasn't far, for the town was tiny. They parked outside a lovely stone cottage that sat nestled near the lake and was quickly being covered by a blanket of snow. It was located in a perfect setting and would command a fair sum in summer, Kelly reckoned. They had to go up a wooden staircase to get to the front door and it looked as though it had once been a barn, perhaps to store canoes. It was slippery and they held on to the rail.

Marvin held the keys and led them to the front door. He'd reported back from his conversation with his wife, who was indeed called Lorna, that an elderly couple were booked in for three months and it had surprised them all. Marvin said he'd had no idea that his wife let their properties for such long stretches. She took care of that side of things and he didn't really get involved. He'd asked what she knew of the couple but Lorna had told him very little. Kelly had watched as Marvin got angry on the phone, asking his wife why she didn't vet their guests. It was quite clear that Lorna Burns had hung up on her husband. As it turned out, Lorna was unable to meet them at the property, as requested by the police, because she was tied up with other business elsewhere.

Kelly wondered what she had to hide. Marvin didn't know exactly where she was and Lorna hadn't told him.

Marvin knocked first, out of politeness, and the door was answered by a sweet old lady. Marvin explained who he was and asked if he could come in. He introduced the two detectives and clarified that they needed access to the property for a short while and they wouldn't be bothered at all.

'Your wife called us, that's perfectly fine,' the woman agreed kindly, and they were escorted inside to a kitchen, where they banged their feet on the mat to knock off snow. Kelly peered around. It looked just like a holiday let should: guidebooks were stacked on the shelves, the furniture was reasonable but not elaborate, board games were placed neatly on the table and the walls were sparse.

Marvin waited for further instruction, adding, 'I'm not familiar with the lets, I leave it to Lorna. I think there are two rooms downstairs, and the lounge is through here on this floor, to make the most of the views.'

'And upstairs?'

'Just an attic, so Lorna told me over the phone. It's empty.'

Kelly nodded and went to the lounge, in the direction that Marvin had pointed.

'Do you have visitors?' she asked the woman.

'No, we don't know anyone here. We're on holiday.'

Kelly nodded again and nosed around the living room. The view over the lake was stunning. Next she went downstairs and instructed Dan to wait with the couple. She'd asked him to check them out by asking some basic questions about their stay and spot any anomalies. She didn't much care to either condemn or exonerate the pair; her mind was open. It was a tall story, that the place might be a brothel, but she was intrigued by Maureen Johnson and her theories. The old couple looked harmless enough, but she'd read Dan's file and he'd qualified as a criminal profiler. She'd be keen to find out what he thought just as soon as they were done here.

Marvin looked just as keen as she was to explore the place. They reached the lower level and Kelly went into each of the bedrooms in turn.

'Do you have anything at all to do with the running of the holiday let business?' she asked him.

'No, that's Lorna's speciality. I run the shop.'

'Is that what she does on a daily basis? I mean does it fill her time?'

'Oh, yes. If she's not cleaning them after a stay, she's searching for others, greeting guests and buying furniture and crockery.'

'How many do you have?' Kelly asked.

'I'm not sure.'

'And the pubs she owns?'

'I beg your pardon?' Marvin's tone was puzzled.

It was clear to Kelly that Marvin Burns didn't really know what his wife got up to.

'Your wife is the landlady of at least two public houses. You didn't know this?'

Marvin looked scared and caught out.

'Mr Burns, it's imperative that I speak to Lorna. Let her know I'll expect her call within a couple of hours, is that clear?' Kelly said.

He nodded.

Both bedrooms were a decent size and the beds were unmade. It wasn't her place to judge if a couple slept separately, but she found the unmade beds odd for a couple of their age; that generation usually seemed to live by more discipline and order, and pride. In the first bedroom, she'd touched the pillow on the bed and found it to be warm. Now, she touched the two pillows on the bed in the second bedroom: they too were warm to the hand.

'Can I see in the attic?' she asked Marvin.

'I have no idea how to get in there. I think it's closed off.'

'There was a hatch in the hallway upstairs.'

'Really?'

Kelly went back up to where she'd left Dan and peered up at the hatch. It did indeed appear to be painted shut, with no key-turn for a ladder, and no hinge. The couple were standing by the window looking at the lake.

'How long have you been out of bed, up and about?' she asked them.

They turned to her, startled, and then looked at one another. It was the woman who spoke first.

'I'm an early riser, I tend to get up at seven,' she said.

Kelly looked at the man, who looked again at the woman. 'I got up about ten, I think,' he said.

'Right, well thank you so much, Marvin. We'll leave you all alone now.' Kelly beckoned to Dan.

They were shown out and Marvin called his wife on his mobile phone. Meanwhile, Kelly wandered around the back of the property towards the lake. Round the back, another wooden staircase led up to a barn-like door, which was padlocked. She tried to work out where in the house it would lead to. Above that, a spiral metal staircase led to the roof level. She went up carefully, expecting it to be treacherous in the weather, and found a flat roof with a locked hatch. She tried it but it wouldn't budge and snow flew everywhere. There were no footprints in the snow, except hers. When she got back to Marvin and Dan she'd finished brushing the snow off.

'It's a shame, you know, it seems as though you've got bags more space in that roof, and a back room that looks as though it's behind the lounge.'

Marvin peered up. He seemed uninterested.

'Lorna said she's busy all day.'

'Call her back,' Kelly insisted.

Marvin started to complain but clearly thought better of it and did as he was told. When the call was answered, Kelly grabbed his phone. Dan stepped in between them.

'Mrs Burns, I wouldn't hang up if I were you. Detective Inspector Kelly Porter. I suggest you get here now, or I'll be forced to break into your attic.'

She hung up. Next she called HQ and ran the information by them to see if the situation qualified for emergency entrance to a property. They agreed that there was grounds to seize evidence possibly within the property relating to a serious crime. She also had reason to believe that evidence within the holiday let could be destroyed if they waited for a formal warrant. Meanwhile, certified warrants would be prepared for all of the Burns properties.

'Dan, get something to break a lock out of my boot; anything. Come with me.'

Dan went to her car and rooted around the boot, finding a toolbox. He grabbed a cutter and a hammer from it. He followed her up the metal stairs at the back of the property and she showed him the hatch. He began working on it and the lock cracked open easily. Dan hefted the large door upwards and they felt a gush of warm air escape. Inside, there was a ladder that led to a landing. Dan went first, helping Kelly down.

'What did you think?' she asked him.

'Both odd. They didn't say a word to one another while you were downstairs, or even before or after that either. In my opinion, they hardly seemed to know one another.'

'What makes you say that? My parents barely spoke at that age. They're, what, mid-seventies? All my father did was work and complain.'

'At one point, they bumped into one another, trying to get past, and they bounced off each other in horror. In my experience, when you know somebody, you don't do that. You either laugh or apologise, stabilising one another, or tut and roll your eyes in a negative manner, depending on how much, or little, that person means to you.'

Kelly was impressed and told him so, before adding, 'Both beds were unmade downstairs, and the pillows weren't cold like they would be if they'd been up hours, as they said.'

'And all this space up here.' Dan gestured around them.

'I wonder what sort of turnover Lorna and Marvin Burns' holiday let business has.'

'As well as the pubs.'

They found themselves in a corridor. Their eyes adjusted and they looked at one another as they both saw a door. They approached it and Kelly turned the handle. It opened.

Inside, sitting on two beds, were three young women and two older men; all looked sheepish and guilty as hell.

'We'll escort each of you out one at a time, please.' Kelly told them who she was and the men hung their heads. As their eyes adjusted further, they could see quite clearly that the men were in a state of undress and the woman wore scant garments fitting for a sexual encounter, if not in reality then in fantasy.

'I'm arresting each of you on charges of soliciting sex for money in an organised place of exchange of services. You do not have to say anything, but if you do and you change your mind if evidence is used in court to the contrary, it may be used against you. Dan, how many pairs of ties have you got?'

'Enough,' he replied.

'Let's get downstairs and get the old couple, as well as Marvin Burns, in for questioning. We need to establish who is running things here.'

Chapter 22

It took a good hour to get the eight people packed off in squad cars, bound for registration at the nearest police station in Windermere. And Lorna Burns never showed up. A request to locate her was added to the Police National Computer. Her absence spoke volumes and she was suspected of running a profitable business related to prostitution, at the very least. Kelly called Craig. She'd missed several calls from him. She put him on Bluetooth as she drove back to Ambleside. The sky had darkened considerably and the snow on the ground had thickened. Meanwhile, Dan contacted Kate Umshaw back at Eden House to begin work on establishing a list of the properties owned by Lorna and Marvin Burns in preparation for a raid on them all.

'Kelly, did you get my messages?' Craig asked.

Kelly filled him in quickly and apologised for not getting back to him sooner. He agreed to take charge of the custody in Windermere, which was a shorter drive from Barrow than it was from Penrith. He whistled. 'Good work. I have something for you too. The sighting of Lisa Lau in Preston was unreliable. It wasn't her. I could see clearly when I reviewed the tape that it was an East Asian woman, but not her. I checked and double-checked. Plus, there was a sighting that fell through the net somehow and wasn't added to HOLMES. Lisa Lau was seen in Ambleside on the second of January, talking to a Chinese guy. Preston are completely uninterested. I'm having the case transferred back to me.'

'Jesus, Craig. Can you repeat all of that, but slowly?'

'Sorry.' He did as she asked.

'What's the embassy doing? Are they sharing their findings?'

'No, and a diplomat at the Foreign and Commonwealth Office who I spoke to when I updated them on the Preston sighting told me that her family is very rich and powerful in China. They're billionaires.'

'And did they tell you who the embassy has tasked with investigating?' Kelly asked.

'No, and it's likely we won't ever know. Maybe it's the parents wanting to find their daughter, and it's as straightforward as that,' Craig said.

'Or something more. If they've sent a diplomat to dig around, and if they're state-sponsored and working for the embassy, he or she would be seen as a foreign operative with diplomatic immunity. They may even be armed.'

'I hit a brick wall with the FCO. I get the impression no one wants to challenge the Chinese. They have too many investments here in the UK to go round offending them. Where are you now?' Craig asked.

'Back in Ambleside, and the weather looks pretty crap. We thought we may as well check out the YHA Lisa Lau stayed in. When we were in Grasmere we were given the name of a local lad, a misfit called Kevin Flint. We called on him but no one answered, so we'll have to try again another time.'

'Who gave you his name?' Craig asked.

Kelly told him about Maureen Johnson and her opinions on local knocking shops, as she'd called them.

'She sounds like a very useful witness.'

'We're going to try to talk to Kevin tomorrow. Can you arrange the interviews for the eight people we've got at Windermere? We've got twenty-four hours.'

Craig agreed.

'Oh, great. Police traffic update just came through, Kirkstone Pass is closed. We'll have to go the other way, up the A591. The YHA where Lisa stayed isn't far so we can pay them a visit. We also got some quite interesting information from the

Scrag End pub, which keeps popping up. All three women were regulars there. Yus Ali said he'd seen Lucinda with an old man in his fifties, small, creepy but wealthy, at a bus stop in Grasmere. It matches the description given by the bartender of who she was with in there, but on a different occasion. He could be a regular punter of hers. Like a sugar daddy figure. We need to find him.'

'If he was wealthy, why would they be heading for the bus stop?' Craig raised a good point.

'Because they'd been drinking?' Kelly asked. 'Non-traceable?'

'Should we meet tomorrow?' Craig asked.

'Sure. The weather is pretty bad up here, why don't we see what it's like tomorrow and if it's worse, we can both head to the services on the M6? Might be easier,' Kelly suggested.

'No problem. Another thing is really nagging me,' Craig said. 'HOLMES was behind the power curve on Lisa Lau when the case was allocated to Preston. It's going to take time to get that case back, so I'm going to add a duplicate case to the current case you opened today and update it with all I know this end about Lisa's disappearance. Could you do the same?'

'Of course. I'll do it when we get back. That is if we get back and don't have to find a hotel for the night. If that's the case, I'll do it on my iPad. There's already loads of overlap here and I'm not sure yet which case file to link them to, so I'm going to merge them on a separate file on HOLMES. That way we won't miss anything. Let me know when you interview the people we arrested today.'

They both hung up.

Chapter 23

The hostel where Lisa Lau had stayed up until her disappearance was fairly upmarket and looked more like a modest hotel. The YHA had come a long way since Kelly had stayed in them on school trips thirty years ago. The foyer was clean and it had a coffee shop. Youngsters milled about, some played pool, and the place looked vibrant and a good place to hang out. The YHA wasn't far away from the main square in town. The snow had begun to take on an ethereal look as dusk crept up on them and street lights were switched on. It was looking more and more like they'd be trapped for the night. Kelly had her phone tucked under her chin and spoke animatedly to Kate Umshaw back at Eden House. Her team had worked tirelessly under the guidance of her second in charge and were busy inputting updates on HOLMES. Kelly felt strangely far from home, and working a case so far south had its limitations. She was itching to solve Dorinne's murder, but her enquiries were producing more questions than answers. She ran her theories past Kate.

The trucks of grit moved easily through the streets, but up on the fells the snow would make conditions treacherous. Johnny was on call tonight and she wondered how many times he'd have to go out. Only last week, three lads in trainers, with no waterproofs and no map, whistle or torches, were rescued from a crag east of Skiddaw. The press had attacked them viciously as morons and called for the law to be changed so that idiots like that could be charged with causing potential harm to life through misadventure, but, sadly, being a fuckwit wasn't a crime. It was a shame, because Kelly reckoned that half her cases had a fuckwit at the centre of them.

'Our last stop is the Heaven nightclub, then we'll make our way back,' she told Kate. She ended the call. She and Dan banged their shoes on the doorstep to free them of snow and went to the reception desk. Lisa's room had been cleared of belongings when the police had first visited on their procedural rounds. No one remembered Lisa leaving with a large amount of luggage, or indeed checking out at all, but the fact was, it looked like she'd packed up and left.

Kelly introduced herself and Dan, and the demeanour of the young woman at the desk changed. They were used to it; the cops had a habit of making even innocent people feel uncomfortable.

'We'd like to ask a few further questions about when Lisa Lau stayed here, if we may?'

'Okay. I remember Lisa – she was fun. It's quieter round here, if you know what I mean. I never thought she'd just leave like that. She talked to everyone and she'd made loads of friends, or at least, I thought she did.'

Kelly noticed that her name badge read Leila.

'Were you her friend, Leila?'

'Not really, I don't think I was… cool enough. She hung out with the popular people.'

'The popular people?' Kelly asked.

The receptionist rolled her eyes. 'You know, the ones who smoke and go to all the parties.'

'You don't go to parties?' Kelly asked.

'Not those kinds of parties. I mean, all weekend, dru—' Leila stopped talking and her cheeks turned pink. She looked around and tried to backtrack, saying she meant alcohol.

'It's okay, you're not in trouble,' Kelly reassured her. 'So, at parties, people get high, and drunk, and they have a good time. Have you any clue where these parties were?'

A couple came to the desk and Leila had to deal with their enquiry. 'Let me shut the desk while I find someone to cover. I don't really want to be overheard.'

Once she had dealt with the couple, Leila put up a sign and locked a drawer. She called somebody on the phone, who obviously agreed to come to the desk, and took them into an unused lounge, where the walls were covered in bookshelves. It appeared to be the hostel's quiet space, and that no one wanted to use it.

They sat down in comfy chairs.

'Were you working when the police came?' Dan asked conversationally, trying to make Leila feel at ease. Kelly had told him to jump in any time.

'No. I came in the next day and somebody said Lisa had vanished, but all her stuff was gone so she must have just decided to leave. We talked about how shocked we were but her bill was up to date, so we just moved on.'

'She paid her bill regularly?' Dan asked.

'Always, it was a direct bank transfer from China. We have a lot of foreign workers with money coming and going from abroad.'

'What was New Year's Day like here?' Kelly asked.

'A mix of up and down. People are missing their families, or might not have family, but we always try to celebrate.'

'How long have you worked here?' Kelly asked.

'Five years.'

'Did Lisa ever bring anyone to stay?'

Leila shook her head as she answered. 'No, that's strictly against the rules.'

'So did she spend nights away?'

'Of course, like I said, she partied a lot. We have a check-in system, in case of fire, so you can look through that to see when she was here.'

'Thank you, that's really helpful. Do you have CCTV in the foyer too?'

'Yes, it was installed two months ago.'

Kelly knew that no CCTV had been looked at because of the case going to Preston. She made arrangements for Leila to send her the whole file of images captured since installation. Kelly regularly gave thanks for modern technology, and that digital CCTV was never erased but simply went to an electronic cloud in the sky. For some, scared of Big Brother invasion, technological advances were detested, but for the cops, they were welcomed with open arms.

'Was there any gossip surrounding her disappearance?' Kelly asked. 'Sometimes people talk about cases and they get ignored, but actually I bet I'd find it quite useful to know what people around here said.'

Leila fiddled with her nails. She looked only in her twenties and she was nervous, but she seemed honest and genuine.

'I overheard one of the men trying to get Lisa to go out with him. He was really keen and he was so good-looking.' She paused before carrying on. 'Lisa kept saying no and I thought she was mad. One night, he was asking her again, and pretending to sing her love songs. It was funny; they were all having a good time. She told him to forget it because he couldn't pay her enough.' She looked at the two detectives.

'So, you took from that she charged men to be with her?'

Leila nodded.

'In a sexual way?'

'That's what I understood. She also had a nickname, which was Lisa-Low, it meant she, you know, would go down—'

'I understand,' Kelly interjected. 'Did you know how wealthy her family is?'

'No idea. I assumed she always looked so good because she worked a lot.'

'So, she never mentioned them?'

Leila shook her head. 'I had no idea how important she was until the Chinese man came asking questions.'

'The Chinese man?' Kelly said, glancing at Dan, who was also paying close attention.

'Yes. He said he worked for her family and had to find Lisa as soon as possible.'

'What did you tell him?' Kelly was frustrated that the receptionist hadn't mentioned this until now, but she kept a neutral tone.

'Exactly what I'm telling you. Lisa did talk about her family, but not about their wealth. About how much she hated them. It's common for conversations to come out like that. A lot of people who stay here long-term are estranged from loved ones, or have been abused by them. It's never a surprise when people say that, and it made sense that she was here instead of there.'

'Her work permit runs out this weekend,' Kelly said. 'She would have had to have gone back.'

'Maybe she disappeared so she doesn't have to?' said Leila. 'The Chinese guy was pretty intimidating.'

'Did he give you his name?'

'Wait a minute, I wrote it down in my notes because I asked him to spell it, but as he asked me more questions he showed me his passport because I wanted ID. He wasn't impressed but I insisted.'

Kelly raised her eyebrows, impressed by Leila's wits. 'Why didn't you call the police?' she asked her.

'I had no idea who to tell, it didn't seem relevant after I read in the paper that the case was closed.'

'You must have followed the story in detail; not much was reported about it.'

Leila nodded. Kelly looked at her phone and the image of the passport. It belonged to Minister Li Qiang.

'Can I screenshot it?' Kelly asked. Leila held it up for her as she did so.

'Can you get that CCTV footage over to me, and hopefully we'll find out when she left. What did Minister Qiang want?'

'The same as you, the CCTV footage but I told him the cameras don't work. He looked straight at them and gave me this look. It gave me the creeps. I told him they're just dummies, and we can't afford CCTV. He asked to see the main computer in the office and I said no.'

'That was a pretty ballsy thing to do given his position.'

'I didn't like him. That's when he told me how powerful Lisa's parents are. I said that I already knew and that he should speak to the police, as I was going to do.'

'But you didn't?'

'I felt foolish,' Leila said.

'Can we see Lisa's room?'

'It's in use, I'm afraid.'

Kelly nodded. That ship had sailed.

'Did you ever hear Lisa talking about the Scrag End pub in town?'

'Yes, I think her room-mate mentioned it to the police at the time.'

'Yes, I've got a room-mate referred to in my notes, but no name. Is she still sharing the room?' Kelly asked.

'No, she left.'

'Any idea where?'

Leila, unsurprisingly, shook her head. 'There was a big turnover of guests after Lisa went. The party moved on elsewhere, I guess,' she said.

'Can we see your guest records? I don't suppose you remember the name of her room-mate?'

'Of course, it was Mandy Williams. If you follow me to the office, I'll log you in.'

Kelly recognised the name immediately. Surely this was the same Mandy Williams from the Scrag End that morning.

By the time she and Dan had searched the entries for around New Year, they'd discovered that twelve people had checked out of the youth hostel on the fourth of January. One male and eleven females. It was the same day that the Chinese minister had visited the hostel. Another resident's name that raised eyebrows was Kian Delaney.

As they walked back to the car, Kelly having transferred the MP4s of the CCTV, as well as the check-in data and guest list to her iPad, she asked Dan to drive to the Heaven nightclub while she called the FCO.

The weather had worsened. They'd have to leave soon and resume their efforts another time; meanwhile, they could work on updating HOLMES and see if that flagged anything new. The FCO kept her on hold for twenty minutes and passed her between three departments. Finally she was transferred to the Home Office and she rolled her eyes when she was put on hold again. They sat in the car park behind the Heaven nightclub and both she and Dan noticed cameras on the side of the building. She was eventually connected to a civil servant, and explained, for the hundredth time, what she was after. All the man at the end of the phone said was that she should call the Chinese embassy direct. She let out a stifled laugh; they both knew full well that embassies didn't answer their phones to anyone without an extension number.

'Why is this so difficult?' she asked him.

'I'm afraid the name you are seeking is in a locked file, so all I can suggest is that you talk to someone with higher clearance, or communicate with the embassy direct.'

The line went dead. Higher security clearance meant that whatever Lisa Lau's name had flagged up was enough to trigger the need for secrecy. Kelly guessed it had something to do with her family.

–

The Heaven nightclub was yet to open but a phone call got them in through the front and they were taken to the office. They had to walk through the cavernous rooms, which reminded Kelly of her university days. The place stank of stale booze and the interior was sad and a little shameful when not in use. She imagined the throngs of bodies pressed in there at the weekend, tunes banging out, wall to wall, with lights blinding swarms of dancers, high on this or that, looking for love.

The manager was called Phil and he was more than happy to chat about his work and the types of women who hung out at his club. Though at the mention of sex work, he became defensive. Kelly calmed him.

'That's not why we're here. We're simply tracing the whereabouts of one woman.' She showed him the photo of Dorinne. He raised his eyebrows.

'No idea, she looks like all the rest.'

'We noticed cameras overlooking the car park,' Dan said.

'All yours, and from in here too. It's not unusual for it to be requested, with drunken fights and the like. So what happened to the woman?'

'It's a murder inquiry,' Kelly stated.

'The body in the bin?'

Kelly nodded.

'Jesus. What's Heaven got to do with it?' Phil became defensive again.

'This was the last place we've got a witness testimony from. It was back in October.'

'But she's showed up dead now?'

'Which is why it's so important we get this footage,' Dan said. Phil looked between him and Kelly.

'Right. I'm afraid that far back, it'll be on file so I'll have to request it,' Phil said.

'How long will that take?'

'Maybe a day,' Phil replied. Kelly nodded and they got up to leave. They had a long journey home and it was fully dark outside now. Kelly thanked the manager and gave him her card.

'My email is on there, can you send the footage direct to me?'

'Sure.'

Outside, the wind whipped snow into their faces and they were thankful for the calm of the car interior. Kelly asked Dan to update HOLMES as they headed back north, while she dictated.

'DI Lockwood has been busy,' Dan said as she pulled out onto the main drag and headed to the A591. Traffic was snarling already and she could see a gritting lorry up ahead. They were more prepared than most of the country for such weather and, usually, the roads were kept clear.

Kelly articulated her thoughts aloud, and Dan inputted data. Being stuck in the car was a great opportunity for admin. She delivered the names of the people who'd checked out of the YHA in Ambleside en masse, including Mandy Williams, presumably the same girl from the Scrag End that morning, together with her friend, Kian Delaney. Next Dan looked up the addresses given to them by Maureen Johnson at Marvin's, and cross-referenced the relevant information to the new investigation into the disappearance of Lucinda Dockie. Everything that was in her brain associated with all three cases, she blurted out to Dan as he tapped away. It was like a huge web of names, addresses and secrecy. HOLMES threw out notifications of matches, and Dan told Kelly that he could see from the screen that Craig Lockwood was typing away from his end too. They neared Thirlmere and the traffic slowed to a grinding snail's pace.

'Very slow traffic and more snow building up. It reminds me of home,' Dan said.

'You have nice weather in Glasgow?'

'Once a year maybe, when everyone takes off their coat.' He smiled. 'How much longer?' he asked, nodding ahead, unfamiliar with the roads.

'At this speed, it'll be hours. Hope you didn't have plans tonight,' she said.

'Not me.'

'We have to follow this road all the way to Keswick, when the traffic will ease on the main road, but if people keep breaking down or sliding around in the snow, it could take us all night.'

'Stop off somewhere?' he suggested.

'Let's keep moving while we can,' she said.

'How big is prostitution in the Lakes?' he asked.

'No idea. We don't go for conviction any more because it's so minor compared to everything else. They get let off with warnings. There'll be some office who can give us the stats on stop and searches and statements. It's something to ask Craig.'

'Isn't it on the PNC as a matter of course? It is in Glasgow.'

'That's the problem round here. Everybody sees sex workers as residing in cities, but it's rife in the provinces, where it's harder to find.'

–

Kate Umshaw called from Eden House to give an update on the Burns properties. Kelly put her on speaker. It turned out they owned twenty, all over the district, as well as the two pubs the police already knew of. The business was called Sunshine Holidays and some of the properties were small, some large. They were all fully booked until next Christmas. Kelly asked Kate to add them all to the computer system, direct from Airbnb, cross-referenced with council tax bills. She also reminded Kate to see if any of them matched the ones Craig Lockwood had been given by David Martin.

Kelly's eyes grew tired and she rubbed them, trying hard to concentrate on the road. What she wouldn't give right now for a bath and a glass of Malbec. Maybe one day, she and Johnny would go to Mendoza in Argentina and taste the real thing where it was made. HOLMES notified them of another match, and Dan read it out. It was another address given to them by Maureen, and another of the Burns properties.

'Shit!' Kelly turned the steering wheel hard. The power of four wheels was never more welcome; she managed to navigate around a turning car in front that was completely blocking the road. It had slewed across the road, completely out of control.

'Do you know where we are?' Dan asked.

'I'm going to see if they're all right. We're near Castlerigg stone circle. There's a small hotel up on the left. We might need to use it, and we'd better make our decision before the rest of this lot.' She nodded to the line of traffic both ways, which was now stuck due to the car. She opened the door and a deluge of icy air and snow hit her. She braced herself and took her coat from the back seat, wrapping it tightly, and slammed the door.

As she reached the car a man from another vehicle, clearly thinking the same, appeared next to her. She knocked on the window, which rolled down. A man and a woman were inside, with a baby in a carrier on the back seat. The baby was crying and the couple looked to be in shock.

'Are you all okay? I'm a police officer, my colleague is calling the emergency services now.'

The man stared at her and breathed deeply.

'That was well controlled. You're lucky you stopped.' Kelly knew that to the right of where they were was a drop of around thirty foot. Given the weight of the falling snow, any nearer the edge and they would have been over it.

'Keep your engine running with the heater on. Someone will be here soon. You'd best put the window up and soothe the baby. Don't under any circumstances try and turn round. I know this road and right down there is a ditch, and you're two feet from the drop that you can't see because of the snow.'

It was shocking for them to hear after what they'd already been through, but Kelly needed to make sure they wouldn't try to drive out of the problem. The guy nodded. The woman took off her seat belt and turned to the back seat and the crying baby. The window rolled back up and Kelly went back to the car. She opened the door quickly and slammed it behind her. Snow blew in with her.

'They'll be lucky to get them out tonight; the road is blocked and they need a truck down here.' Dan relayed to her what the police had told him. 'We'll have to manoeuvre the car ourselves.'

'It's too dangerous, there's a drop that side.'

Dan peered through his window. 'I'll take a look,' he said, and opened his door and disappeared into the night.

Dan walked around the car and Kelly watched him go to the driver's side. Two more men appeared. Traffic was building up both ways and this was the only way north or south, with the Helvellyn range to the east and the Langdale Pikes to the west. She called Eden House and was put through to fire and rescue. They told her that the A591 was blocked further north due to two overturned cars, so a vehicle had been sent from the south. They were putting out a radio and TV announcement, plus updating all of their social media accounts, that travel should be avoided tonight unless in an emergency. As far as their predicament went, they could make no promises. Kelly didn't really want to leave the couple alone out here with a baby. She got out of the car and braved the wind again.

When she got to Dan, he was discussing options with the small group of people who'd gathered.

'The wheel arch is stuck on a tree stub,' he shouted into the wind.

Kelly made up her mind. 'We should take them to the hotel, it's a five-minute walk. I'll tell all of the vehicles to pass on the message, and I'll let the emergency services know roughly how many people are out here.'

She went back to the car and grabbed everything she might need for an overnight stay, then went to tell the couple in the car the bad news. Reluctantly, they began preparing the baby for a brisk journey into the freezing night. She passed messages down the line of traffic and Dan did the same northbound. Some people left their cars but others chose to stay. A group of them set off to the hotel. Kelly hoped it wasn't too busy.

They were in luck; the hotel had enough rooms to give them all. They had hot food as well, and a bar. People made themselves busy calling relatives and she called Johnny. He didn't answer and she imagined him on a hillside somewhere, searching for a lost climber. She wished he was here, in front of the burning fire.

Chapter 24

Kevin decided to spend the night in an abandoned bothy, high up on Rydal Fell. He'd got his bike all the way up and he took it inside. He knew no one would be there; it wasn't like a self-catering bothy, where provisions were left and fires burned – this one was only used by sheep and strays now. He seethed with rage towards his mother, who'd pissed in his bed and destroyed his clothes. The desire to put his hands round her throat and keep squeezing until she stopped breathing had never been more real.

He'd got home to find his father passed out on the sofa downstairs and his mother waiting for him on the landing, ready to pounce. She had berated him for not coming home. Thoughts of leaving for good whirred around his head. He had everything he needed to survive on his own and never go home again. He had money from his disability allowance in an account opened by his key worker that his mother knew nothing about. Her money, for having to bear the burden of a son who brought shame on her, was paid into her account. His key worker said that he was not obligated to tell his mother. It was the first time he'd heard the word 'obligated'. It meant something you had to do, and Kevin was surprised he'd never heard it because that's all he'd ever done: what he was told to do.

Until recently, when his walks had taken him into the path of a stranger – a stranger with specific desires – for the first time ever, he had been pursuing a course that he was in control of. He made the decision to follow, and wait, and watch and fantasise, over and over again.

And it felt good.

All at the same time, he was breaking free, physically and mentally, from his mother. She was losing control and he could tell that she could sense it. That was why he hadn't strangled her to death tonight, because it had been more powerful to laugh at her: she'd done those things in his room because she was desperate, and, for the first time ever, he felt power.

When he'd got in, he read it all over her face. He'd stood there, in the hallway, taking everything she threw at him: the vile language, the demeaning insults and the damaging accusations. With every word, his heart closed off towards her, and he clenched and unclenched his fists. Then he'd seen his room.

She'd gone to come to him but he'd backed away and she'd stopped, reaching out to him, then dropping her hand and opening her mouth to give him more filth, but it didn't come; her voice dried up and words failed her. He stared at her and felt heat well up inside, and he'd begun to sweat. His eyes narrowed and his mouth grimaced and, though he wasn't aware until later, he'd bitten his lip.

Now it stung and he touched it with a finger. It hurt more than all the grazes that covered his body. But he felt alive. That's when something stirred inside him and he'd laughed. He stood in his doorway, with her in the hall, growing smaller and smaller, howling with laughter until he couldn't stop. He coughed and spluttered as he fought for breath to laugh harder and her eyes grew wider with understanding. A transfer of power was taking place before them both, and it was intoxicating.

He didn't see her face when he left, he just heard her voice, cracked and unfamiliar. She'd simply said, 'Kevin…'

Now, he listened to the wind outside the bothy, bowing dark silhouetted trees in the distance. Snow fell ghoulish in the moonlight and he remained mesmerised, fantasising about what he'd seen tonight.

He'd managed to get through to St Brigid's, despite the thick snow. The road had been gritted. He only needed to get to the turn-off and he could then carry his bike and walk to the churchyard to see if the stranger was there. When he'd arrived, there had been no fresh footprints in the snow, but he trudged through anyway, to the old ruin. His walking boots sank into the drifts and he was glad he wore a thermal jacket. It had been dark when he got there and the stars were fully bright. The moon was waxing gibbous – the full moon was expected on the tenth of the month – and it looked like a rugby ball, deflating a little on the left. The craters were brightly visible and Kevin wished he could go there. Space would suit him. He'd seen the movie *First Man*, and what had struck him was the silence. Another planet would be even better. He wouldn't miss anyone, not a soul: except perhaps the stranger.

He'd been disappointed with the weather; it meant that even the stranger might not venture out tonight. But after he'd been there about two hours, freezing and having almost given up, he'd become aware of headlights. He heard a car stop and the engine was cut, the lights went out. He held his breath and heard voices. He recognised the man's voice and excitement flashed through his body. And he was with a woman.

'Somebody else is here?' he heard her say. She must have noticed Kevin's footprints. His heart sank as he believed he might have ruined an opportunity.

'Looks like a large deer,' the man said, reassuring her. Kevin wanted to laugh but he held back: the woman must be very stupid because deer prints were nowhere near like a man's.

The man was convincing. Kevin's excitement grew because he was pretty sure the man knew what had made the prints, and he was coming into the graveyard anyway. Kevin knew in that moment that the man liked to be watched as much as it thrilled Kevin to watch.

The woman accepted the explanation and the voices grew louder as they approached and entered through the gateway, where vines centuries old were weighted down with snow. Kevin marvelled that the stranger had managed to talk the woman into coming to the cemetery on a night such as this: his power was that potent. Then he saw them. The woman was on the stranger's back, piggy-back style, and she giggled as he carried her towards the back of the church. He watched as the man stopped to put her down and clear a tomb of deep snow with his hand; he then spread his coat over it, like before. Kevin crouched silently behind a plinth and tried to control his breathing. He checked his pocket for tissues. The woman lay down on her back, laughing and staring wantonly. Kevin took in the details of the woman's face and her body. He wanted to remember everything about her, every last detail, like the others, to consume and memorise so that he could relive the moment over and over again. He wondered what happened after they left the graveyard: did the man ever take them home? Kevin considered briefly what the man might do with the women if he was to have them all night.

The man began rearranging her clothes so he could have what he wanted. Kevin held his breath.

The light from the moon shone down on the trees, making them appear like ancient temple pillars, framing their place of worship. The tops weighed heavy with snow and the gravestones stuck up out of the ground, like worshippers called to prayer. Everything was still and pure, and perfect, with the crystallised snow sparkling and glinting, giving a noble topping to the site, and throwing more light on the clandestine ritual. Kevin felt as if he was part of a sect, and this man had invited him in.

The woman was noisier compared to the others, and her voice carried on the wind and whipped about them. She threw back her head and laughed and groaned. He pinned her on the tomb, holding on to his coat. Kevin slunk into a shadow caused by the old church itself, and watched, mesmerised and zoned out, inside a world where, for once, he had some control. He was being treated like an honoured guest, he was wanted, and he was a partner.

He forgot his own pleasure, until it spilled over his hand and he was reminded where he was and what he was doing. He wiped it on his jeans and his senses returned, and he watched her lie panting, with him on top of her. She took out a cigarette from his jacket and lit it. The smoke billowed into the night and it began to snow again, having given them a break of about an hour. He only remembered how thick it was when it began to fall again. The flakes landed on the woman's body and melted with her body heat and dripped down the crevices between her breasts, her legs and her waist. Kevin felt the cold now and he shivered.

'You earned your money,' the man said.

'You pay me well.'

Kevin wondered if he could someday pay a woman to do that for him. He watched as the couple finished sharing their cigarette and she threw it into the snow. Slowly, he helped her up and gave her his coat. She shivered and snuggled in her wrapping. She climbed onto his back again and the man began to walk towards the archway and Kevin held his breath. His jeans stuck to him and he crouched down, hoping she wouldn't see him. They got closer and Kevin's heart pounded. His hand went up to his face, in a bid to sink further into the shadows. They were virtually next to him and suddenly he felt a shockwave of electricity through him as the man reached down and covered Kevin's own hand. It lingered there, but for a second, and then it was gone.

Kevin froze as the man floated by with the woman holding on to his back and Kevin watched them leave. His breath came in bursts as the couple passed through the arch and disappeared. Kevin couldn't move for minutes until after he heard the car pull away. It took many more for his heart to still and, by the time he stood up, his legs were weak. He looked down and, in his hand, saw a folded piece of paper. He unwrapped it, dizzy with excitement, and saw scribbled on it a phone number.

Chapter 25

The snow meant that most of the punters couldn't go home, which meant they paid more, but it also made the girls tired.

Deep in the heart of Birkhouse Moor, at the foot of the mighty Helvellyn and next to the rushing water of Grisedale Beck, three cottages had been renovated and let to large groups. Or at least that's what it said on Airbnb.

The oldest trade on earth, and not an illegal one if one knew how to navigate the law, was in full swing, safe from the battering of the snowstorm outside. However, the organisation of the timeless commerce into a business involving more than the two willing parties *was* illegal. Which is why those in charge got jumpy when the police turned up at the door. They'd heard about the incident in Grasmere, and luckily, the house was in order by the time the coppers turned up asking questions, like they do. *But* a copper with nose had pushed further until they were exposed, and it put them all at risk. All the houses had been warned now.

Paul Knight sat in a chair next to a window, with no lights on, to help his eyes adjust to the darkness outside, peering into the night, looking for headlights. There weren't many places to go up here, next to the old quarry, but forewarned was forearmed and they could easily make it look like a party, with enough time. It had happened before.

Music wafted through the rooms from a sound system. All the clients had to be introduced by somebody already on the inside and were strictly vetted, then paid a hefty deposit to join the agency. Paul had learned a lot about how to hide information that was easily discoverable – if you knew where to look. A network of firewalls, diversionary software using Tor (shorthand for 'the onion router', due to its many-layered mystery), virtual private networks and fake IPs (internet protocol addresses) had all been expertly manipulated by the mastermind behind the agency. It had been a marvel to realise that behind the veneer of Sunshine Holidays, men – and the odd woman – were being introduced to the world of the agency, where they could book their purest fantasy and have it played out, for a price. After a careful vetting process Paul had been introduced to the genius behind the web of deceit. Zhang Wei, co-owner and the brains behind the company. Paul wasn't a fan, but he paid wages on time and rewarded loyalty. He stared into the night, wondering if Mr Wei would gift him another holiday to Spain this year.

Every bedroom was taken and a soft orange glow escaped from under each door. The music had been introduced to muffle the noises of lust: grunting, moaning, the odd squeal and thud. It made things run smoother. Different songs played in each room, and could be changed according to the client's wishes.

It was the inaugural year for these three houses and it was a period of transition and celebration. The agency was doing well. The girls came and went, as one might expect for such an exhausting and risky job, but they were looked after and paid well. Of course, most had other work and were probably also on the game outside, but as long as they stuck to the rules when they were in here, they'd be invited back. After all, in this trade, discretion was guaranteed.

No drugs, contraception at all times – unless prearranged and the price was right – regular STI and HIV testing, and strict confidentiality were the absolute baseline of the business. There were MPs in parliament calling for the exact same set-up, to protect the workers (minus the paying extra for bareback), so girls and women didn't have to work on the street, but they were always voted down. And so the trade remained in the shadows, where faint orange light showed the way, and the whimpers of girls and the creaking of bedposts signalled illicit activity.

A man left one of the bedrooms and Paul stood up. He had no interest in faces – in fact it was better that he didn't get to know anyone; he waited until the man signalled that he was ready, and opened the front door.

'You going to take your chances?' Paul asked.

'It's barely two miles to Glenridding. It's only a bit of snow,' the man said.

'Good luck.' Paul shut the door and continued his watch. His phone vibrated and he answered.

'All quiet,' he said. He looked around. 'One just left; it looks like the others will stay. Do all the girls know?'

He listened for a moment and hung up. This wasn't his only job; he worked for a postal sorting office in Kendal, driving a delivery truck; that's how he'd met her, the woman who ran the whole rig, together with Mr Wei. It suited him; he earned treble what he did during the day, and it meant he'd almost paid off his mortgage. His wife asked no questions, because they had separate bank accounts, and he was waiting happily for his retirement, which would definitely come early. She watched him go to work in his van every day and marvelled at his ability to save so diligently to afford a holiday to the Costa Del Sol.

Life was good.

A woman wandered into the hallway. She wore a robe and rubbed her eyes.

'You all right, love?' Paul asked.

'I need some more water,' she said.

'You've got a sink in your room.'

She stared at him. He understood. She needed a break. He nodded to the kitchen and she padded away. They called them girls but they were all ages, races, shapes and sizes. 'Girl' flattered all of them. He caught glimpses of them as they arrived and went to their rooms. Some of them were pretty and he couldn't understand why they were on the game. Some were old and ugly, with fat bellies. But then he'd long worked out that this lark was all in the mind. Self-respect was something that went deeper than pretty eyes and a wide smile. The most beautiful women in the world were insecure, and perfect for this job. Similarly, men – and some women – really didn't give a toss what the person looked like if they were delivering their filthiest perversions.

Paul's aim was to earn enough over the next five years so by the age of fifty he could retire and move to Spain. He took good care of himself and worked out in the gym every day, so he could enjoy his future, but also in preparation for trouble. He'd only witnessed it once, but one couldn't be too careful. A guy, thinking himself a cut above, had swaggered in one night – this was in another place, in Bowness – and Paul hadn't liked the look of him then. He found it odd that he'd made it through to become a member of the agency. Anyhow, a couple of hours in, one of the girls had pressed her alarm; they all had them fitted under the bed, so they were easily reached. It was in case a customer forced them to do something they didn't want to do, or got rough, or brought drugs, that kind of thing. It was true that the agency was slick: it had sources of money Paul could only speculate about, but the operation impressed him, most of the time. He'd walked into the room to find the girl battling to keep this guy off. The door had banged against the wall and the punter had swung round, surprised, his erection proudly pointing at Paul. A line of coke sat expectantly on the bedside and the girl was spread out on her front, bleeding. It hadn't taken long to overpower the man and calm him down. They'd shared a smoke outside and the guy explained that he was going through a rough time and it wouldn't happen again. Paul wasn't confident he was telling the truth.

'I'll have to let the agency know,' he'd said. The man hung his head and put it in his hands. This was the risk factor: only time would tell if the guy would blow and leak them to the coppers, or his desire to partake in the agency would win out and he'd behave himself in the future, but not with the same girl. Desire was triumphant. He hadn't caused trouble since. Mr Wei made sure anyhow that any breach of security was dealt with swiftly and IPs shut down reliably.

—

Tonight, Paul followed the girl to the kitchen.

'Anything wrong?' he asked her. She turned to him with wide eyes and he was at a loss as to what to say. He recognised the look as a mixture of resignation and disgust, and he knew her days were numbered. The agency had to be sure of the girls' mental and physical health; otherwise, they'd collapse, compromising the operation. He went to her and held her, soothing her. But then the tears came and they didn't stop. She sobbed into his chest and snot covered her face. And it was loud.

He heard a door open and a man came towards the kitchen, from her room, naked.

'What the fuck is going on?' the man asked, oblivious to his state of undress.

Paul held up his hand and made a gesture to the man that he needed to hang on, but the man didn't intend to be told what to do. He strode towards the kitchen, cock jiggling around, and Paul let go of the girl.

'Hang on, she's having a break,' Paul said.

'And I'm paying for it.' The guy rubbed his nose angrily and squared up to Paul. Paul noticed the guy's eyes and realised that he was high on something. Drugs and alcohol changed behaviour: that's why they were banned.

The girl cowered behind Paul.

'I paid for extra. I want my money back.' He looked behind Paul.

'It'll be arranged,' said Paul, eager to defuse the situation. After all, it was a brothel; clients paid for whatever they wanted, and got it.

There was a tense few seconds when it seemed that Paul might have to physically remove the man, then the guy's agitation evaporated and he went back to his room. Paul heard banging and slamming, and it wasn't long before the man left without saying anything else. Paul looked at the girl, who was crouched on the floor. He knew the score and so did she: he had to tell the people he reported to and she wouldn't be allowed back. If you couldn't hack it, then you weren't up to the job: there was no sympathy for girls who were too sensitive. The man would be recompensed, and Paul wouldn't mention the suspicion of drugs to his bosses. For the most part, the customer was always right. He pulled the girl up off the floor and walked her back to her room and closed the door behind her. She'd sleep it off and face the agency tomorrow.

He thought about the villa in Spain that he always envisaged: it was built of stone and painted white, and overlooked a hillside next to the turquoise blue Mediterranean Sea. Palm trees wafted in the breeze and the hot sun danced off the surface of the pool. If he closed his eyes for long enough, he saw himself there; he could even smell the BBQ and the fat juicy prawns cooking; he could taste the Rioja and feel the hot sand under his feet.

He went back to his seat by the door and peered out. The snow had stopped and the wind had died down. He decided to take his alarm belt and his phone with him and go to shovel some snow, so maybe some of the clients could get their cars out safely.

Chapter 26

Kelly listened as Johnny told her about his mission to the top of the Fairfield Horseshoe to rescue two campers who thought it clever to be at one with nature, on top of a mountain, in a snowstorm, in winter. They'd finally found a signal on one of their phones, after the other dropped theirs in the deep drifting snow, by walking for a mile in a direction that they then forgot. By the time they retraced their footprints to take them back to their tent, it had blown away, with half their kit. Wandering around trying to find it, they'd got themselves lost. In their haste to find a phone signal, they'd only worn sliders on their feet and jumpers over their sleep attire.

Johnny had taken the Whinlatter route and another team had taken the Coledale Beck route. The phone hadn't yet been traced as they had trouble with signals all night. The gusts were too dangerous for a chopper and besides, there was nowhere to land. Finally, by using the signal from the dying mobile phone, and good old-fashioned shouting, Johnny had found the pair, half hypothermic and huddling together in the middle of a snowdrift.

'What's the hotel like?' he asked Kelly.

'Cheap and cheerful. The owners are very friendly, and we've probably doubled their winter earnings in one night. My bed is lovely and warm. I'm knackered.'

'Maybe you should cut your hours,' Johnny said.

'Policing doesn't work like that, you know as well as I do. I can't investigate half-assed; it's a contradiction in terms. Part-time murder inquiry just doesn't cut the mustard.'

'But what about the baby?'

'It's what my body is designed to do, or so the doc said. He said carry on as normal and listen to any signals to stop. I can run, dance, climb, and hike if I want to, because it's very well protected,' she said.

'But you being tired all the time is a sign that maybe you should listen to,' he said.

'I know I should but I can't, not now,' Kelly reminded him.

'It could be too late by the time you do.'

'Good God, Johnny, don't say things like that. What are you trying to do? Scare the hell out of me? If I get any pain or bleeding or anything like that then I'd be the first to act, trust me, but a bit of fatigue? Isn't that par for the course with pregnancies? Women work up until the full forty weeks now.'

'They're not all policewomen.'

'I haven't got the most taxing job in the world,' she said. She was stretched out on the bed in her room, listening to the wind roaring outside.

'But it's emotionally stressful and very traumatic, you don't know what that can do.'

'Were you like this when Josie was an eight-week-old foetus?'

'I was in Iraq. I was selfish. I'm not that person any more. I want you to be careful. I want to look after you. I love you, Kelly, I want to protect you, and working all hours and getting stuck in blizzards isn't my idea of giving you what you need right now.'

'That's not your fault,' she said.

'What took you down to Ambleside anyway?'

'The murder case. You know the Chinese woman as well?'

'Yes.'

'It turns out the sighting in Preston was inaccurate and we've reopened the case. My team have unearthed more evidence for the murdered woman being a sex worker and I wanted to visit some sites myself.' She told Johnny about the arrests they had made after finding the sex workers and their clients at the cottage earlier.

'It's a risky trade. Do the police investigate missing hookers seriously yet? Or are they still seen as dubious women of questionable morals who take risks that sometimes don't pay off?' he asked, half tongue-in-cheek.

Kelly sighed. He was absolutely right to be cynical. It wasn't long ago that if a woman was the victim of crime and found out to be a prostitute, the police wouldn't put as much resource into the case as they would if, say, the victim was an innocent child. Only just before Christmas, two women had been stabbed in Penrith: one in Potton Park and the other on the Beacon Estate. It was felt, by some, that the woman in Potton Park was the more high-profile because she was a well-to-do mother and wife, minding her own business. The other had links to gangs and hung out with the wrong crowd, taking drugs and sleeping around. It wasn't fair, but it was human nature. Kelly wasn't going to allow sloppy police work on the cases of Lisa, Dorinne and Lucinda. And she knew Craig felt the same.

It didn't matter what these women did to earn money, they were human beings with families. *There but by the grace of God go I*, thought Kelly. Life had a habit of chewing you up and spitting you out if you were born on the wrong side of the tracks. Funny how women who slept around on a council estate were called hookers, but TV personalities doing it on live TV were fawned-over celebrities.

'I'd like to think that they'll be investigated the same as any missing person. I'm meeting the DI in charge of Barrow tomorrow, it could be Cumbria-wide.' She paused for a bit. 'Have you ever heard any rumours about brothels near us? I know it sounds like a stupid question, but you know so many people. We know they exist, because we have raids every so often that are successful, but we can't seem to trace any of the women to a particular address. And you talk to some right bell-ends in pubs.'

'Thanks. Maybe they were working alone? I get told gossip all the time at work. We've got a volunteer who is, how can I put this? In the army, he'd be a called "thing"; it means...'

'I think I know what you mean. He's enthusiastic about the ladies, right?'

'Yeah, he shows me some weird shit on his phone, I mean, not that I watch it, he just shows you, over morning tea. He'll say, "Johnny, look at this one." It'll be a woman on Tinder who he met in some toilets the night before in Bowness, and gave the good news to, paid her a twenty, pulled his trousers up and buggered off.'

'Nice.'

'I could ask him.'

'He sounds like the right type of guy.'

'But you say these girls are missing, so you think there's something more sinister going on?' Johnny asked.

'There are similarities between the murder case and the missing person cases that I can't ignore.'

'It sounds like you're not going to sleep tonight with all that whirring round,' he said.

'This bed is so comfortable though, I don't think I'll have a problem.'

'I wish I was there,' he said. 'I've started packing a few things to move in, and I've asked around. I know someone who has a large enough van to help.'

'Have you told Josie yet?'

'I want to tell her together,' he said.

Kelly felt peace. Suddenly she no longer felt scared. Johnny had been suggesting moving in together for ages. Now she was allowing herself to become excited. They'd get a good price for Johnny's place and could build an extension on the side to make the kitchen bigger.

She yawned.

'You'd better get some sleep, I'll see you tomorrow,' he said. They hung up.

But despite her tiredness the last thing she could do was sleep, and she opened the files from the YHA in Ambleside. Her call with the FCO and Home Office bugged her. Of all the embassies to be dealing with, China and Russia were the two the UK had least sway over. No one in Whitehall was about to challenge any decision made by the Chinese government. Her concern was not that a diplomatic minister called Li Qiang was investigating Lisa Lau, but what might be lost or tampered with along the way. Who was he? But, more importantly, where the hell was he?

She checked to see if the CCTV had arrived from the Heaven club yet. It hadn't. She stared at her screen and opened Lisa Lau's attendance record from the YHA. It showed her leaving the hostel at four p.m. on New Year's Day. She never checked back in. She was reported missing on the third, and Li Qiang visited the hostel on the fourth. That was a discrepancy of over twenty-four hours. She opened the CCTV file and found the correct time on New Year's Day and found Lisa walking out, happily checking her phone and seemingly singing to herself.

She had no luggage.

Chapter 27

Kevin approached the house, smiling widely. He felt armed and dangerous. He felt renewed, enriched… whole. He put his key in the lock and turned the handle and went inside. He reckoned he could run a marathon; maybe that was his calling: something physical. He fancied himself superhuman, with a hidden, game-changing power.

Until he heard his mother.

He stopped walking and smiling, feeling his face return to its usual frown. The lines on his forehead were so deep that his mother always said he looked fifty years old. Now his body betrayed him and he bent over like an old man of those years. His shoulders fell slightly and he exhaled with resignation. All the bravado left him and he was rendered just Kevin again. The lad who everyone felt sorry for. He knew that when Marvin gave him his top-shelf magazines, he was doing it with pity. He knew that when he saw Maureen Johnson shake her head, she was thinking he'd have been better off not born at all. He imagined the entire church congregation recoiling in horror when they found him behind a gravestone with his trousers down.

He experienced the weight of guilt and failure. It was like a great burden on his shoulders, pressing mercilessly downwards. It was as if he'd taken a pill that drew the life out of him, slowly seeping through his gut. He looked down towards his shoes.

Maybe he'd made the wrong decision to come back. Again.

'Where have you been, bastard boy?' she growled. Her brutality was back. She'd been drinking.

He slowly lifted his head and allowed his eyes to adjust to the sight: she was wrapped in her pale cream silky dressing gown, smoking a cigarette. There was an empty bottle of cheap whisky next to her. He could see her eyes glinting and didn't need to see her mouth to know that she was snarling like a rabid rat, hiding in the shadows ready for its next filthy meal.

His father was no doubt passed out somewhere: either here, or at the pub, or maybe in a street. One day they'd find him in a ditch and they'd have to find money to fund a funeral.

Kevin's hands were still deep in his pockets and he could feel his thighs through his jacket. He touched the clearly defined muscle of his quadriceps and the sensation distracted him. The mass was hard and lean and it gave him a glimmer of confidence. He began to rub his hands up and down and tense his leg muscles against them to create a satisfying resistance. With every stroke, he grew braver. It was true that his body was strong and fit from all the cycling he did. Sure, he was heavy and thickset, but he was strong.

His shoulders raised a little and his breath came quicker. He lifted his head and looked at his mother.

'I've been out,' he said.

'Out! You disgusting pervert!' She stood up and stubbed out her cigarette, then stood facing him with her hands on her hips. She scowled at him and his mouth began to curve upwards in a grin. His heart rate sped up further and he took his hands out of his pockets. He flexed other muscle groups: his back, his buttocks, his biceps...

She remained where she stood, defiant, menacing and malevolent.

He took a step towards her so he appeared in the light of the moon, shining through a split in the curtain.

'I made a friend,' he said.

The muscles in her face softened and her eye twitched.

'You? A friend? Don't be ridiculous. You're a day-dreamer, Kevin! You need to get upstairs and prepare yourself while I run a hot bath. A very hot bath.'

Kevin experienced a flood of butterflies to his belly and he swallowed hard. His mother's face hardened again. He registered her ugliness almost for the first time. She came towards him and before he could figure out what he was going to say next, she slapped him hard across the face. His head flew to the side and spittle flew out onto the carpet.

'Dirty boy!' she screamed. She went to slap him again, but this time he caught her arm in a grip so hard that she wriggled and gasped.

'Ouch! Kevin! You're hurting me! How dare you! You...'

He squeezed harder. His belly burned and his head pounded, and a foggy mist descended on his brain. There was only one thing on his mind, and it completely filled his psyche: to stop his mother. He grabbed hold of her other arm and began shaking her. She tried to scream and get away, but he was too strong.

As suddenly as it started, the shaking stopped and he stared into her eyes. He'd never seen that look before, and he tried to work out what it was. He'd always seen his mother as looking like he always saw the police, or doctors, looking: in charge. Now, this was different. She looked like a dog might look should his owner kick him. Or a frightened child who has lost his mother at the mall.

She reminded him of himself: someone with needs that were so special that they couldn't take care of themselves, and who were completely at others' mercy. Her eyes were wide and her chest heaved up and down. He forced her backwards to the chair she'd been sitting on, stewing and fuming, waiting for him to come and get his punishment.

'Sit down,' he demanded, and threw her backwards. She landed in the chair and he thought she'd stopped breathing, but her chest still moved up and down rapidly.

'Kevin,' she whispered.

'Shut up!' It was the loudest he'd ever heard anyone shout. The noise boomed around the room and shattered the space in his head.

'Shut up!' he bellowed again. She closed her mouth and tears flowed from her eyes. Her breath came in irregular whimpers and she stayed glued to the chair.

Kevin's body shook and the fog lifted. His whole body began to loosen as the tension in his muscles released. His face softened and he watched his mother's face carefully, trying to decide if he liked it or not; he was so unused to it being anything but domineeringly powerful.

'I'm not having a bath tonight,' he said in a normal voice. His mother nodded her head briskly.

'I'm going straight to bed,' he added. She nodded again, hastily. 'You'll find your pissy mattress in the hall for you to clean,' he said. She nodded again.

He left the room and climbed the stairs, not realising that he still had his boots on.

Chapter 28

The man unlocked the gate to the small pen and covered his mouth. The body had already begun to putrefy. It happened.

It was too soon, but it was expected. He wore boxer shorts, a T-shirt, heavy-duty gloves and an easy-wipe apron. Her face was set in a look that he'd seen before, in a recent film. He couldn't think what it was now, but a woman had been burning alive and she'd screamed as the flames melted her skin.

Her skin was slippery and she smelled bad. It was a good job she was leaving, because it made room for the others, but also she'd allowed herself to become unclean and he no longer desired her. He heard whimpers behind him and peered over to the other cages. The orange lamp revealed a ghoulish scene from a horror movie. None of them looked at him. A camera sat silently in one corner of the cellar and the blue light told him that it was functioning normally. He worked quickly, seemingly mindless of the other life forms surrounding him.

He took the woman by the hair, which was disgustingly oily, and dragged her out of the confined space. Her scalp was still holding together. She was heavy, but dead bodies usually were. Her flesh wobbled as she travelled behind him and when he'd got her fully out of the cage her legs flopped noisily on the stone floor. He heard a gasp and a woman crying and he stopped what he was doing to look at where the noise came from. He crawled over to the cage and crouched outside, peering in.

Her eyes were pure white, except for the dark purple pupils, and her skin glowed honey-like in the orange glow. She was a bit skinny, really, and there had been a couple of occasions when he thought he might kill her with his broad hands round her throat. But she'd pulled through. He liked that about her: she had spirit. She stopped making noises when he tilted his head and spread his hands.

He followed her eyes and realised that she was staring at his hands. That's what she was afraid of most. He wanted to spend a bit of time with her now, but he had work to do. He couldn't risk them being tainted by the dead woman and catching some kind of infection from her. When a body expired, he tried to get rid of it as soon as possible. But he'd been working crazy hours lately.

He'd tried lots of different methods of disposal, all with varying degrees of success. His last one hadn't ended well and she'd been found. He gave himself a stern talking-to after that. It was all because of the smell. He'd better wrap this one tighter and, this time, he would take her to the waste disposal yard himself; not the one run by the government and full of cameras, no, the one just at the end of Church Lane, where people dumped stuff and no one cared. Fly-tipping was illegal of course, but only tramps and drunks lived down the end of Church Lane. He'd take her inside an old chest freezer so she wouldn't stink and encourage enquiry. Occasionally, the council got bored of incessant complaints and, instead of building expensive barriers and manning the place, they simply filled the ditches in. If they did that soon then the freezer, along with the woman inside, would disappear for ever.

There'd been talk of a refugee camp down Church Lane, accepting foreigners from war zones and the like, such as Syria, but the local residents had petitioned the council, and won. The camp had been built elsewhere. In Wales, he fancied. He kept abreast of the news. It never ceased to amaze him how negative a place the world was. War, disease and famine: all the population controls that Malthus predicted in 1798. His own opinion was that they were close to another Malthusian catastrophe now, and they approached another apocalypse like the 1918 Spanish flu, or something similar.

There were simply too many people, and Mother Nature always found a way to heal and kill off a few parasites until she had time to recover. He saw himself as part of that noble process: scourging the population of the unclean.

He hadn't meant for the body in the bin to be found. He'd watched that road for weeks, judging it to be foolproof. But the weather was milder that week, and she must have stunk to high heaven: a distasteful shame. He reckoned a high wind must have opened the lid, or something. He'd thought the smell wouldn't carry as far in winter, with the bin covered in snow, but he was wrong. His biggest fear was that the bin had some kind of hidden barcode attached to it, making it traceable, but he knew that was mere paranoia.

'Please…'

He turned away from the woman and towards the cage behind him. His face was set in a scowl and all thoughts of spending time down there enjoying himself evaporated.

'I'll do anything… Please… I need to get back for my daughter…'

He bashed the door of the cage so hard that it rocked and she sucked in a gasp of air, terrified. She pushed herself backwards against the metal and covered her mouth. The woman opposite her shook her head in warning.

He stared at her and pushed his face against the gate. 'Shut. The. Fuck. Up.' He said it very slowly and it was more of a hiss than a sentence. The woman nodded vigorously and shrank in size as much as she could.

He breathed less rapidly and his shoulders dropped a little. He hated swearing.

Good.

He turned round and checked the other cage one more time. Happy, he went back to the dead woman and grabbed hold of her hair again and began to drag her to the door. He opened it and manoeuvred the body through it, tutting and sighing as he went. It was hard work, and he still had to get her upstairs to the garage where his tools were. Already his apron was wet with the oily stuff oozing out of her from every opening. Now, in better light, he noticed the discolouration on her limbs and torso. He almost expected her to fight back and laughed at his extraordinary imagination. He'd come back to clean up later on.

Out in the small space at the foot of the stairs, he took a heavy-duty waste bag from a bag hanging on a hook and wrapped the top of her body in it, tying it round her waist. He did the same with the lower part of her body. He managed to get her sitting upright, and held on to her shoulders as he got himself into a lunge position so he could get her on his shoulder, like a fireman's lift. It worked. Now he could negotiate the stairs up to the garage. Halfway up he stopped to have a break, but he didn't put her down. His thighs screamed and his back ached, but if he put her down now, he'd never get her back up there.

He made it and kicked open the door. He wasn't getting any younger.

He'd already prepared the workbench, and the floor was covered in plastic. A drain collected water and oil at the centre of the garage and today it would act as a receptacle for blood too, though dead bodies didn't bleed much, but there'd still be a bit of mess. He'd considered hanging them up, like deer and game, to set the blood and make the whole process less contaminated, but human bodies didn't age well like a good piece of venison.

He bent over and she slid off him onto the bench, her head making a cracking sound as it landed on the wood. He stood, panting, getting his breath back, and looking around to make sure everything was as it should be. He went to a fridge in the corner of the room and took out a cold bottle of beer. He popped the top open and sank half in one go, then got to work. He'd taught himself how to satisfactorily dismember a human body. It wasn't hard. What was hard was surgical butchery, but he wasn't in the business of selling pretty cuts of meat, just getting rid of them.

He had an arrangement of knives: long ones for sawing, small ones for sinew and heavy ones for chopping through joints. He sharpened them lovingly, then set his iPhone to Bluetooth and played music through the speaker on top of the fridge. He played 'Nimrod', and it soothed him. He often cried when listening to his favourite classical pieces. It was something to do with hormonal changes when senses are deeply stimulated.

He'd read about the quickest amputation in history. The world record was twenty-two seconds and performed by a doctor called Robert Liston in 1822.

'Tell me, gentlemen. Time me.'

He had no gallery, no operating theatre full of smoking colleagues in outdoor coats, coughing germs that no one knew existed yet all over the screaming, conscious patient, trying to writhe in agony, only to be given a shot of whisky, held down, or punched into unconsciousness.

He didn't aim to break world records. He simply wanted the body to go away, and this was the hardest part. He'd rushed the last one and the memory made him angry and he had to put down his tools. He had to make his peace with it, and he admitted, now, his weakness that he simply couldn't butcher her into many pieces because he liked her.

It was simple, really.

He'd grown to harbour real affection for her, which was why he'd left her body in the lounge by mistake, with the heater on, encouraging decomposition. It was a depressing end to a beautiful relationship.

Move on.

It was similar to jointing a chicken, really: a slit over a joint, then a bit of pressure to separate the limbs was all that was needed. He decided to do this one in more pieces. He decided to chop off her arms, and looked at the head. A thought occurred to him that he'd never put a knife through a neck. He'd been too busy admiring his work with his hands round throats to think about knifing them. He wondered whether it would be a task and decided to give it a go. In the end, it was soft and yielding, except the vertebrae.

—

After almost forty-five minutes he had seven packages, wrapped up tight, ready for the old freezer. He opened the top and put the lumps of flesh inside, one by one, letting the top fall closed when he was done.

Now to tidy up.

As he mopped the floor and wrapped up the last remnants of a life, his thoughts turned to the young boy. He was a handsome chap and reminded him of himself at the same age. There was no doubting why the lad was there, each night, in the graveyard, waiting for him. He'd once had the same vicarious need to watch. And learn. But that was a long time ago. The lad couldn't be trusted, no one could. He worked alone, and that wasn't about to change. Unless...

He toyed with the idea of an apprentice and all the complications and risks involved with such a perilous proposition. But the boy was simple: easy to control perhaps, but was he trustworthy? He hadn't ratted him out so far, and he knew his face. Maybe the boy didn't read the papers. And yet, every night when he took a woman to St Brigid's the boy was there, like a loyal hound waiting for his master to say 'Kill!'

Chapter 29

Harry worked late. He listened to the radio and it made him feel at peace. He had only a few more packages to deliver. Some people preferred the late slots and, as he couldn't sleep, sometimes it suited him. Time was money and the more he got done before midnight, the more he could charge for that twenty-four-hour period and start all over again tomorrow. The only problem was that the weather had closed in and it was slow going. He heard on the radio that some roads were blocked and he swore under his breath.

His mind wandered to the police and he thought carefully about what they'd said about spotting brothels. He decided not to reveal the deliveries of sex toys despite being asked outright. It was hardly his business, and the tips he received were appreciated. He totted up in his head how many times he'd witnessed the tell-tale signs and shook his head. The whole Lakes was at it, if what he'd seen was anything to go by. Were Maureen and Marvin being melodramatic? Maureen seemed convinced. He had last seen Marvin heading with the two coppers to the address Maureen gave them. Harry didn't really know Lorna, but he listened to what he heard when he was in the shop. She didn't seem a nice woman, but she did seem to be a shrewd one.

He remembered that Maureen had once joked that Lorna was really a county lines drug lord, and her property lets were a front. Marvin hadn't seen the funny side. Harry knew she'd only meant it as a jest, but Marvin had reacted with such a lack of humour that Harry knew that he was at least a little sensitive to what his wife did when she was out and about, which was most of the time. He'd caught a glimpse of her once. He hadn't known it at the time; Maureen had told him after. She'd been outside arguing with Marvin, and Harry had been about to step in but Marvin had cut him off. Harry got the message loud and clear and went inside the shop to collect his parcels. It was then that Maureen told him who the woman was.

He thought of her now: she was well dressed and perfectly groomed. He could smell her perfume from ten paces and her hair was recently styled. She was no spring chicken, but she clearly looked after herself. Harry couldn't help thinking that a woman like that would be a challenge, but she was way beyond what he could handle. Harry liked to keep it simple. He was unattached in so far as he held down no lasting relationships. It had always been so. Along the way, he'd often been assumed to be bent, a pansy, a gayboy. Well they could think what they liked. He kept his counsel. When he took a woman out, he liked to look the part and wore his best clothes and he shaved, and took plenty of cash to impress. He had his fair share of dates and kept a steady stream of those interested enough to keep him ticking along.

The snow shone under the moonlight and every so often would gust in waves across his windscreen. His wipers worked hard and he squinted into the thick black canvas, dotted with white lumps, facing him and threatening to turn him dizzy. He didn't see a soul on the street and was thankful he had no deliveries deep in the Lakes tonight. They were mainly around Bowness and Windermere, and those towns had been cleared of the worst of the snow by big lorries spewing dirty grit over the roads. The South Lakes area was a well-oiled machine when faced with adverse weather, unlike the less accessible central and northern fells.

–

He pulled into a long driveway belonging to one of the more expensive pads along the shore of Windermere, Cumbria's largest lake. The private road was thick with snow, but his van could cope comfortably. Since his encounter with the police, he was more keenly evaluating every property he visited. This was a new one. Perhaps he should start a book. The place was huge. It was built of Cumberland stone and slate, and looked as though it had been there for centuries. He marvelled at how much money one would need to earn to be the owner of such a place. It was the stuff of dreams and he counted seventeen windows just at the back. All had soft glows escaping through the shutters and Harry's interest was piqued. Maybe it was a hotel? But the addresses on the parcels he had for the property didn't mention a hotel, business, or care home. He parked up and went to the rear of his vehicle, throwing open the doors against the falling snow. Light from the house gave him enough of a visual to see the parcels for the property. He pulled out his wheelie crate and loaded the boxes, checking the source of each as he handled them. Occasionally, a box or two would go missing and never be delivered. It was statistically inevitable. Some customers complained, and others didn't. He wagered that those who didn't were unwilling to have a consignment investigated because of the contents therein. This was another thing to add to the list, perhaps, of what hinted at a whorehouse.

He wheeled the crate to the rear, as he'd been instructed on his tracking data, and rang the bell. The rear of the property was darker, but he could still see enough, and his eyes had adjusted. The door was opened by a young man who looked to be in his thirties, and who wore what looked like a bouncer's uniform: black jeans and black jumper. He didn't make eye contact and simply waited patiently for the crate to be unloaded. He said nothing. Once the job was done, he closed the door gently, without saying thank you, or even acknowledging Harry's presence.

As he walked back to the van with his empty crate, Harry reckoned he'd found what the detectives might describe as a property displaying suspicious markers of questionable activity. He climbed back into his van and rubbed his hands, blowing into them. He reached over to the dash for his phone and opened the Notes icon, adding the address to a substantial list. The truth was that Harry had been taking notes on the properties on his rounds for a long time now. No one had asked him to do so until this afternoon, and now he saw his list with fresh eyes. In the wrong hands, the information could be very valuable indeed. He whistled gently as he pulled away and wondered how badly the detectives needed his singular knowledge of suspicious activity at certain addresses all over the National Park.

Chapter 30

Kelly woke to the sound of diggers outside. She stretched. She'd slept fantastically well. She reached into her bag beside the bed and got out a ginger biscuit. She'd worked out that if she nibbled one before she got out of bed, then her blood sugar wouldn't dip so drastically before breakfast. She realised that she was quite hungry and remembered that after her pasty last night she hadn't eaten anything else apart from a bag of nuts, a can of Pringles and a packet of Wheat Crunchies that were complimentary in her room. She ate three biscuits to compensate.

She got out of bed and went to put the kettle on, and popped a herbal tea bag into a mug. She hated hotels without tea-making facilities, and considered it tight-fisted. The room was lovely and warm and once the kettle was boiling, she looked at her phone: it was gone eight o'clock. Satisfied she'd had a good rest, she felt positive about the day ahead and sharing updates with Craig.

She peered behind the curtains; a vision of winter beauty assaulted her. She could see the tiny bridge over St John's Beck. The water was flowing freely, so it couldn't be that cold, she thought. The snow sat on the small archway, and upon the surrounding fields and trees. She couldn't see the main road, as she was the wrong side of the hotel, but she heard voices outside and they sounded emphatic and male. She imagined men standing around with yellow hard hats directing traffic and loading cars onto trucks with winching equipment. She stretched again and went to take a shower.

The night away was like an illicit treat and she felt revived. After her shower, she towel-dried her hair and turned on her Toughpad. She caught a glimpse of herself in the mirror and was taken back by the vigour in her eyes and the shine on her skin. She looked the healthiest she had in months – since her holiday to Florida with Johnny, when the sun and relaxation had made her look ten years younger. She always kept an emergency overnight bag in her car and she packed it now, looking around the room to make sure she hadn't left anything.

Logging in to HOLMES, she could see perfectly clearly that, like her, Craig had stayed up late into the night looking at the data from the YHA in Ambleside. He'd noted his sightings of Lisa Lau, as well as a large group of people checking out on January the fourth, all around the same time, and had worked hard to try to match names with faces on the CCTV. It was quite obvious from watching the footage who was checking out, and he'd inputted each of the twelve names.

What was most interesting, though, was the tag he'd flagged up for her, which was footage from the fourth of January that he'd watched on a hunch. Craig's hunches were the result of almost thirty years' service, observing human beings both at their most brazen and their most vulnerable. There was no word for it; and there was no shortcut or certificate, it was just a sixth sense that occasionally leapt out of nowhere, guiding the seasoned copper to a new lead.

Clear as day, standing at the reception desk and speaking to Leila, just as Leila had told her, for a full four minutes, was a tall, well-dressed man of East Asian descent who, at twenty seconds in, showed an ID document: a frame that Craig had made into an enlarged still. The ID was a Chinese diplomatic passport. Kelly thought at first it was a UK passport, because it was the same colour – burgundy – but she read Craig's notes and they brought to her attention the Chinese characters on the front and the distinctive logo of the temple under five stars. She would have missed the word diplomatic, had Craig not been so vigilant. She reckoned he would have had to have gone over that footage twenty times to spot it, but then, she'd have done exactly the same; she smiled at how similar they were.

Along with the visual, Craig had created another tag that showed he'd already been in contact with the UK Border Agency and found out that access and information regarding this particular diplomat was classified as highly restricted. One would need the highest level of vetting clearance, such as that afforded to ambassadors and senior civil servants, to gain access to the information. Of course, this was no surprise – serving UK diplomats in other countries would have the same level of protection – but it confirmed that the person sent on behalf of the family of Lisa Lau to investigate the disappearance of their daughter was a government official, and this made things tricky. Diplomats could (and did) get away with murder.

Kelly gave the room another final glance and went to find Dan. He was waiting for her in the foyer, cleanly shaved and fresh. He smiled at her and stood up to greet her. He'd been reading the local paper and he reversed it now to show her an appeal on page two. There were photographs of Lisa Lau and Lucinda Dockie next to one another, with a short piece about who to contact with information. Separately, an appeal for information about Dorinne's murder took up more space.

'Good, that paper has a distribution of twenty-five thousand a day. Have you read HOLMES this morning?'

'Yes. I'm assuming we're going to see DI Lockwood as soon as we can?'

'I'm calling him in a minute, but I want to find out where breakfast is first. I can smell bacon.'

Dan watched her as she found an employee, who directed her to a dining room. He followed her and she managed to find a table, despite the place being heaving as a result of last night's fiasco. Kelly spotted the couple with the baby and went to their table.

'Good morning, did you sleep well? How's the baby?' Kelly looked at the tiny human in her car seat, next to the mother on a chair. The baby played with her toes and smiled when Kelly rattled one of her toys. She was cute. Kelly didn't generally see babies as attractive, but this one was. Most of them looked like wrinkled old men, loved only by their deluded parents.

They confirmed they'd slept well enough, as much as is possible with a young baby at least.

'Have you been told any news about your car?' Kelly asked.

'It's been towed away and we're waiting for a hire car to arrive. The road is clear now and traffic is moving quite freely,' the man replied and the mother nodded.

'Great, well, take care.'

'Thank you for being there,' the mother said. Kelly smiled and went to find a large plate.

Dan ordered coffee and Kelly noticed that it didn't make her gag as much now. She ordered tea. After she sat down with her plate, she noticed Dan staring at her food over his banana and blueberry muffin.

'I'm starving,' she said.

'I can see.'

'Don't tell me you're a diet Nazi?' she asked.

'I've gone vegan. It was my wife's idea.'

Kelly didn't know what to say. She couldn't imagine a life without meat, and a life without eggs and cheese would be never-ending torture.

'Don't you miss cheese?' she asked.

'There are fairly good substitutes now and she buys soy bacon. We eat a lot of tofu.' He didn't sound convincing.

'I won't tell if you want to go and get a few sausages,' she said.

Dan looked at her and towards the breakfast bar.

'Hasn't that muffin got egg and milk in it?'

Dan stared at his treat and stopped chewing. 'She knows I'm still learning what's in stuff,' he said.

'I heard that avocados aren't vegan because bees are harmed during their production.'

'I read that too.' Dan looked glum.

'How long have you been married?' she asked.

'Seven years.'

'Kids?'

'No, we erm…'

'Oh God, sorry, it's absolutely none of my business. I just thought I'd get to know you a bit better,' she apologised.

'It's fine, it's no secret. We've done five rounds of IVF and now we've given up. We're looking into fostering.'

Kelly stopped eating. 'That's amazing. I truly admire that. There are so many kids out there who need good, loving homes. I sometimes think we are so overpopulated anyway, we should concentrate on the ones we've got.'

'What about you?' he asked.

'No kids. No husband. But a wonderful sixteen-year-old who is my boyfriend's daughter.'

'Perfect. Like you said. We should look after the ones we've got.'

Kelly concentrated on her food and changed the subject.

'You managed to source a razor?'

'They sell bathroom packs at reception. Very clever and a good earner, I'd bet. Sleep well?' he asked.

'Like a baby.'

Satiated with fat and carbs, she wiped her mouth and checked her phone.

'We need to freshen up properly. Let's head home, and I'll drop you in Penrith.'

Next, she called Johnny, who was relieved to hear that traffic was flowing again.

'I've got an appointment with the estate agent at eleven,' he said. 'I told Josie, she's over the moon. I couldn't help it, I'm sorry. I know I said I wanted to do it together. She overheard me talking about selling the house. She's thrilled, she thinks the world of you and she's already planning what to do with her room.'

Kelly smiled into the phone. He wasn't messing about, but that's what she loved about him. A part of her had been nervous about Josie and her wanting to share her father, but now she was reassured.

'That's awesome. I'll see you tonight.'

As Kelly put on her coat and went to the foyer, she saw Dan at the breakfast bar, standing in front of the sausages.

Chapter 31

In Windermere police station, Marvin was just waking up in a cell. The room had an extraordinarily narrow bed (more like a bunk) with a small pillow, like those you get given on cheap flights to Malaga, and one blanket. He felt wretched. He had no idea if they'd questioned Lorna or, indeed, what all this was about. All he knew was that, in one of their holiday lets, several people seemed to be having a bit of a gang bang, in exchange for money. Maureen would have a field day when she found out.

His phone had been confiscated and so he hadn't been able to communicate with Lorna at all. The detectives had told him they would find her, and when they did she'd be arrested on suspicion of running whorehouses.

It was almost laughable, if it wasn't so serious an allegation. Surely it couldn't be true? Of course it wasn't. His eye was drawn to where his watch had been. That had been taken off him too, along with all of his belongings he stood in. All of it had been logged in by a smug police officer behind a computer screen, as the arrest charge was read against him.

He'd been read his rights and told they had twenty-four hours to hold him, while they investigated the suspicion. Then, if they decided to go further upon any substantiation of proof, he'd be fully charged and held indefinitely until prosecution. It was like living inside a bubble. He could hear nothing, except the odd cough and sneeze from the next cell, and he could see nothing because the cells walls were so high, with one window at the very top, and that was tiny. The only light he'd seen was superficial and it hurt his head. He craved sunlight. At no other time did he truly understand the reality of incarceration like he did in this moment.

The watch was an expensive one and he remembered Lorna giving it to him as a gift.

'I think it's very beautiful, darling,' he'd said. 'It looks expensive,' he'd added.

Lorna sighed. 'Sunshine Holidays is doing so well, Marvin, don't spoil it, please. You never wanted me to take the risk but now it's paying off, I'm going to enjoy the fruits of my labour. And I'm going to spoil you.' She kissed him on his cheek. 'You said you never wanted to get involved, so don't moan when I buy you something nice. It ruins it. Look, I bought myself this.'

He'd looked at her outstretched hand and gazed at a ring of a beautiful smoky grey stone, set in rose gold.

'It's quite something. Are we really making that much money?' he'd asked.

Now, thinking back, he felt a fool. Maureen was right: there was never smoke without fire; but little did she know that she was standing right on top of the pyre. It all made sense now. The secrecy, though admittedly he hadn't shown much interest. Thinking back, Lorna kept everything to do with the business separate from their lives at the shop. In fact, Lorna never went into the shop any more. He'd assumed her happy and busy with her new venture, never thinking to ask questions about what she was doing. It seemed obvious now.

He scolded himself. The police might have it all wrong, he reassured himself. Lorna might not know anything about what was going on in the cottage. Christ, the old couple might have just arranged a party; they'd looked shifty from the moment he turned up with the police. He was damned sure that properties all over the Lakes were full of swingers and adulterers and kinky groups, meeting up to do God knows what, every single season. He and Lorna were unlucky, that's all. They'd been victims of deceit. He'd heard about it before; how could all landlords and holiday lets be vetted for what took place inside them?

He put his head in his hands. He'd never seen the people in that cottage before in his life, but the police were trying to make out that he was in on it all along. He had no evidence to the contrary. All he had was his sense of right and wrong, and the hope to appeal to good nature: person to person, face to face. He'd never been arrested for anything in his whole life and he didn't know how the game worked. They used clever phrases that caught him out, and they tricked him with information he'd given without knowing it. He'd had two interviews so far, and felt as though he'd dug an enormous hole for himself without meaning to. He couldn't remember his answers from the night before and struggled to figure out what he should do next. He didn't have a lawyer; why would he? He didn't normally need one! And he'd used his two phone calls up trying, without success, to get in touch with Lorna.

Twenty holiday lets and two pubs. It was a veritable empire, and he'd known little about it. He searched his memory, as the police had asked him to do, to see if he could recall anything out of the ordinary. He'd let slip about her nice clothes, handbags and shoes. It was an innocent remark to start with, but before he realised what they were doing, he'd said too much. Everything he told them was made to be incriminating about his wife.

The jewellery, the new car, the restaurant meals. L'Enclume in Cartmel had cost five hundred pounds alone. He'd complained but she'd told him they deserved it and a rich American was staying in her newest holiday let, for which, because it overlooked Windermere, she could charge a premium. He enjoyed seeing her happy and saw it as her little hobby.

He trusted her. Or did he? Was he simply grateful that such an attractive younger woman paid him attention in return for him allowing her to do what she wanted, with whom she wanted? He was a stupid old man.

He rubbed his eyes and stretched. He dreaded the thought of another interview under caution. Every little detail was being recorded and he knew that every time he opened his mouth, he made things worse for Lorna.

Then he remembered something.

Last year, he'd dropped her off at a property. Her car was having a new windscreen fitted, after a nasty crack from a stone had begun to grow larger. She said she was looking at a possible new let. They'd driven deep into the Lakes, to the shore of Derwentwater, to a large grand house with private grounds. He'd asked her if the place was divided into flats, and she'd laughed. It stuck in his memory because it was an unkind laugh: the kind that was condescending. She'd been vague as she got out of the car to meet the person selling. But when he drove off, a hunch made him stop and look back. He'd seen his wife greeting the man supposedly selling the property like an old friend. They'd laughed together and talked animatedly from the get-go. He'd watched his wife exchange kisses with the man on both cheeks.

It had been particularly memorable because the man was so distinctive-looking. He was either Chinese or from somewhere like that. Marvin had once watched a documentary on Hong Kong, and knew full well that Chinese people in formal situations nod and shake hands, they never kiss. This was no business meeting. He remembered now telling Maureen about it; regrettably, but he'd needed to offload.

He questioned himself on why he hadn't challenged her then. He shocked himself at how easily he'd wanted to push the vision out of his head. He'd wanted to erase it from his memory because to retain it was too painful. Lorna was an attractive woman. She'd used her extra cash, which he thought hard-earned, to preen and groom herself.

And he'd ignored it. Wilfully ignored, not just simply forgotten; he'd actively pushed it down into the dark recesses of his brain, where it could be washed away. When he'd picked her up, later that afternoon, he hadn't even mentioned it to her.

Chapter 32

Kelly drove. Dan was quiet. The gravity of what lay ahead sat between them and both mulled over their most pressing activities. Last night she'd seen him on an animated phone call, probably to his wife: first night on the job and he doesn't come home. The fresh blanket of snow gave the Lake District a charming, innocent facade, which belied the intentions of one man, working in secret, trying to hide the fact that he'd killed a woman and dumped her in a waste bin. The knowledge of the fact made the desire to stare out of the window, and gaze upon the beauty of mountains covered in snow, less alluring. Swabs from the wheelie bin were being processed in a lab in Carlisle, as well as the items bagged and tagged by Ted Wallis, especially the metal fragment and fibres. But it took time for these results to come through.

Overnight, the call centre had received hundreds of tips regarding the two missing women, as well as new leads on Dorinne. Going public on Lucinda Dockie, only a day after the body in the bin, had renewed the public's interest in Dorinne. But all leads had to be processed and followed up; Highways England CCTV from the area surrounding the Heaven club was being trawled through, and the residents along the road where the contents of the bin had been discovered were still being interviewed, and Craig had followed up with David Martin, formally interviewing him at Barrow police station. Craig had assured the guy of discretion, in as far as he wasn't about to Snapchat his wife about it. It was all the guy was worried about and Craig was happy from watching his body indicators, such as leg position, fidgeting, eye contact, open or closed stances, as well as tonal changes in his voice, that the guy liked hookers; he didn't kill them. His DNA had been run through the system and no matches with previous crimes were found. Usually in a murder, previous was a given, and more often than not murderers nowadays were caught out by it years after their crimes, as the DNA database grew. When shown the photo of Dorinne, Mr Martin had looked nonplussed. They were also trying to track down Kian Delancy. This morning, while Kelly went home to get a shower and change clothes, it was down to DS Kate Umshaw to get the ball rolling and prepare a morning brief for her, which would commence shortly. Kate had DC Emma Hide, and a clutch of uniforms, at her disposal. The gritters had been working hard all night and most of the roads were clear, but more snow was expected this afternoon.

A call came through Bluetooth and Kelly answered it. DS Kate Umshaw's voice filled the small space. She was chairing the first briefing of the day, with Kelly on speaker.

'We've had several sightings, boss, of all three women. They vary wildly in timeline, but I'm assigning each one as we get it, and dispatching officers to take witness statements, giving priority to Dorinne Callaghan. There's been a hit overnight on the man described by both Yus Ali and the bartender at the Scrag End pub: the man whose appearance has been logged as short, plump, in his fifties and well dressed. We've had a sighting of him with being with Lucinda Dockie on a separate occasion. We're working on a mixture of old and new statements, all from scratch.'

The stranger was quickly becoming a person of significant interest.

'Go on,' Kelly said. They were on the ring road around Keswick now, and they'd be home shortly. She'd have to drop Dan in Penrith, where he'd bought a terrace not far from where her mother, Wendy, had lived. Then she'd drive back to Pooley Bridge. Once again, Kelly would spend the day in the South

Lakes, and hopefully meet up with Craig Lockwood. It was a tough decision, leaving her team for another day, but with the profile from Demi, the snooping around of Minister Qiang and the lack of transparency from the Chinese embassy, as well as the questionable business parameters of Sunshine Holidays, Kelly had come to believe that finding Lisa Lau and Lucinda Dockie was somehow the key to unlocking Dorinne's case. She was further convinced of this fact because of the discovery of a witness statement from the October inquiry into Dorinne's disappearance linking her to Lucinda Dockie. And the statement was from none other than Kian Delaney.

'He worked at the same diner as Dorinne, and it turns out that Lucinda Dockie worked there too. It's the Lakeside Bar and Grill. Delaney said, back in October, that he saw a man meeting the description matching the one given by the bartender at the Scrag End waiting for her outside, after two separate late shifts. He also stated that he'd seen him before, and described a man who looked well dressed and smart, but who was a lot older and shorter than Dorinne, and that's why it stuck in his mind. Lucinda worked at the diner for five or so years, overlapping with Dorinne for a few months last year.' Kate waited for her boss.

'That is a blinding coincidence,' Kelly said. 'I can drive through Glenridding on my way to Ambleside. DC Hide, meet me there and you can check out the Gate Inn, as well as visit Lucinda Dockie's house. It's been sealed off but we haven't had a forensics team there yet.'

'Yes, boss.'

'DS Houghton and I are almost back now, we're coming around Keswick. I'll send him down to Glenridding with you, Emma, so wait for him to get into the office. I'll head off as soon as I can. I want Yus Ali picked up to give an artist's impression, and we need Kian Delaney to do the same. DS Umshaw, can you try and find Mandy Williams, please. I want to know why she omitted to tell me that she was Lisa's room-mate.'

'Yes, boss.' Emma and Kate spoke in unison.

'Any news on Lorna Burns yet? Lockwood is going to take charge of the interviews in Windermere, though I think Marvin Burns has already thrown himself under a few buses overnight. He was easy to crack, by all accounts. I'm pretty sure that he had no knowledge of what was going on in that cottage, but I need someone checking all the other properties and we should have a warrant for all of them, including business records for Sunshine Holidays, very soon. They should come through today.'

Kelly and Dan heard a distraction in the office and Kate informed them that Rob Shawcross had turned up, demanding to be put on the case.

'Paternity leave is overrated,' Kelly heard him say.

There was a communal murmured agreement around the incident room, palpable from the interior of Kelly's car. She felt a twinge of sadness for the colleague sat in her passenger seat after what he'd told her about having kids. She knew it'd be hard, when the time came, to tell him her own news.

'Great to have you back on board, Rob,' Kelly said. 'I've got the perfect job for you. Kate, can you fill Rob in on Sunshine Holidays and I want you, Rob, to go through the business and find out if the figures balance. If not, why.'

She wondered if she would take her maternity leave when the time came. She was entitled to a year off with half pay, plus the government allowance. In her head, she'd already made up her mind about coming back to work as soon as she could, to allow Johnny to be a dad in his own time, and in his own way, without her meddling. She knew that disagreements on childrearing were the biggest single factor in divorces. Not that they were married, but she wanted him to be a proper home parent, not just in name. At the moment, she didn't know what it felt like to be maternal and feel the need to spend time with a child: her child. Maybe that would change. Her mind was wandering and she forced herself back to the team discussion.

'Magistrates hate anything to do with sex work. As soon as the warrants I authorised come through, I want raids on Sunshine Holidays properties.'

'Yes, boss. It's good to be back in the office.'

'How did Mia take it?' Kelly asked about Rob's wife.

'She agreed that if I spent another day at home, one or the other of us would end up leaving. She's in a routine now. But seriously, guv, we're good.'

'Glad to hear it. And how is the gorgeous little man?'

It wasn't like DI Porter to gush. At Eden House, the team shared glances. All except DS Umshaw, who knew exactly where the sentiment came from. She smiled.

'He's cracking. All smiles. Not sleeping through yet, but I'm used to disturbed sleep. I hear you had a holiday in Thirlmere last night?' Rob jested with them. Kelly laughed.

'What a treat! Mind you, the breakfast was fantastic,' she said. 'Right, guys. Let's get to work. DS Umshaw, can you chase the lab, please? We should be getting the first results through today. I want to trace that wheelie bin.'

'Yes, guv.'

Another day of graft awaited them. Legwork was the back-bone of any investigation, and they'd only just got started.

Chapter 33

Mandy Williams was depressed, and it was clinical. It wasn't just the 'I don't want to get up, I'm having a bad day' type of low, which hits everyone when life's drudgery catches up, or if it's dark and cold outside. It was cold all right, but the morning had chased the dark away; but still she wrapped herself up in her duvet, preferring to stay there.

She had a sickly feeling in her stomach and it was because of the police officers who came to the Scrag End pub yesterday. Her anxiety had gone through the roof, and she couldn't shake the feeling of intense paranoia, agitation and twitchiness that accompanied the thoughts. She wished she could turn back the clock and make different decisions. The need to get out had pushed her into a foolish mistake. She wasn't supposed to be out and about, but she felt like a zoo animal cooped up in here.

That was another thing that was making her nervous and down in the dumps: regret. It was a toxic emotion, but she couldn't help it. She'd made so many poor decisions that had led her to her life as it was today that she looked back with resentment and shame. She saw the faces of Lisa and Lucinda in her dreams. Beautiful Lisa: exotic, funny and, like the blue heart of a flame, mesmerising. And sweet Lucinda, who talked of her daughter often, and of breaking the cycle and getting out of the game. But she couldn't get clean. No matter how many times she stopped using, she always picked up again, and her loser boyfriend just stood and watched. And now Dorinne, dead in a waste bin. They'd all assumed she'd just taken off.

It was Lucinda who'd first told her that the fat old man was going to give her and her daughter a better life. But Mandy knew better. She'd warned her and she'd warned Lisa. The man wasn't all he seemed. She'd gone with him one night, after meeting him at the Scrag End. He came across as civil, pleasant even. He'd made her laugh and he offered her plenty of money. But there was something about him that made her change her mind. They'd left the pub and walked to his van and that's when he'd said it. It hadn't really made any sense at the time and he'd given her what he thought was a reasonable explanation, but it was the way he'd said it that made her stop.

'You remind me of my sister,' he'd said. Mandy was no angel; she'd had customers ask her for all sorts of weird shit, and sometimes she'd played along. But ordinary guys have fantasies; she accepted that. It was the freaks you had to look out for and the difference between them was the way they emphasised stuff. One could never be 100 per cent certain, which is exactly why hookers got abused. However, there was something called a nutter scale for clients who were genuinely whacko. And he fitted the bill. His soft features, his pot belly, his dress sense and, finally, the hint that he was about to pay for a sexual encounter with someone who reminded him of his sister, all conspired to make Mandy walk away. She told him she'd forgotten something at the pub and never saw him again – until yesterday at the Scrag End. She'd frozen and it was only Old Bobby who'd saved her, asking her to join him for a sherry. They'd watched him leave when the coppers turned up, and she hadn't mentioned him to the detective. He'd been standing slightly to the left of the bar and had slipped out before the detective began her monologue. No one seemed to notice, and Mandy reckoned she was the only one who saw him arrive, and leave just as quick. It only served to make her even more fearful of him: what did he have to hide?

Her self-esteem was on the floor. Another reason not to bother getting up. Not only had she given the police officer her mobile number because she was terrified not to, she'd blabbed about Lisa, and that was exactly what she'd been told not to do by the man at the youth hostel who introduced himself as Mr Qiang. Her mouth was her biggest liability. Technically, though, she hadn't told the police everything, so, in her head, she reconciled her actions with the money he'd given to her on that same day.

Her mobile phone rang and her stomach turned over hard, making her pulse rate go through the roof in seconds. She felt under the bed for it and stared at the number. It wasn't the police. It was a number she'd stored on the fourth of January. She answered.

'Hello?'

'Mandy. We need to meet. I'm sending a car.'

'Er... right,' she replied, not daring to refuse.

'Good. It will be outside your address at quarter to eleven exactly.' He hung up.

She'd been put up in a room in a small guest house in Glenridding, and she'd not dared go out. She didn't know who was paying but could guess that it was probably Lisa's family. Maybe she was in danger?

The Chinese man who'd introduced himself at the hostel was well dressed and manicured. He had an air of authority and safety about him that she trusted. She felt relaxed with him around. It didn't make sense in her brain because he was a complete stranger, but he had the ability to calm her and make her feel as though her stress could be put aside, at least for a while. The police detective had the same effect on her: the woman who'd come to the Scrag End pub; but that was different. She trusted her personally, and had held her eyes for important seconds during their exchange. Those moments had made her want to tell the detective everything, but then there was a break that stopped her and she didn't know where it came from. Something told her to hold back and so that's what she'd done. She valued her life more than the truth.

She stared at her mobile phone and looked at the time on the screen: she had an hour to get ready. She felt unclean and fatigued: a common sign of melancholy. Her hair needed washing and she had to choose some decent clothes to wear. Her tall, thin frame felt weak as she went to the bathroom. She'd never stayed in a hotel like this before. She'd visited them, but never as the paying guest. She'd played with the light controls when she'd first arrived: they were turned on and off by wafting one's hand in front of the fixture. It was fun for ten minutes; now it was quite irritating and she yearned for a proper switch. The TV had Netflix, which kept her entertained for a few hours; now she was bored of boxsets. She phoned Kian, who had also been given a room at the guest house. They chatted about Lisa, and about where they thought she'd gone. Kian was able to pronounce the name of the Chinese man who'd promised to find their friend: Li Qiang. He told her to trust him, that was what his gut told him, and she said that she would.

–

Mandy had slept badly for a week. She searched for answers that never came and she lay awake at night, wondering what was going on and where Lisa was. She suspected that the detective knew nothing about the smart Chinese man, who Mandy believed was connected to the Lau family. He was warm, kind, thoughtful and attentive, but he said little and never answered her questions directly.

'Is Lisa all right?' she'd asked.

'You are a great friend to be concerned about her,' he'd replied.

'Are you working with the police?' she asked him.

'The police are doing what they have to do, and I'm doing the same,' he said.

'Who do you work for? Where is all this money coming from?'

'Do you need some more?' he asked.

'No!'

It was frustrating. Originally, when she was first moved here, he'd given her an envelope. It had seemed the most logical thing to do at first. A Chinese man, assumed to be related to Lisa, turns up at the YHA, suggesting you need to be moved for your own safety – without an explanation why – but presents a safe option; you take it. Kian took it too. Only now was she looking back and beginning to question. The envelope had sat on the desk for a day, until curiosity won and she opened it to find a wad of cash. She'd counted it and it totalled a thousand pounds. Mandy had never seen a thousand pounds before and she'd put it swiftly into a drawer. Whenever she asked Mr Qiang what the money was for, he'd deflected the question, cleverly moving on to something else.

She'd been bought, but for what? To keep secrets about Lisa, or to help find her?

–

As she stepped in the shower, in a desperate attempt to revive herself and her lank ginger hair, she couldn't help feeling that the path she'd chosen to take that day when Mr Qiang had walked into the YHA in Ambleside was now irreversible.

Chapter 34

Kelly dropped Dan off at his house and waved goodbye. She called Johnny, who had already made arrangements for the van to move stuff from his place to hers and was there now.

'Maybe this weekend we can go shopping for Josie to do her room?' he asked.

'Great. I told Dad. He said he wants to buy us something special as a house-warming present and knowing him it's probably very expensive. But it also depends on the case. Let's see.'

Johnny was used to Kelly dropping everything for a case.

'I might have mentioned that you like those green BBQ egg things,' he said.

'Johnny, they're so much money!'

'But it'll look great on the terrace. Come on, he loves spoiling you. He's making up for forty years. It gives him a lot of pleasure, which is why I said he could come shopping with us this weekend.'

'So, you already arranged it? I should have guessed! I'm just pulling in now. I told you, I need to see how the case develops.'

They hung up. He came to the door and took her bag. She'd pack another overnight bag just in case the same thing happened again. She wasn't going to let a dump of snow get in the way of this investigation, and it was Ambleside and Grasmere that connected all three women. The glacial mass of granite and rock between her and them was mere geography.

'So you slept well?' Johnny asked and she nodded. They kissed.

'Ah it's good to be home. I wish I could stay for a bit, but I'm going back to Ambleside and I need to pack a bag in case I get stuck again.'

'What's taking you down there so much? Isn't that South Lakes?'

'Not technically, and the case revolves around the wheelie bin discovery, which is North Lakes. I'm working with the DI in Barrow anyway.'

'You look tired,' he said.

'Thanks! This morning when I woke up I felt so fresh – you know how to schmooze a woman! And stop worrying. Women give birth all the time, without prolonged enforced "rest" that they don't need. Pregnancy is not an illness and the last thing I need is you wrapping me in cotton wool. That's not why I fell in love with you and it's not a way I can even begin to think about existing.'

'Sorry. I'm overreacting. I've turned into a bag of nerves over this.' He went to her and placed his hand gently over her abdomen. 'It's knocked me for six. I never thought this would happen.'

'We have sex. It could always happen.'

'We were careful.'

'Not in Florida we weren't. Can't you remember, the night we got so smashed on tequila that we skinny-dipped and I threw up for two days after? I reckon I vomited my contraceptive pill two days in a row,' she said.

'Is it that sensitive?' he asked.

'Apparently so. Anyway, we are where we are. It was a shock for us both but I want to look forward. You know I thought you'd be the one to avoid having more children, not me. You have this demeanour of a rolling stone, which is what attracted me in the first place.'

'The fact that you thought I'd be difficult to keep, and so it was safe for you to hang around?' he asked.

'Yes. You always psychoanalyse me perfectly. But now, I want it. Maybe that thing you said, you know, the hormones kicking in, maybe that's started now. I told Kate at work. She rumbled me when I kept leaving full coffee mugs on the windowsill. She's got three teenaged girls, so to her it must have been obvious.'

'Josie is excited. In fact, she said she was heading over here when she was dressed. It's an INSET day apparently.'

'They're always having INSET days.' Kelly had become more aware of school arrangements since Josie came into her life.

'I know. I thought it might be a ruse to choose her room and move in today, but I checked with the school. They're random over the year.'

'I'd better get a shower. Make me a herbal tea?'

'Of course.'

'Are you on call today?' she asked.

'No, I've got the day off and I'm going to move stuff over here if that's all right?' he asked.

'You don't have to ask, it's your place now.'

Kelly went upstairs to change and repack her bag. This time she threw some supplies into a small wheelie case. A thick jumper and pyjama bottoms were crucial for surviving another night away. She added her hairdryer too. She felt ready to face what the day threw at her.

She switched on her iPad and noticed an update from Craig Lockwood to say, firstly, that the weather wasn't bad on the roads in South Cumbria, so should they meet in Ambleside? And secondly, to query the CCTV footage taken from the YHA yesterday by her and Dan. She opened it and read the marker flagged up next to her name. *DI Porter? Diplomatic plate check traced to Sellafield nuclear plant.*

She read further and opened the footage tagged by Lockwood and saw a street view of Minister Qiang leaving the YHA on the fourth of January. It was a fantastic view and clear too. The camera must have been set up because of the junction further down the street. It had come in late last night and Craig had spotted it. Qiang could be seen getting into a car with diplomatic plates and this was what Craig was referring to: the vehicle had then been traced as travelling to Sellafield. All eligible officials registered with the FCO have to be registered with the DVLA, and so they could be traced, even though they technically couldn't be pulled over or followed.

Sellafield nuclear power station dominated the little seaside town near Seascale on the Cumbrian coast, between Ravenglass and St Bees. It was a bleak coastline made more ominous by the huge concrete carbuncle. Cancer rates in under-twenty-year-olds had soared there between the periods of highest use, up to around 1990. Kelly thought that the plant had been disused for some time but that scientists and engineers still operated it. They had to. It was no secret that the place was the most toxic industrial site in Europe; but why would a Chinese diplomat be going there? This was the question that Craig had asked Kelly. She looked out of her window across the River Eamont and watched as snow dropped off laden branches.

She researched the plant and started reading about its history, and was still reading about it when Johnny came to check on her and tell her that Josie was here. She gathered her things and went down to see her stepdaughter.

They hugged and Josie stood awkwardly, stealing glances at Kelly's stomach.

'What do you think? Is it okay?' Kelly asked. Josie smiled and her cheeks turned pink.

'I think it's cool. Can I look after it? Is it a boy or a girl?'

'We don't know yet, and yes, you can do as much as you want. I'll need you. Your dad will need you! The plan is for him to stay at home and me to carry on working. So your dad tells me that we're taking you shopping for your room on Saturday?'

Josie smiled broadly. 'Do you mind? Is that okay?'

'Which room do you want? Is the big one all right? It's got built-in wardrobes that are huge. Big enough for a young lady anyway.'

'I love it!'

'We can decorate.'

'No, I love the colour. I'm thinking go big on accessories.'

'My thoughts exactly. Accessorise all the way. You know Ted is planning an extension, so we can help him decorate that too. It's my favourite bit.'

Josie sat in the lounge. She looked as though it was hers already. She fitted. They all fitted.

'I need to go to work, but I hope you make progress today,' Kelly said. She kissed Johnny, and Josie waved goodbye.

'What are your plans for your INSET day?' Kelly asked, tongue in cheek.

'*Crime Investigation*, there's a new one today.'

'Maybe one day you'll join my team,' Kelly said, and left.

In the car, she called DS Umshaw and asked her to find out who owned Sellafield and if she could get hold of a staff list. The plant had been commissioned in the 1950s to produce nuclear power, but controversy, and a decline in reliance upon the power, meant that it was in the process of decommissioning. It would take another hundred years, and billions of pounds, but it had to be done properly. Meanwhile it was a disposal site for anyone who paid for it. The Chinese were said to be buying up swathes of energy firms across Europe and she wanted to know who had the money to purchase a nuclear plant spanning two miles across. The Chinese did. The French owned several UK power companies but Sellafield would have to have been negotiated carefully: it was a political, as well as an economic, hot potato. The only reason she knew this was that in her enquiries into money-laundering a few years back for a case, she'd come across many European companies being bought up by Chinese interests under umbrella names, registered offshore. If the general public knew how many companies foreign governments owned on UK soil, there would be outrage. Huawei was a case in point. Conspiracy theories abounded about why China might be interested in getting the keys to foreign power and communications, but it didn't take a rocket scientist (or nuclear physicist) to see why. Perhaps Li Qiang was on official government business. Perhaps not.

She sensed déjà vu as she pulled into Glenridding, but this time she found the turning for the Lakeside Bar and Grill and parked. She'd called ahead and they'd confirmed that members of staff were in there setting up.

She went inside and met a woman who looked senior and in charge. Kelly showed her ID and the woman nodded that they should sit down. It turned out she was the day manager.

'I'm trying to find Kian Delaney. He works here, correct? He gave a witness statement to the police back in October about Dorinne Callaghan, who also worked here.'

'I haven't seen Kian for a week, he's off sick,' the woman said.

'And Lucinda Dockie? She worked here until December?'

'Yeah, I remember her.' The day manager confirmed Lucinda's ID from Kelly's photo.

'Did you happen to notice either of the women meet a man in the car park after their shifts?'

'Now you're asking. I've no idea, I don't pay attention to how the waitresses get home.'

'Did Dorinne work here when she went missing?'

'Yes, she did and she was lucky she wasn't fired before that. She turned up late, looking dishevelled, and she was a shit timekeeper, excuse my French.'

'You now know that she is dead?'

'I heard that was her in the bin.' The manager's voice softened.

'It's really important that I find Kian. I need to speak to him about the man he said he saw in his statement.'

'Let me look at the shift book, it'll have his address, if he gave one.'

'Thank you,' Kelly said. The manager got up and went to the computer at reception and tapped keys.

'Right, here we go,' she said. She gave Kelly Kian Delaney's shifts and his address.

'Oh, wait a minute, he recently moved. He was at the YHA in Ambleside like a lot of them, but now it says he's – that's funny.'

'What?' Kelly asked.

'Well, it's a post office box. But I still have his mobile number.'

'When's the last time Kian worked a shift?'

'It says the third of January.'

'Could you print out a full staff list for me?' Kelly asked. The manager tapped away and a piece of paper churned out of the printer. She handed it to Kelly. She also gave her Kian's number.

'Thanks for your help,' Kelly said, taking it. She gave her a card. 'Call me if you see Kian or hear anything about where he might be. Or if you remember either Lucinda or Dorinne meeting anyone in the car park.'

'Of course,' she said.

Kelly left, mulling over the significance of this merry band of misfits with interweaving stories. She called Kate as she drove south over Kirkstone Pass once more, experiencing déjà vu again. She updated her on Kian Delaney and learned that Kian's number so kindly given to her by the manager was already on file from his statement. Neither he nor Mandy were answering their phones.

—

The snow had been pushed to the sides of the narrow road and left a brown slush behind. But it was pretty clear. People were staying at home, not wanting to get caught out again like last night. The heater kept her comfortable and she relaxed as she enjoyed the scenery. It wasn't long before Kate came back to her on Sellafield. It had been bought in 2003 by an umbrella company. Fifty-one per cent of the stakeholder share in that company came from the Chinese government. Kate also told her that there were Chinese scientists employed on site as part of a joint venture between governments, funded by the UKRI (UK Research and Innovation) department of government, one arm of which included work with China.

'UKRI China acquired twenty-two billion pounds' worth of joint ventures, mainly chemistry and power based, between 2016 and 2019. That's a lot of money.' Kate stated the obvious. But to government giants it wasn't really a lot. It was merely the profit a bank like HSBC made in a quarter. An Asian bank.

'Do we know what ventures they were?' Kelly asked. She looked outside at the fells and felt a longing to be up there. She spotted little dots of colour that she knew were walkers' jackets.

'The stats are transparent to a point. For example, all UK trading has to be logged and available to the public, as well as salaries, pensions, profits and tax, but once you get to particular projects, it gets trickier to pin them down. They have grand names but don't have to publish details; it's considered a security risk and covered under data protection.'

'Okay, so we have Chinese scientists at Sellafield, and a Chinese diplomat paying them a visit. Does that make sense? Why would the same diplomat tasked with finding Lisa Lau be checking up on government business?'

'Do you want me to ping over the list of employees I have? The Chinese names all work in one department that is responsible for the UKRI Chinese-funded research into how rocket fuel behaves in space.'

'Really?'

'Really. Did that make me sound intelligent?' Kate asked.

'Almost. Find out if any of the employees live near Ambleside. It's my understanding that most workers there, no matter where they're from, live in local digs. Somebody more senior might live further away and be chauffeured, for example,' Kelly said.

The sighting of Lisa Lau talking to a Chinese man on the second of January concerned her. Maybe they weren't looking for the same perpetrator who'd abducted and murdered Dorinne at all. Maybe Lisa's disappearance was entirely coincidental, and she'd been smuggled back to China to face her parents. It was crazy and she hated coincidences.

'Kate, find out who was responsible for the sightings of Lisa Lau in Preston, as well as Dorinne in Lancaster, and then trace whoever saw Lisa in Ambleside on the second with a Chinese man. Maybe it was our Li Qiang.'

'Yes, guv.'

Kelly arrived in Grasmere and drove past Marvin's post office and corner shop. It was closed. She found the address for Maureen Johnson and parked out the front on the street. Maureen's curtains twitched and Kelly had hardly had time to ring the bell before the door was answered.

'What happened to Marvin?' she asked. 'I've been round there countless times, and since he went off with you lot, I've heard nothing.'

'There's no need for panic, Maureen. We needed to ask him some further questions, that's all. I'm sure you'll be able to talk to him soon. May I come in?' Kelly asked.

Maureen stepped backwards and allowed her to go in. The place was immaculate, as Kelly had anticipated. The woman had looked well preened the first time she'd seen her at Marvin's, and it was no surprise that her home reflected this.

'I just wanted to tell you that we're working on several of the helpful leads you told us about. I wondered why, though, you implicate the young Kevin Flint as somebody who might be involved. He's not been mentioned by any other source. I wonder if you could expand for me.'

'Why are you questioning Marvin? He has nothing to do with what his wife gets up to.'

'And what might that be?'

'If she's the one running the knocking shop I told you about then she must be in charge of more. Do I need to do your job for you, detective? It's all common sense isn't it? He never sees her. I can't remember the last time I saw her in the shop. She's always buying him expensive gifts and booking holidays he doesn't want to go on, so she ends up going on them herself. Or maybe not by herself.'

Kelly waited patiently. The information on Kevin Flint, for background purposes, before she barged into what was obviously a complicated domestic environment, could wait. She could feel her eyes drooping. The room was warm and outside it was freezing: the combination resulted in a recipe for a perfect nap. She removed her scarf and took off her coat, and witnessed Maureen Johnson's body language relax. The woman took a deep breath and looked at her hands.

'I know I'm a gossip, detective.'

'Please call me Kelly. You have a lovely home. I get the impression that you're very protective of Marvin, and that you've been friends a very long time.'

'We have. He was flattered when a woman twenty years his junior wanted him. She fawned over him and he bought her presents. But I cottoned on early. She's what some people might call a gold-digger.'

'But, if what you are telling me is correct, she doesn't need his money.'

'Not any more. But it wasn't always the case. I saw him struggle with the shop as she spent and spent. He never complained, all the while coming up with new lines and products to make the business work. And it did.'

'You're very proud. You must have been an important part of the success.'

Maureen nodded and smiled. Kelly perceived a little puff of her chest.

'So, I wasn't surprised when it finally happened.'

'What?' Kelly asked.

'She's got a fella.'

'Really?'

'Oh yes. Of course, he's younger than Marvin and he seems rich too. It was the boob job that gave it away for me. I sat Marvin down and gave him a stern talking to, and finally he agreed with me that she was taking him for a ride. He told me something in confidence and I promised never to tell a soul, and, God help me, I meant it. But now, after this, she makes my blood boil, Kelly, she does. I can't see it go on any more. You think he's got something to do with this and he hasn't, I swear on my life.'

Kelly waited and allowed the woman to breathe and recover from her tirade.

'He told me that he dropped Lorna off, last year sometime, at a huge plush mansion-type house on the shore of Derwentwater. He reckoned she was buying it, but do you know how much something like that sets you back, Kelly?'

Kelly nodded. 'Couple of million?'

'Exactly. Where did she get that sort of money from? I can tell you where: on her back, that's where. Marvin told me, God forgive me, that he hung about after dropping her off to meet this fella. He had a hunch, you know, he just *knew*. She said it was business. All the time I had my suspicions she was having an affair and all the while it was under Marvin's nose. He later found out that this guy was – and still is – Lorna's business partner in Sunshine Holidays.'

Kelly nodded. Maureen took a long inhalation of air.

'Marvin said the man kissed Lorna but to Marvin there was more than affection, or business, in it. He was Chinese.'

Kelly's pulse quickened and she felt butterflies in her stomach, but she didn't flinch.

'So?' Maureen asked, expectant.

'Did I miss something?' Kelly asked.

'He's foreign, rich, and buying up property with a woman running knocking shops. It's a takeover, I tell you, and she's in on it. They're up to something. Foreigners have been buying up the Lakes for years, haven't they? My point is, you're looking in the wrong place.'

'We are trying to locate Mrs Burns, Maureen, but if she doesn't want to be found, it makes our job harder.'

'And why wouldn't she want to be found, I ask you. You're the police! Why can't you find her?' Maureen raised her voice.

'You're absolutely right. Are there any other locations that you can think of, somewhere Marvin might have mentioned perhaps, that Lorna could have gone?'

'That place on Derwentwater, Marvin said she spent most of her time there. She said she was getting it ready to show him. Likely story.'

'Do you have the address?'

'It's impossible to miss, Marvin said. It has a private road,' Maureen said.

'And what about Kevin Flint?' asked Kelly.

Maureen looked at her squarely. 'I never had a good feeling about the boy. He's a pervert. But I already told you that. I don't suppose you've spoken to him yet, have you? Otherwise you wouldn't be asking me.'

'The weather closed in on us yesterday. We have to do things when we can. And so far you haven't told me anything to implicate him in a crime.'

'The family moved to Grasmere about four years ago and stories started circulating almost straight away about the mother. She took to wandering around at night, wailing and carrying on like a madwoman. We've called ambulances, GPs and the police. Then one day, she stopped. Then we started to see Kevin going out late and wandering around, like she used to.'

'Who saw him?'

'Plenty of us. If I hear a noise, Kelly, I'll look out of my window, like any decent worried folk might. It's odd, going out in the middle of the night like that, aimlessly.'

'He might be employed on a night shift somewhere.'

Maureen laughed. 'He's unemployable. I keep telling you. He doesn't have a job. He goes out looking for women and I reckon Lorna Burns knew it. If anyone knows what happened to those poor girls, my great-niece included, then she does.'

'Hang on a minute, Maureen, are you implying that Lorna Burns had something to do with Dorinne's death? I thought you suspected Kevin?'

'What do I know? I think you should check them out, that's all. Patty Flint has passed on her retarded genes to him and now he goes looking for his desires, wherever he can get them.'

'And you think that might be at some of the establishments allegedly run by Lorna Burns?'

'Exactly,' said Maureen, sitting back, happy with herself and her detective work. To Kelly, none of it made sense. The idea that Lorna Burns could, or would, provide an outlet for the indulgences of a seemingly sex-crazed boy was bizarre. Surely Lorna Burns (and her business partner) was driven by profit, and the boy had little means to pay. There was simply no incentive. But Maureen had given her enough to follow, and if some of it linked up, even if not in the way Maureen suspected, then it might at least lead her to the enigmatic Chinese man with whom Lorna Burns had an unspecified relationship. She put in a quick call to Craig for him to ask Marvin to describe the man he'd seen with his wife.

She thanked Maureen and left. From the car she called Kate to see if she could run a check for a large property on a private road on Derwentwater and locate the owner. It wasn't long before she came back. Kelly answered her phone just as she reached the house of Kevin Flint.

'There is one property that fits that description. It's registered to Mr Zhang Wei,' Kate told her. 'He's owned it for eighteen months. He pays council tax, utilities and water rates, so it's lived in. It's not advertised on any holiday let sites. But the thing that

I thought you might be more interested in is his work. If he lives at this address, he's got a lengthy commute.'

'Where?'

'Sellafield.'

Chapter 35

The journey to Glenridding, through Pooley Bridge and then along the northern shore of Ullswater, was uneventful. DS Dan Houghton and DC Emma Hide arrived in the small pretty village mid-morning. They had much to do and decided to split their tasks to save time. They agreed to meet up for lunch at one of the many eateries along the shore. Ullswater snaked away from the land at its south-western tip, before disappearing round the corner to the south, where water sports were available in the summer. In wintertime, the boats, launches, canoes and paddleboards were packed away in large huts, and the yards were silent. But Glenridding itself remained busy due to the demand for winter walking. The sun shone brightly and Dan had to put the screen visor down as he negotiated a place to park. He'd take the Gate Inn, and Emma would head to Lucinda Dockie's house. Both were in walking distance of the car park. They'd chatted about the cases in the car and Dan had got to know his colleague fairly well. He thought her steadfast and reliable, from what he'd seen in such a short space of time. He'd managed to meet DC Rob Shawcross before they left the office this morning too. At first, Dan had suspected that he might be treading on toes, when he came face to face with a man whose stature matched his own and whose steely eyes reminded him of himself, patrolling the Gorbals in Glasgow, being assaulted with missiles by kids no older than ten or eleven. Rob had that look already. He joked that it was because he had a newborn, but Dan was never mistaken: Rob had seen a lot of shit.

But, after a few minutes, Dan's fears were allayed. Rob was a good sort and trustworthy; he could see it in his eyes when Kelly Porter was mentioned. She'd created a team around her who'd never let her down and, he realised, the rumours were true: Kelly Porter was a legend. He held up his head as he walked in the direction of the establishment owned by Sunshine Holidays. His brief was straightforward: find out where Lorna Burns was, question anyone working there and ask to look around. Dan preferred being out and about rather than in the office, so he was happy with the assignment. He'd already worked out that DS Umshaw liked to fact-crunch, and Rob Shawcross was often trusted with vital computer algorithms, as he had been today. Paperwork was vital, he knew – as did every decent copper – but it could be soul-destroying. It was another reason he'd asked to join Kelly Porter's team: the geography and population of Cumbria meant that small teams had to be willing to do the legwork themselves. Vast armies of police in the cities, like Glasgow, could afford to send uniforms on fact-finding missions, collating the work digitally from the comfort of a central office. Here, they didn't have the manpower, so you were more likely to see detectives chasing their own leads. It was exhilarating and he was buoyed by his conversation with Emma.

The Gate Inn was a smart establishment. The building was set apart from the road that ran through the centre of the small village, popular with walkers tackling Helvellyn then seeking some refreshment. The swarms of tourists generally parked in the National Trust car park across the road, Emma said, near the information centre, and paid ten pounds a day for the privilege. But it was worth it: there was nowhere else to park. The locals decried the intervention of the National Trust and bemoaned the days when one could park at the side of any road, to take a quick hike up any route they pleased. Nowadays, the only option was parking in NT-designated areas, skewing the eighteen million tourists through a few routes up the same mountains. It had made the hiking life very dull indeed. The only way around it was to bus or cycle to a chosen spot and go an alternative route, avoiding the crowds and thus enjoying the Lakes as they used to be: unspoiled and quiet. To be fair, the NT had little choice. They had to manage the constant pounding on the popular routes to avoid catastrophic erosion, and hundreds of stone paths had been built on the most common routes to that end in recent years. A path had even been laid up Scafell Pike by volunteers spreading boulders, bit by bit, every time they scaled England's highest peak. The bags of tonnes of broken stone were dropped by helicopter and distributed by mindful citizens, stone by stone, until a complete path took shape, which would protect the route for years to come.

They'd driven past the Lakeside Bar and Grill, where DI Porter had already visited this morning, and admired it. Dan couldn't help wondering why Lucinda and Dorinne would choose to work there, if they were on the game, unless it was a respectable front for tax purposes. The Gate Inn promised, on a board outside, home cooking in friendly surroundings. Dan wished he could stay for a pint and a bowl of local Cumberland sausage and mash, before remembering that he was vegan. This morning, when he'd lingered in front of the food warmer staring at the bacon and eggs, he'd been tempted to have a small feast when Kelly wasn't looking. He grappled with the moral dilemma of letting his wife down, but at the same time, a voice in his head told him that what she didn't see wouldn't hurt her and that what was important was to keep her happy, rather than trying to be a purist. She was doing it for her body, believing that she might conceive, and that was commendable, and he supported her wholeheartedly, but his personal trainer back in Scotland had told him not to be so bloody stupid as to cut animal products from his diet, if he wanted to continue building and maintaining muscle. It was a predicament that only he could find a way through, on his own. As long as he told his wife what she wanted to hear, keeping her happy, they could carry on as normal. Assuming he didn't get caught.

He'd taken a takeaway plastic container from the hotel this morning. Inside, while Kelly was paying at the front desk, he'd filled it with sausages and bits of cheese. It was in his backpack, so his wife wouldn't find it, and he'd taken treats out of it when Emma filled up with petrol, or like now when he was alone. He stuffed a sausage in his mouth and licked his fingers and tasted the fat. He followed with a lump of cheese and held the creamy mushed-up food in his mouth for longer than was necessary, then gulped it down alongside his bottle of water, and instantly felt nourished. He'd had a panic moment at one point, wondering if his wife would be able to smell the animal fat on him, but then he'd told himself to calm down and convinced himself that it was his protein-starved brain that was skewing his outlook.

Fortified, and pleased with himself for finding the Gate Inn on his own with no dramas, he looked around. He banged on the door. A young man appeared at the window and mouthed that they were closed, until Dan showed his ID badge. The man unlocked the door to let him in. He looked in his twenties and said he worked mornings, setting up. A faint whiff of burnt fat lingered in the air, indicative of a fry-up brunch. Dan had noticed outside a sign for B&B.

'Who deals with the rooms to let, pal?' Dan asked. The lad nodded through to a desk. They stood in a small bar.

'Are they taken?'

'No idea, I don't have anything to do with the B&B.'

'Really? Don't they need breakfast?' Dan asked.

The young man shrugged and leant against a bar stool.

'Have a look at this.' Dan showed him the photo of Dorinne. 'Have you seen her here?'

The young man's cheeks burned bright red. 'I saw her in the paper.'

'Go on,' Dan said.

'She used to come in here from time to time.'

'What about these?' Dan showed him the photos of Lucinda and Lisa. He got another reluctant and nervous affirmation.

'And did they come in here alone or with anyone else?'

'No, not alone, usually other people.'

'Remember any of them?'

'It's difficult to say. It gets busy in here at weekends, it's dark and crowded. Usually with a fella, I think. This one hung around with a scruffy-looking guy. They normally ended up shouting. He wasn't from around here.' He pointed to Lucinda's photo.

'Can you describe him? Age? Dress? Accent?'

'Twenties, thin, like I said; scruffy.'

'Does the name Yus Ali mean anything?'

'Not to me.'

Dan produced a photograph of Yus Ali they'd taken from the passport office.

'Yup, that's him.'

'What about an older guy? Portly, well dressed, balding on top?' Dan asked.

'That describes 90 per cent of our customers,' the young man joked. It was a fair point.

'Any vans park up out front?' Dan asked, knowing that a vehicle large enough to transport a wheelie bin was central to their enquiries.

'Vans?'

'Aye.'

'A couple. Local delivery drivers wanting a pint, and the like.'

'Any you know?' Dan was aware that most bar staff tended to know their regulars well.

'Most of them.'

'I'll wait here for your guests to wake up.'

The man looked uncomfortable but Dan made it clear that he wasn't budging. He called DI Porter to tell her what he was doing. More positive IDs for their murder victim, and more information linking all three women, was a welcome distraction for Kelly, who'd just found out that Marvin Burns had positively ID'd Zhang Wei as the man his wife had met.

Chapter 36

After parting company with DS Houghton, it didn't take DC Emma Hide long to locate Lucinda Dockie's house, which she had shared with her three-year-old daughter. Lucinda's mother had given the police a key and was happy for the place to be searched. It hadn't been treated as a crime scene as yet, but the increasing tension surrounding both missing women had elevated the importance of one of the last places Lucinda might have been before disappearing into thin air. Forensics were booked in later in the day, but Emma had been instructed by DI Porter to do a preliminary search. She had gloves with her and evidence bags. Sometimes it took a while to pin forensics down. They were busy working on the evidence collected from the body in the bin, and that – rightly so – had taken many hours from their already busy schedule. The cases of Lisa Lau and Lucinda Dockie were lower down the pecking order, and as such, they needed to be patient.

The maisonette flat was stone-built and nestled in the middle of a long terrace, behind the main shops and hotels in the centre of the tiny village. It was a beautiful place to live. So far, they knew that Lucinda worked late evenings at the Lakeside Bar and Grill, but they knew little of her other activities, apart from what Yus Ali had told them, and that was far from reliable. A wronged boyfriend – and a jealous one at that – was likely to embellish information.

She parked outside on the road and took the key with her. The house smelled clean. She closed the door behind her and entered a narrow hallway. There was no noise at all. Light flowed through large windows on the stairs landing and from the first room she came to. It was a front room with a couple of sofas, lots of toys, tidied away nicely, and a TV. She browsed the DVDs stacked up in front of the machine and recognised some of them but not all. Emma had no children, and no small nephews or nieces, but she recognised Peppa Pig and Thomas the Tank Engine. It was a sorrowful realisation that she was prying into the world of a mother whose child had been abandoned, for whatever reason: be it by design or accident. She went to the back room, which was the kitchen, containing modest fittings and a small table set for two. A box sat on the table and Emma opened it. It was one of those pretty patterned cardboard boxes where one kept mail or cut-out recipes.

Inside, there was a pile of letters, and Emma leafed through them. Some were bills, and there were a few pay cheques. At the bottom was a newspaper cutting of a witness appeal for sightings of Lisa Lau, a week ago, from the local paper. Emma put the lid on the box. She opened a few drawers and found more bills and unopened mail. The letters were from banks and internet providers, and general junk. She turned her attention to the upper wall units and opened tins and jars and peered into them. She found a tin containing small change and smiled, seeing her own habit reflected. Next, she reached down to the cooker and opened it. It was very clean and looked unused, but then she noticed the microwave on the counter, which looked pretty well used: the print on the start button had worn off and there were splashes of food on the counter in front. It was the only thing in the kitchen that wasn't spotless. On a hunch, she opened the cooker again and got down onto her knees and peered in.

There was something at the back.

It was a plastic bag. No one in their right mind would keep a plastic bag in a cooker, unless they never cooked in it. She reached back and took the bag out, looking inside. A quick, rough calculation, based on experience, led her to believe that she was looking at around three thousand pounds.

Wherever Lucinda Dockie had gone, it was not on her terms, because if she was going somewhere for any length of time, she would take the two most valuable things in her life: her daughter, and her stash of cash.

She'd brought with her some sterile evidence bags, just in case, and now she placed the bag of money inside a large one, sealing it. Next she went out into the back yard. The back door key had been left in the lock. The space was well looked after and there was a swing set up, alongside a large toy car that would fit a toddler, and a sandpit, covered over. Emma lifted items up and looked under plant pots. She put a glove on and sifted through the cold, damp sand. There was a small shed in the corner; it was locked, so she went back to the kitchen to see if she had missed a key.

Inside a glass, among the cups, she found a small key that looked as though it would open a padlock. She took it back outside and tried it and it worked. It never failed to amaze Emma how lax people's security measures were: people hide stuff in the most obvious places.

Inside the shed she found various bits and pieces of equipment with which to look after plants. There was a washing line, which Emma assumed was put to use in the summer. Sports bags hung on nails, containing squash racquets, balls and a small pop-up tent.

The life that Emma was piecing together didn't fit with that of a hooker, but then a lot of call girls were normal women, trying to earn a little extra cash. But three thousand quid wasn't just a little extra cash.

A Titleist golf bag sat in the corner. Emma recognised the logo from her father's golf kit, which took over their shed at home. This wasn't the full rig, it was just a ball bag, but still, it was out of place. She unzipped it and peered in. This time the plastic bag she found was stashed with, she guessed, around five thousand pounds. She placed the whole thing in its entirety into an evidence bag and put it to one side while she continued searching. Satisfied there wasn't anything of further interest in the shed, she took the Titleist bag outside and put it by the back step while she made a note of what she'd found. The air was bitter but she left the back door open as she made her notes. The rest would have to wait for the forensics team; she couldn't remove the evidence by herself. Officers no longer did it, as it could completely destroy an investigation at the court stage, should a savvy defence pick up on it and accuse the lone officer of tampering.

Gone were the days when police officers were taken at their word.

Inside again, she ventured upstairs. The landing contained one cupboard and Emma nosed around inside. It was where the hoover was stored, and spare bags. Emma rifled through each one. She found nothing of consequence. There were two bedrooms and she entered the little girl's room first. A cot sat lonely and neglected in the middle of the room. Emma imagined the room full of life and laughter and noted the teddies and other tokens of love inside the cot. Lucinda was a caring and thoughtful mother.

She opened the girl's wardrobe and sifted through clothes, blankets and various items apparently necessary for a little life: a potty, a large bag, a bottle steamer, dozens of pairs of shoes and more toys. It would seem that Lucinda spent most of her income on her daughter, and why wouldn't she?

Nothing suggested that Lucinda had planned to go away for a holiday or to visit somebody. She went into Lucinda's room and straight away noticed a shift in atmosphere. The bed was badly made, the wallpaper was coming off, it was damp and musty, and the wardrobe door was ill-fitting. She looked under the bed and found dust that must have accumulated over years. She opened the drawers of the mismatched bedside cabinets carefully, expecting them to be overflowing.

She was wrong.

They were more or less empty. One contained three vibrators and various other sex toys – she guessed at their various uses, but gave up, unfamiliar with the urge or need to garnish her own sex life, when she got it. She found baby oil in another and thought it odd that Lucinda would entertain clients in her own home. But then she remembered that the girl stayed with her grandmother in Bowness frequently. Maybe those nights were her work nights? Or the toys could have been purely for private use.

Inside the forlorn-looking wardrobe, she found more convincing evidence of Lucinda's potential after-hours activities: a whole array of outfits any paying punter would be happy with: crotchless and feathery, gaudy and inviting. Emma was overwhelmed with pity for anyone who thought they must adorn their body in such a degrading manner for money. Assuming it wasn't simply a personal fetish; but it didn't look like it.

Moving to the bathroom, she found propranolol, the beta blocker used to treat panic and anxiety attacks, in the medicine cabinet. She also found a notable collection of lubricating gels, as well as amyl nitrate: used to relax muscles and associated with anal sex.

The more she foraged through the detritus of this woman's life, the more downcast Emma grew. In between bottles of citalopram, she found Calpol, dummies and sterilising tablets. Emma wondered what demons drove a twenty-four-year-old to antidepressants, but then remembered the toys in the drawer and the outfits hanging up and the double life that was quickly emerging.

As she bent over the sink to see what was on top of the cabinet, her leg touched the bath panel and it wobbled, attracting her attention. She put her finger behind it and it popped off effortlessly. She removed the whole panel and bent over to look at what might be under there.

It was a small suitcase.

She dragged it out and opened it carefully, wearing gloves again. Inside was more cash, around two thousand pounds perhaps. Alongside the cash, Emma found a book. A quick flick though confirmed that it was some sort of diary, with notes in. It was so unusual for people to keep such a thing in modern life, especially someone of Lucinda's age: it was more linked to teenage love and angst; but still, Emma felt as though she imagined one might upon winning the lottery.

Chapter 37

The Flint family home was an end of terrace and the front garden was neglected and forlorn. The winter light made it look sadder than Kelly guessed it might in summer, though she saw no plant life that might have a chance. Three wheelie bins stood at odd angles, cardboard covered in snow flapped against the broken fence and she noticed that all the curtains were closed. Without jumping to conclusions, it was reminiscent of many domestic facades she'd seen in her career to date, behind which had dwelled some very unhappy people. It frankly depressed her. Something inside her hoped that Kevin wasn't involved, but she didn't know why. She didn't even know him.

She knocked and stood back. There was no answer, so she tried again, this time harder.

She heard a sound and saw a figure emerge from behind the dirty glass pane in the door. A face appeared at the side window next to the door frame and Kelly felt the hostility through the glass. It was a woman and Kelly began the instinctively human habit of judgement: she was haggard, not necessarily old, with deep lines carved through her thin skin showing the hallmarks of alcohol and cigarettes. Her eyes were heavy and red and dark pits framed them. Her hair was dishevelled and she could see that she was clasping a thick grey dressing gown around her.

Kelly pressed her ID card against the window. Straight away, the woman's demeanour changed and her eyes widened. Kelly waited as she unlocked the door and held it open. She clasped her garment even tighter and she looked scared. Kelly felt sorry for her and wanted to reassure her somehow. It was an odd response, but the woman looked so vulnerable. She moved aside to let Kelly in.

'Has something happened?' she asked.

'Nothing to worry about, madam – I assume Patty Flint? – I just want to ask a few questions regarding your son, that's all. It's part of a general enquiry,' Kelly said.

'What's Kevin done?' she asked. Her lips pursed and her eyes narrowed. The place stank. Kelly stepped past her and went into the hallway. She almost asked her not to close the door, to get some fresh air into the place. She hated visits like this because her clothes would smell all day long. She felt her stomach churning already. There was something about cigarette smoke that her body didn't like at the moment. She'd read plenty about it, and also that the feelings should lessen as the placenta kicked in to do its job. In the past she'd enjoyed the odd cigarette herself, mainly in London when she worked for the Met. It was the nerves. Now, she felt like she might run for the door.

'I'm not aware that your son has done anything.' She waited. Patty Flint closed the door fiercely and walked past her, along the corridor to the back. She followed without being asked. As Patty reached the doorway she paused and arched her neck up to the ceiling. 'Kevin!' she screamed. Kelly winced. 'Kevin! Get down here!'

When they were inside the kitchen, Patty Flint turned to her, folded her arms stroppily and sighed like a teenager caught in the act of something illegal or immoral. Her sympathy for the woman dissolved.

'I was wondering if you know any of these women,' Kelly said, producing photographs of Dorinne, Lisa and Lucinda. Patty Flint glanced at them.

'Nope.'

Kelly heard footsteps above and listened to them come down the stairs. She turned around and faced who she assumed to be Kevin Flint. He was almost as tall as Dan Houghton, but much wider. The young man was pale as death and had a terrible case of acne. His hair was scruffy and he kept his hands deep in his pockets. He wore casual shorts and Kelly noticed that his calves were unusually thick. The lad was enormous. If it wasn't for his face, Kelly would've prepared for trouble, but his expression was peaceful and warm: the exact opposite of his mother.

'Kevin?' she asked.

The lad nodded.

Kelly extended her arm. 'Pleased to meet you, I'm Detective Inspector Kelly Porter.'

Kevin shook her hand and Kelly noted the weakness of his grip. He struggled to maintain eye contact and kept glancing at his mother, who scowled at him.

'May I speak with Kevin alone please, Mrs Flint?'

'Sorry, Kevin is special needs so you can make him say anything you like. I can't allow it. He's simple in the head, he's got the brainpower of a six-year-old, so I need to be here.'

It was the most Kelly had heard out of the woman since coming inside the house. It was like a mantra that she spewed out. Kelly noted that Patty Flint seemed almost proud of the mantle she wore: that of a mother of a child who was different. Did it give her power? She saw Kevin's demeanour change and watched with interest.

'Mother,' he said. Patty flinched and straightened like a rod. Kelly watched closely as the dynamic between the two played out. Maureen had painted a picture of a seriously vulnerable boy, abused and manipulated, crying out and acting out in perverted ways because he knew no different. What she was seeing here was not that at all. The lad seemed in charge.

'I don't need my mother here. I can help you myself.'

Patty Flint, to Kelly's surprise, lost her assertive grin and held on to her grubby dressing gown, as if it would help her to decide what to do. She walked past Kelly and her son, and slammed the door behind her. Kevin looked at Kelly.

'I hate the term special needs,' Kelly said. 'I'm sure you're more than capable of answering any of my questions. Do you work, Kevin?' she asked.

He shook his head. 'I'm not allowed. I hate noise. I get angry.'

'Right. So you have worked in the past?'

He nodded.

'Kevin, we're going door to door in the local area. You might have heard on the news that a woman was found dead in a wheelie bin, and two others are missing. Do you recognise any of these?' Kelly showed him the photographs all units were using to identify the three women. He stared at them but shook his head. Kelly didn't perceive any indication that he was lying, but his display of a lack of empathy was concerning. He didn't show any concern at all for the dead woman she'd mentioned.

'Did you hear about them?'

'Who?' It was the first time he'd looked her in the eye and she saw behind them a deep tragedy. They were lifeless and she was reminded of the eyes of children who had witnessed war or deprivation on a dramatic scale. She held his gaze but he looked away.

'The ladies, Kevin. Did you hear about them?'

'No. I don't listen to news. It's always bad.'

'You haven't heard about them? It would be hard to avoid that news, it's everywhere. The body in the bin?'

He looked her in the eye again and appeared to be studying her. It made her feel cold.

'I heard about it but I don't know why you're asking me if I knew her; I didn't.'

'What do you do when you leave the house to go for long cycle rides?' Kelly recalled Maureen mentioning that he did this.

A shadow fell across his face. 'I ride.'

'You enjoy getting out of the house?'

He smiled. 'Yes.'

'Where do you go?'

'The—' He stopped.

'Where? The what?' she pressed him, but he'd clammed up. 'What do you do? Do you meet anybody?'

'No.'

It was said too quickly.

'A friend perhaps?' Her phone buzzed and Kelly saw that Kate had sent through two photos: one of Lorna Burns and another of Zhang Wei. She showed them to Kevin. 'Do you know either of these people, Kevin?'

This time he looked carefully at the images, then shook his head. It was a more animated movement than last time, more natural. It was Kelly's first indication that perhaps Kevin Flint was lying to her; not about Lorna Burns or Zhang Wei, but about the three women.

'And you're sure about these?' She forced him to look at the photos of Lisa, Lucinda and Dorinne once more. This time, he recoiled.

'No.' It was said without focusing on the photographs.

'They might have looked slightly different when you saw them? Maybe they were scared or worried about something? Maybe they were with someone.'

At the mention of somebody else, he stiffened.

'You've seen them with someone else?' she pushed him.

'No!'

Kelly didn't flinch. She'd been in the company of worse. She noticed that Kevin had begun to hold on to the counter behind him in a pensive, stabilising manner, as if he was about to pass out, but he showed no signs of fainting. His knuckles were becoming white and his breathing had quickened.

'Thank you, Kevin,' she said. She needed to get him into a secure interview situation, but there was no way she'd risk attempting that on her own. 'I'll see myself out. I'll leave my card in case you remember someone's face. Please call me any time.'

She walked past him and held her breath as she came level with him. His hands were like shovels and would make short work of her neck, should he be so inclined. She got to the door and pushed down on the handle, letting in fresh air and causing it to suck against the vacuum. She didn't look back as she shut it behind her. She walked swiftly to her car and got in, sitting behind the steering wheel. It was a minute before her heart rate calmed. There was something about the young man that spoke of his potential for chaos. It puzzled her; it was like being in the presence of the very essence of human frailty and weakness.

She shook her head, as if that would clear it, and the smell of foetid air wafted from her clothes, causing her to retch. She found a tissue and spat in it. She gathered her thoughts and went back over their brief encounter. He'd been about to tell her where he went. 'The—'

As she drove away for her meeting in Ambleside with Craig, she was left with the feeling that Kevin Flint knew something about the three women she was investigating. He'd seen them before, of that she was sure.

Chapter 38

Yus Ali had skipped work for the third day and was avoiding his landlady. He couldn't pay his rent. His wages, when he could be bothered to work, were cash in hand, and he was short at the moment. He'd hitched to Glenridding to get into Lucinda's house but he had a problem: someone was in there already. He knew she kept cash for a rainy day under her bed; he'd seen her take some of it from time to time, but she was clever, and when he'd gone to steal some, it was no longer there. He figured that she moved it around. He'd been walking up and down past the house, on the other side of the street, for a good twenty minutes and now he watched as a woman came out, talking on her mobile phone. Yus could clearly see her police tag dangling round her neck and she was wearing plastic gloves; he sighed heavily, walking in the opposite direction. He was the only person on the street apart from her, and she looked at him, but only for a moment, uninterested.

He saw no one else.

He went round the back of the small row of terraces and entered the deserted passageway, stopping at the wooden door leading to Lucinda's back yard. He took a deep breath, not daring to stop to examine the madness of what he was about to do. He pushed the door, which was never locked, and straight away he saw that the back door of the house was open. On the ground he saw some kind of sports bag sitting inside a plastic bag. The outer bag looked like a forensic-type one and he realised that the female police officer was conducting a search.

Without thinking, he opened the top of the bag and unzipped the odd-shaped bag inside. It was full of money.

His heart pounded and he felt hot suddenly. He heard a door close and looked up to the back windows. Satisfied that no one was watching, he took the bag and sprinted out of the yard, only pausing to make sure he didn't slam the metal latch of the tall yard gate. It was a full door size, rather than a small gate like some of the others had, so once on the other side of it, he couldn't be detected as he ran as fast as he could down the alleyway and along the street. He looked back over his shoulder a couple of times, but after he'd turned the corner and entered another street, he slowed down to walking pace and recovered his breath. He hadn't run that fast or exerted that much energy in years and now the cigarettes and booze caught up with him and he bent over, his chest heaving up and down. A woman with a pram walked past, but she was busy cooing to the baby inside and didn't look at him. He crossed the road and, finding a shady public garden, went in and knelt down under a tree. He looked around and made sure he was alone before he transferred the paper bills to any pockets he could stuff them into. He filled his jacket and his jeans and stuffed money under his shirt. He folded up what was left in the plastic and tucked it under his arm. The red and white bag, which he could see now had a logo on the side saying Titleist Pro-Golf, he discarded under a bush.

He knew that was the most distinctive thing likely to identify anyone in the area around this time, when the police eventually started to ask. There were two scenarios: Lucinda had left the bag wrapped in plastic outside and left in a hurry, or the police-woman had found it with a mind to take it as evidence. The latter was far more likely and his priority now was not getting caught.

He had fuck all of any worth in his dingy little room, and he had no desire to go back there. He walked in the direction of the National Trust car park and headed for the toilets. Once inside a cubicle, he rearranged the hastily hidden cash and felt courageous enough to slip a few quid separately into his wallet, which was normally empty. His next stop was a small tourist shop, to buy a large cotton shopping bag with I LOVE THE LAKE DISTRICT emblazoned over the front, with cartoon sheep in the background. It was the perfect size. Back in the toilet, he stuffed it full with money. It all fitted in nicely. He did a rough calculation as he went and reckoned he had a couple of thousand pounds.

The temptation to go shopping was powerful, but he couldn't risk showing off and drawing attention to himself. He needed to get to Penrith and the least obvious way to get there was by bus. But buses left Glenridding for Pooley Bridge only infrequently. He looked at the bus app on his phone, which he used a lot. He didn't drive, couldn't afford cabs, and Lucinda was gone. Now he could afford a cab, but he shunned the idea as too risky. It would be a longer journey by two buses, changing at Pooley Bridge, but it would be worth it. From there, he'd go north, into Scotland, and decide what to do next.

Chapter 39

Marvin Burns looked very small and feeble behind the table. He was clearly exhausted from a disturbed night, having been woken at odd times to give statements. Now, Craig Lockwood entered interview suite two at Windermere police station, and sat down in front of him.

'Morning, Marvin,' he said. He was due to meet Kelly in Ambleside for lunch. They'd agreed he should see what Marvin had to say first. He was due to be released without charge at around three p.m.

'I'm tired, I should like very much to go home soon.'

'I know. I hear you loud and clear. I understand what you must be thinking. We've kept you overnight and disturbed your sleep; I apologise for that, by the way. It's just routine. We have a certain amount of time to charge you or release you.'

'Your pals have told me that every time they've got me in here, but I don't accept any of the accusations. My wife would never be involved in any of the things you say, and I have never heard of any business taking place other than holiday lets.'

'But that's our problem. We've been investigating Sunshine Holidays as a matter of urgency and officers have been working their balls off to collate a list of the properties owned and let by your wife. It's a long list, including two public houses linked to the disappearance of two women and the death of Dorinne Callaghan. Did you know she ran so many?'

'Like I told you before, the holiday let business is hers and she runs it. I run the shop and the post office. I don't pry into her business accounts and she takes no interest in mine. What on earth have Lorna's properties got to do with murder?'

Craig ignored the question. He spread out a printed sheet in front of the man and allowed him to read the data on it. It was a list of all the properties registered to Lorna and Marvin Burns.

'She used my name,' Marvin said simply.

'Assuming you are claiming that your signature has been forged then yes, she did. That makes you liable for all of them to the tune of 50 per cent. Your tax returns don't list them, so we're looking at charging you with tax fraud at the least. The thing is, we'll have to pass your details to HMRC, who'll deal with the case independently. I wouldn't book any holidays for a while; you'll need to be contactable for the foreseeable future.'

'How much profit are we talking about?' Marvin asked. His voice had grown small.

'We're not sure of exact figures. We've got specialised officers working on the maths. But I've been told it's in the millions in turnover.'

Marvin's face went white.

'You've identified this man as knowing your wife.' Craig showed Marvin the picture of Zhang Wei. The man had been confirmed as working for UKRI China at Sellafield, and named as Lorna Burns' business partner by Maureen Johnson.

'Did you know that Sunshine Holidays is run jointly by your wife and this man? He has a 49 per cent stake in your company.'

'It's not my company.'

'It is on paper and that's all that counts for HMRC.'

Marvin slumped forward and put his head in his hands. 'Christ, what is she doing?'

'I think I can tell you the answer to that,' Craig said.

'I didn't want to know the answer.' Marvin looked into his hands.

'And you're still saying that you knew nothing of their business arrangement? How they co-run these properties? There are massive discrepancies in revenue, which, to anyone familiar with the way these things work, suggests that massive amounts of cash are being handed over. There are only a few trades, Marvin, that deal in cash: betting shops, tanning salons and...' Craig had been informed by Kelly of DC Shawcross's preliminary findings of his work on Sunshine Holidays, and it was looking likely that at the very least, they'd be able to get them on financial criminal activity.

'Knocking shops.'

'Indeed.'

'Christ.' He looked down at his shoes and Craig saw a tear escape from his left eye. It trickled down his cheek and landed on his lap.

'At this stage, Marvin, it's prudent to let you know that you should really be getting yourself a lawyer.'

'I don't need a lawyer.' Still, Marvin's voice was a whisper.

'Can you prove that you're not involved? Indeed, at the very centre of these operations?'

'No. But I can prove my own personal use of my accounts. If I had access to the amounts you're suggesting, there would be evidence of me spending it, wouldn't there?'

Craig nodded. It was a good point but legally not watertight.

'And there isn't.'

'We're looking into your personal accounts as well, and, as yet, we haven't found anything suspicious. Can I make a suggestion?'

Marvin looked up.

'You help us and we'll help you. Contact your wife and arrange to meet her. We'll be there to surprise her and we'll take care of the rest. You'll only be further involved if we find proof that you were indeed running the show with Lorna. How about it?'

Marvin rubbed his neck. 'Entrap my wife?'

'Your wife who is involved with another man? Who has built an empire of wealth with that man?'

They locked eyes.

'I'll do it,' Marvin said.

Chapter 40

Kelly ended the call to Emma. The fact that Lucinda Dockie was sitting on so much cash appeared to confirm that the woman had not gone missing of her own free will. It further elevated the case.

Lorna Burns seemed to have disappeared into thin air, and according to Craig, who'd interviewed her husband, Marvin, he had no idea where she'd gone either. She decided to send a squad car to the home address of Mr Zhang Wei, on the shore of Derwentwater, where Maureen had said Lorna met him. Back at Eden House, Rob Shawcross had thrown himself into the accounts of Sunshine Holidays and his digging had unearthed some interesting questions to put to both Lorna Burns and Zhang Wei, not least why he was her business partner. They already knew that he owned 49 per cent of the business, but how far did he go in running it, when he had a job as a respected scientist at Sellafield? Kelly also wanted to know if Minister Li Qiang had paid a visit to him recently and why. International diplomacy was a minefield of political intrigue and corruption: she had to be careful. The cloak of secrecy they were encountering every time they tried to get answers from the FCO rang alarm bells for Kelly. She'd come across something similar in London, when she'd discovered undeclared agents working at the very heart of British industry to gain scientific and military intelligence. Sellafield, of course, would be the perfect place to do that, posing as a scientist. But she was getting ahead of herself. On paper, Zhang Wei was a Chinese national with a work permit for the UK. And why would he risk his position by running brothels? Unless it was a sideline that his bosses didn't know about.

Her phone rang again and this time it was Rob from Eden House.

'Guv, I've been working on how clients can gain access to bookings at Sunshine Holidays properties if they're always fully booked. The phone numbers go to one central line and then you're diverted to an IP address, registered to Lorna Burns. One of the people that you arrested yesterday in Grasmere also admitted that they had been at a brothel and voluntarily gave access to a laptop he used to book arrangements. The IP address uses the same server as that registered to Lorna Burns.'

'You're wasted in the police force, Rob. But I'm glad I've got you on my side,' Kelly said. 'So, if you find out where the common IP address leads to next, you might be able to find their system of booking and their client list?'

'Exactly. The same IP addresses might be used for payment too. It might even have a list of workers.'

'They'd take that risk?'

'If you know what you're doing, it's not really a risk. Typically the police can't chase as fast as they can run electronically.'

'I bet you can,' she said.

'I'll give it a go,' he said.

–

Ambleside was busy, as always. Slush clung to the sides of roads and made the quaint village appear tainted, which, of course, it was. Newspaper stands on every corner displayed headlines about the body in the bin, found not too far away in Patterdale. Tourists stopped to read them and shake their heads; it could damage tourism, but that wasn't Kelly's concern. Airtime was also being given to the missing women and rumours that the women were prostitutes made the articles more sensational. She parked in a public car park and left a permit in the window. She'd suggested a café out of the centre to meet Craig.

As she walked, her mobile rang again. It was Johnny.

'I've been asked to suggest something to you,' he said.

'Who by?'

'Josie,' he said.

'Right, I'm waiting.'

'She wants to know if she can cook you dinner tonight. And what you might like.'

Kelly smiled into the phone. 'That is so sweet, what should I say? What can she cook? Have you moved some stuff already?'

'I think it's probably spaghetti or chilli.'

'Chilli then, please.'

'I haven't seen her like this in years. She's in her room, listening to music, working out where she wants everything.'

'There's only one snag,' Kelly said.

'You might not make it home? I know. She's going to have to get used to that like I have,' he said.

'So that's your day sorted then, I hope you had no other urgent plans.'

'I think I'll be helping Josie. It's my chance to make up time.'

'Johnny, you're already doing that, and she knows it,' Kelly reassured him. 'I don't know how today will go but I'm hoping to be home at a reasonable hour.'

Kelly felt thankful that she had a partner at home who was comfortably off without an accompanying stressful career. Johnny had given his pound of flesh to Her Majesty's armed forces and left honourably with plenty of savings and invest-ments. After Josie's mother kicked him out, he'd found himself in single digs in the officers' mess, with a load of disposable income and nothing to spend it on, aside from the generous child maintenance payments for Josie. He spent as much time away on operational tours as he possibly could, primarily to take his mind off how much he'd fucked up his personal life, but also to occupy his mind. He also invested wisely.

A pal of his from his Sandhurst days had left the army years ago and began investing private cash in South America. Johnny had made a killing, withdrawing the lot before the crash of 2008. The money sat safely in ISAs and premium bonds, doing steadily well, which was good enough for him, and now the three of them. He needn't sell his house in Pooley Bridge if he didn't want; he could easily rent it out to tourists. But they'd work that one out when they were settled.

'You still there?' Johnny asked.

'Sorry. Look, I need to go. I'll see you later. I love you.'

'I love you too,' he said.

After they hung up Kelly took a moment as she watched random strangers mill about, taking in shop windows full of portable chairs, camping equipment and sleeping bags. Her thoughts were on the cases. They were doggedly chasing all the leads on Dorinne's last movements, and waiting with bated breath for the lab results to arrive, hoping at least to get some workable material to refresh the investigation. The time lapse between her disappearance and turning up in the bin had seriously undermined the case, and it could mean that it would take months, maybe years, to solve. They had to be patient. The most promising lead was her last known location: the Heaven club in Ambleside; they were expecting the CCTV footage from that evening in October imminently. Meanwhile, the cases of Lisa Lau and Lucinda Dockie were being used to discover new links between all three women that could prove promising, such as the witness statements about the overweight, balding man, the sightings at Heaven, and the fact that it seemed convincing now that all three women knew one another. She entered the café and saw Craig sitting at a table for two. He waved.

Craig Lockwood was a large man, strong and solid. He was greying at the temples, and lines framed his warm eyes. He was the kind of person you wanted to hug instinctively, unless you were breaking the law, and then you'd want to pelt it as quickly in the other direction as you could. He wasn't to be messed with. She knew that he'd been at the coalface in

Manchester for over a decade, and, like her, cut his teeth as a city copper.

City coppers burn out quickly. The incessant waves of crime, and the constant hunt for murderers, rapists, violent thugs, drug dealers and child abusers was overwhelming, and threatened to desensitise a person to the horror of what people did to one another, for kicks, money, sex or hate; or all of the above.

He'd headed up the Barrow office for the last ten years or so, and had been a friendly face straight away when she'd first moved back to Cumbria. They'd shared the case that eventually made her name and secured her position. And now they were to work together again. Kelly felt a flicker of excitement at the prospect. They'd spoken over the phone regularly enough over the last couple of years, but to chew things over face to face gave her a sense of security that was more than welcome. Now more than ever.

He stood up and held out his arms for her. Handshakes were for formalities. They embraced.

'Coffee?' he asked.

'Erm, no thanks, I'll have water.'

He looked at her oddly, as if coffee and investigations went hand in hand like mac 'n' cheese, or chicken wings and BBQ sauce.

'Is that why you're looking so radiant? A new health drive? Are you training for some crazy fell race, or something?'

She grimaced. 'God, no, I don't do stupid things like that. But thank you for the compliment.'

'Straight to food, then? The specials look good,' he said.

'I did spy a shepherd's pie on the board. That'll do the trick,' she said.

'Hungry?' he asked.

'Cold.'

He went to the counter and came back with a bottle of water for her and a coffee for him, as well as a number on a stick for their food. He placed cutlery on the table and took the tray back.

He sat hunched over in his chair, leaning over his coffee, and resting his elbows on the table, propping his hands together with his fingers. It was an interview pose. It was the perfect opportunity to update him on what Dan and Emma had reported back to her. He responded by rubbing his face and chin and changing position frequently, indicating that he was perturbed. His eyes were like deep pools and gave Kelly a glimpse of how suspects must feel when being interviewed by him.

'Marvin Burns is, in my opinion, straight up. He's devastated by his wife's betrayal. Same with David Martin; but he's supplied some useful information.'

'It was a close friend of Marvin's – Maureen Johnson – who told me about Kevin Flint, and she also told me that Lorna Burns is having an affair with her business partner, Zhang Wei.'

'Zhang Wei has a 49 per cent stake in the Burns business, so Marvin and his wife are in deep shit over tax fraud. Pending that investigation he'll be a free man this afternoon. He agreed to be tailed and bring Lorna in as bait. I'll arrange that,' Craig said.

'I've also got an officer working on trying to crack the business open and I'm hoping it might give us some names. All I need is one client of Dorinne Callaghan,' Kelly said.

'So, Lorna Burns and Zhang Wei are literally in bed together.'

She nodded. 'Looks like it. A squad car was sent to the address on Derwentwater but no one was home. We're trying to trace him through Sellafield but were met with a flimsy "he's busy right now, blah blah." I asked one of my team to get a more detailed trace on whoever reported seeing Lisa at Preston station and Dorinne at Lancaster, and it seems like it could have been the same person,' she said. Craig raised his eyebrows.

'Red herring?' he said.

'That was what I was thinking. They were both anonymous, from payphones here in Ambleside. It doesn't mean they were the same person but it's an interesting similarity, don't you think?'

'To report sightings fifty miles away?'

'Exactly,' she said.

'Have the call boxes been traced?' he asked.

'I'm on it. Let's hope they're covered by CCTV, but it's unlikely. Only private companies can afford to do that here, or a few major traffic junctions, unless residents club together, like the one near the YHA, which is how you spotted our Chinese diplomat getting into his car and travelling to Sellafield.'

Again, his eyebrows rose. It was a comforting gesture that she remembered from working with him last time. 'Next steps?' he asked her.

'Eat shepherd's pie, follow with an indulgent cake, and think about it in an hour?' she said.

'Good plan.'

They caught up on news about family, weather and Kelly's favourite topic of late: food. When they'd finished eating, Craig turned the conversation to the footage of Lisa Lau leaving the YHA in Ambleside on New Year's Day.

'Lisa leaves the YHA on the first. The diplomat turns up on the fourth and twelve further people leave. I've managed to trace half of them, and her room was cleared at some point in between.'

'Is there CCTV of the rear, I wonder?'

'No, I asked,' Craig said.

'We absolutely need to find out where Lisa went on New Year's Day,' Kelly said. 'I've got a phone number for Mandy Williams,' she added. Craig had read the name on HOLMES.

'Is it genuine?' he asked.

She pressed the numbers into her phone and it went straight to voicemail. She left a message.

'I thought she seemed a decent kid. Well, not a kid at all, but innocent, you know? Turns out she was hiding that she was Lisa's room-mate.'

'Don't beat yourself up, people lie; it's what they're good at,' Craig said. 'Keep trying her. Where's that PO box number registered to?' He referred to the one given for Kian Delaney's whereabouts. It was clear that, finally, they were reading each other's HOLMES updates as soon as they could. Her team was doing the same.

'It's in Lancaster. Apparently it's simply a mailbox, run by a small post office. We're looking into it. Don't you think it's all very sleek? A bit too well organised for mere knocking shops, as Maureen Johnson likes to call them. I paid Kevin Flint a visit this morning before coming here. He's odd, there's no doubt about it, and I was nearly sure he had seen the women when I showed him their photos, but I can't help thinking he's too simple to be involved. He doesn't strike me as a sophisticated thug, or part of a large organisation operating behind the smokescreen of holiday lets. It's too obvious.'

'I can't say I profess to know much about him, so I'll go with you on that one,' he said.

'I've got a list of holiday lets to get started on. Some are in Windermere and along the A592. These struck me as stand-out because they're so large. Lorna Burns has only been in the holiday industry game for a couple of years, but, as you've seen, she's amassed quite a portfolio for such a short space of time.'

Eyebrow raise.

'What about the old couple who were arrested at the property in Grasmere, with the girls and clients?'

'They've been subject to interview pretty much all night. We're making progress. We've linked the IP address used by one client to Lorna Burns. When the place was combed afterwards, we seized plenty of cash and various toys, but it's notoriously difficult to get anyone at the CPS interested, you know that. The sex trade is so passé – people are bored with it, unless there's a concrete scandal.' She hoped that Rob would find undisputable evidence of interactions on the dark web, between the people arrested there, and confirm the link to Lorna Burns and Sunshine Holidays.

'Or kids are involved. It's not as sexy as cybercrime or fraud any more, is it?' Craig's cynicism was laden with sarcasm.

'Which is why Cumbria is the perfect place to hide, for someone who's in the rig of the good old-fashioned sex industry.'

She nodded. When the case of Dorinne Callaghan first came to Kelly's desk back in October, she'd had no idea that she'd be sitting here with Craig discussing prostitutes, with the wife of a proprietor of a local post office potentially involved in soliciting them for a Chinese businessman's profits. But all this had to be proven.

Craig told Kelly the name of a female officer in HQ who had a high profile when it came to protecting vulnerable women from being exploited. She'd been firmly in Craig's camp when he'd exposed a chain of brothels years back, and they still kept in touch.

'I'll have a warrant by this afternoon and we can divide the county up and go in hard. Someone, somewhere will want to talk to us. These girls are well looked after sometimes, but there's always one thing that hangs over them: fear. They fall into the game, then they can't get out, even if they want to. Take your girl finding all that money at Lucinda's house: even with all that saved, she still couldn't get herself out. She had a regular, clean job, a child, a supportive mother and she still found herself propping up the bar at the Scrag End, with some short, old bald guy – do we know who he is yet?'

'Dan's supposed to be making an appointment for our artist to see Yus Ali. I haven't heard from him yet. Also, I dropped by the Lakeside Bar and Grill to speak to Kian Delaney, but he's been off sick since last week and he's not answering his phone.'

'Kian Delaney was staying at the hostel where Lisa Lau stayed. Has this anything to do with Dorinne?' he asked.

'On flicking through the diary of Lucinda Dockie, my officer found references to other people who she spoke to as confidants. One was Kian, and another was Dorinne.'

Chapter 41

Kevin Flint parked his bike at the Kirkstone Inn. It had been a long hard cycle to the pass, but he was used to it; his leg muscles were strong and his calves up to the task. He'd been cycling the fells since they first moved to the Lake District four years ago. Before then they'd lived in Lancaster, on a grim estate near the castle. He hadn't much cared for cycling back then; he'd been more into sitting around the castle grounds on his own, smoking and what his mother called 'fiddling'.

'You don't know right from wrong!' she'd holler. How was he supposed to know? How was anyone supposed to know? Every time they moved, she made no secret of the fact that it was his fault. Every day he saw the burden on her face, and every day he wished he'd never been born. Until now. He felt his pocket: the piece of paper was still there. He'd folded it neatly, as the stranger had done. He locked his bike against a railing, near the entrance to the field behind the old pub. The walk to Rough Edge was short but brutal. In parts it meant scrambling, but it left him exhilarated and strong of mind and body: a feeling he was unaccustomed to until his first summit, some three years ago. It had only been Lang How, behind Grasmere, overlooking the lake; but it gave him a sense of peace that he'd never experienced before in his short life. It gave him a diversion, a feeling of freedom, and it unburdened him of the terrible guilt that sat between his shoulder blades all day long. His heavy heart lightened and he gulped the air. Other walkers greeted him and a profound sense of belonging engulfed him.

That was when he started to doubt the power of his mother. Now that was complete, he could move forward with self-determination, safe in the cognition that he was truly liberated. He'd seen it in her face. She knew. For the first time in his life he'd seen something in his mother's eyes that he only ever saw in himself. Fear. The moment unlocked in him a flood of awareness and suddenly he was a man.

He wasn't sure if there was a phone signal at the top of Rough Edge, but he had to make the phone call somewhere private and comforting. Nerves shattered his coordination and his hands slipped on rocks, wet with melting snow. His powerful grasp meant that he held on and managed to drag himself up to the ledge, whereas a weaker individual would have plummeted downwards head-first by now. No one would hear his screams for help up here. It was one of the true wildernesses of the National Park. The bleak bogs of Caudale Moor didn't attract visitors looking for pretty picnic spots; it was merely a meeting of sky and heath, but the solitary slog was worth it to get away from the incessant chatter of people hell-bent on communicating. He didn't understand why folk needed to constantly whine and whinge to one another, about the weather, or politicians, or their wages or what they ate last night. Maureen Johnson was a fine example – but he pushed thoughts of the old hag away and managed to clear his head. He got the impression that the man from the graveyard didn't like to talk much either. The noises he made when he was seeing to his women were ethereal and floated telepathically across the night sky. Kevin's admiration for the stranger had grown to godlike proportions and the anticipation of making contact was almost too much to bear.

He could taste the change in his saliva as he neared the top. It always happened when he got overexcited: a bitter-sweet liquid gushed out of his glands and into his mouth. He swallowed and tried to concentrate on the job before him. One slip and it would all be over.

A few more craggy bits to negotiate and he'd be sitting on top of the edge, looking out over the pass, down to Brothers Water one way, and The Struggle, and Ambleside beyond, the other way. Apart from the wind, threatening to snow again, whispering to him and urging him to go on, the only sound was the trickle of water running over the black shiny rock, down to a natural beck that would eventually join up with other tributaries cascading off the mountains, ending up in Brothers Water below. He stopped and cupped his hands, catching some of the clear freezing water, and supped until he felt refreshed. He was a heavy man, and it wasn't an easy task heaving his vast frame up bare rock faces without equipment. It wasn't obligatory to bring along climbing equipment for such scrambles, but it wouldn't have been out of place either.

Finally, one more thrust had him over the edge and he twisted his body around and sat facing the Kirkstone Inn below. A mere five hundred metres away as the crow flies, nevertheless it looked like a toy house because of the elevation. Kevin got his breath back and took out his mobile phone. He felt the dampness of the rock soaking into his jeans but he didn't mind. Dirty wet clothes never bothered him; only people bothered him.

His hands shook.

He had a signal. He took the folded piece of paper out of his pocket and smoothed it out. His hands were like ice and they moved slowly. He placed the piece of paper back inside the safety of his pocket, together with his phone, and spent a few minutes massaging his hands to get some circulation going in his fingers. Slowly, he felt warm blood return and the flesh became malleable and soft. He took out the piece of paper once more as well as his phone, and dialled the number.

After a few rings, a man answered and Kevin's heart leapt. His voice was crisp and clear. Kevin didn't know what he'd expected but it wasn't this. He'd thought the man would grunt like an animal, or spit curtly at the intrusion, but, no; he was inviting, warm and ordinary.

'Hello? Who is this?' the man repeated. Kevin panicked and pressed the end call button. He pressed the phone against his head and banged it slightly. What a fool! He hadn't thought through to the stage where the man might actually answer, he'd only planned for making the call itself and how that might feel, to contact the stranger who he saw with those women.

The policewoman had shown him their photographs and he'd seen their faces all over again, as fresh as if he was seeing them in the graveyard for the first time: pleasured and willing. In the policewoman's photographs, they looked proper, formal and dull, like real women he saw on the street, not the beasts he saw with the stranger, full of spirit and daring. They were chameleons of surprise, acting to their very best standard, and he realised that was what the stranger wanted. He was with them, and he took them there, to that place of spirits and ghosts, for a reason; and that was to set them free. They were probably unremarkable women in their day-to-day lives, but the stranger enabled them to go to another place with him, and act out a different play to the nondescript roles of pedestrian life.

It was the same for him. The stranger empowered him to dare to go to another place: a place forbidden by his mother and all the doctors and social care workers who told him he was 'hard work'. With the stranger, he could fly.

He admired the women who sought the same, and felt a conspiratorial affinity with them. They were like a secret sect of souls wanting more but never understanding how they could ever get it; never quite believing they were worth it.

He dialled the number again and the man answered straight away.

'Is that you?' he said.

Kevin breathed into the phone and his breath escaped over the edge of the rock in vaporous clouds. His heart beat in his chest and he was no longer cold.

'Yes,' he whispered.

'I've been expecting you.'

Chapter 42

Mandy Williams knocked on the hotel room door and was let in by Li Qiang. He looked smart as always, and he didn't say much, simply beckoning her to a sitting room. She saw Kian straight away, and it made her feel relief that he was here with her. Seasonal workers like them all knew each other and hung out in the same bars, listening to the same music, wearing the same clothes and dreaming the same dreams. He had a kind face, but he looked nervous. She supposed that it was an unusual situation. With Lisa and Dorinne gone, they were all on edge. Only this man seemed to make any sense and give them some kind of reassurance.

However, now that they found themselves in an unfamiliar place with a man they barely knew, after being hounded on their mobile phones by the police, suddenly the severity of the position they were in hit Mandy and her heart began to beat faster. Another Chinese man came into the room and stood with his hands in his pockets. She recognised him. It was Zhang Wei from the agency.

'Sit down, Mandy.'

She did as she was told. The man stood in front of them and unwittingly Mandy moved closer to Kian.

'Please don't be nervous. I want to thank you for your cooperation while I have been conducting my investigation into the disappearance of Lisa. I'm pleased to tell you that the inquiry is now concluded and I'll shortly be leaving the country, to return to China, to give a full report to Lisa's parents.' Li Qiang seemed pleased with himself.

'You found her?' Mandy gasped. Qiang smiled but shook his head.

'That is not your concern. But what is important is that the authorities here in the UK never find out what I know. With your help, that has been made much smoother and, again, I want to thank you for that. The Chinese government also would like to extend their gratitude.'

Mandy and Kian looked at one another. A door opened from an adjoining room and the man who'd driven Mandy to the hotel came in, along with another man of similar build: broad and muscular. She hadn't noticed his physique until now. He'd been sitting behind the wheel of a car, anonymous and plain. Now small details came back to her, such as the tinted windows, the expensive suit, the sunglasses, the Mercedes...

Mandy swallowed.

'We find ourselves with a conundrum. We are on the sovereign territory of the United Kingdom, and so we cannot arbitrarily dish out, shall we say, my country's bidding,' Qiang said. Mr Wei had yet to speak, but Mandy knew he was a man of few words. Qiang threw his hands around in a gesture indicating throwing corn to chickens. It sent a chill down Mandy's spine. He turned his back on them. Mandy looked down at her feet and a coldness spread throughout her body. Kian stiffened next to her.

'So, to prevent the possibility of the authorities using you to find out what happened to Lisa, we have to make sure you are not tempted.'

Kian stood up. 'I'm leaving, Mandy, come with me.'

Before she could take his outstretched hand, one of the men had shot across the room and taken Kian by the neck from behind, lifting him off his feet. Kian struggled but it was useless. The element of surprise, as well as the inequality of strength, left him defenceless. Mandy went to sprint to the door but she was blocked by what felt like a brick wall. She bounced off the man and fell to the floor. Burning pain shot from her elbow to her ear and she bent over to vomit. Before she could fully retch, she saw feet coming towards her and was swept up off her feet by hands round her throat. She was aware of whispers and commands.

'Be careful, no unnecessary marks. Make it look authentic.' It was Zhang Wei who spoke, before leaving the room with Li Qiang, the man they'd both trusted. Now, the reality of the fact that they'd been used hit her. She felt sick again.

The hands round her neck tightened and she felt herself become drowsy. She was barely conscious when she became aware of being taken to a bed. Her blouse was torn open but she didn't have the strength to struggle. An enormous weight bore down on her and she saw her own limbs give in and splay apart. Her mind played tricks on her: was she about to be raped and left in terror for the rest of her life so she wouldn't go to the police? Through her fuggy brain she saw Kian go limp in the hands of the other man. Her eyes darted about, as he too was stripped.

She couldn't work out what was going on. But when the realisation trickled through her muddled thoughts, it was far too late. She wasn't being raped. And Kian wasn't a target for molestation either. The plastic cover being spread on the floor beneath them, the gloves, and the speed with which the two men worked: it was all set up. In her head, she saw her mother's face and wanted to be held by her. A strap was placed round her neck and she was winched upwards by an unknown force. The last thing she saw, before everything went black, was Zhang Wei come back into the room and sit down in an armchair, like a spectator of live entertainment. She watched his face tilt to one side and his mouth spread to a grin: whatever was planned for her, he enjoyed the thought of it. She remembered the night she'd seen him arguing with Paul, at the cottages at Birkhouse Moor. Lovely, caring Paul who always looked out for them. Her eyes watered and her throat felt as if it was on fire.

'These sex games, they're so risky,' he said.

Chapter 43

Emma spoke frantically to Dan over the phone as she paced up and down outside Lucinda Dockie's house. She hadn't had the balls to tell DI Porter what had happened. It hadn't been intentional; she'd left the evidence in the yard for just minutes while she gathered other items together in the house. Maybe somebody had been watching her? The thought made her skin crawl. There was no reason to think that anyone was coming to the property, and there'd been no intelligence to suggest it. Sometimes perps do stalk the houses of their prey but according to all accounts, the streets around Lucinda's place had been uneventful. It could have been an opportunistic action. But would DI Porter see it like that, or would she perceive it as sloppiness? Emma remembered the man outside, on the other side of the road, when she was talking to DI Porter on the phone; he was the only person she'd seen while she was at the property, but he had seemed to be going on his way, like any resident might be.

'What did he look like?' Dan asked.

'Scruffy, skinny, baseball cap, big baggy coat. To be honest I thought he was a college kid. He was minding his own business and walked the opposite way to the house. Wait a minute. Shit. That was the access point for the lane behind, off which the back gates are.' Emma groaned and closed her eyes, rubbing them with her thumb and forefinger. This was a major fuck-up and her stomach turned over at the thought of going in front of DI Porter.

'It's only a guess, but it does sound like Yus Ali, from the one time I saw him yesterday. DI Porter said he hasn't been seen at his digs. He's way behind on his rent.'

'Well, there was five grand in that bag, so he'll be laughing. Fuck, how can I admit this? It's embarrassing,' she said.

'Just be honest with her, she's reasonable, and if it *was* Ali, he went there with intent. Maybe he knew that Lucinda stashed money away?'

'Good point. I feel such a twat.'

'Aye, well there is that,' Dan conceded. 'I'm done here, let's go for that lunch. We can update HOLMES over a coffee.'

They agreed to meet at Jake's Café, which was opposite the newsagent's, over the bridge towards the town's only cash machine. Leaving the Gate Inn, having established that all the rooms upstairs were in fact empty, Dan enjoyed his stroll through the quaint arrangement of gift shops, the odd pub and signs for the tourist information office. He felt as though he knew it well now, after a couple of ambles through the centre. Despite the cold, the sky was crisp and he immersed himself in the charm of the wee place. This was what he'd come to Cumbria for: the tranquillity, the peace and the delightful rhythm of the place. A woman smiled at him and a walker stood by to let him past. Dan promised himself that when things slowed down a tad in his new job, he'd get himself up on the fells. From Glenridding, he couldn't see the summit of Helvellyn, but he could sense it, far in the distance beyond the signposts, and he watched the hikers following the beck up to her foothills, looking giddy with anticipation. He couldn't help but smile at them.

He spotted Emma and sympathised with her. Her face was knotted in guilt and she frowned forlornly, looking down at her shoes. Jake's Café was easy to find and he waited outside for her to catch up. Everybody fucked up at least once in their career. That was the whole point of software like HOLMES: humans make mistakes.

'Hey, stop beating yourself up,' he said when she arrived outside the café. 'Do you want me to tell her?'

'That's just dodging the bullet isn't it?'

'Christ, stop being so stoic. You weren't to know that someone was lurking about the property just at the same time you were expecting forensics to turn up. It was completely sod's law,' he tried to reassure her. 'Yus Ali is a scrotum sac, and I wager he'll have known about the money and would've gone there anyway. Look at it this way: if he'd come earlier and taken it, we'd have never known it was there, and he might have taken that diary you found too. That's gold dust right there. It's not often you find diaries nowadays. Not like the old days. Now everything is instant and unrecorded. And she's chuffed to buggery about you finding references to Dorinne and Kian Delaney in there. Look on the bright side.'

Emma cheered up a bit. It was true; making the link between Lucinda and Dorinne was hugely important.

'Let's eat and I'll call the boss. This is a lovely wee place. Is the lake used for sports and the like?' he asked.

'Absolutely, in the summer, it's full of windsurfs, dinghies, paddleboards and day trippers on the steamers. It's my favourite lake because it's not as busy as the others. You can park opposite a pebble beach and spend the whole day there.'

'It's really bonny,' he said.

They looked at the menu on a board behind the counter and Emma chose the quiche, with Dan opting for game pie and chips. Emma didn't need to know he was supposed to be vegan. Jake's was that kind of place: catering for the delicate and the brawny. An edamame bean salad sat quite comfortably next to a BLT. They took their tickets, found a table and sat down. The place wasn't overly busy but equally it wasn't quiet and Dan was impressed.

'What are all these people doing?'

'Walking mainly. Winter is a popular season; the fells look so different in the snow and people love it.'

They took off their thermal coats. Emma's cheeks were ruddy and she rubbed her hands. They each got their iPads out of their bags and began updating the model on HOLMES for their investigation. They could see DI Porter's updates for the day already, as well as the work being done by staff back at Eden House and on the ground. It was a live template that constantly moved around as it flagged up markers and changed patterns, using its inbuilt algorithms, which were endlessly updated as new technology became available. An army of computer geeks sat in vast offices up and down the country, making sure that the system was not only safe from hackers, but also bang up to date. For example, new software had come in late last year to triangulate mobile phone signals to within ten metres. Complex specialised programs were being developed every minute of every day, to ease the burden on criminal investigations all over the world; it was affording them that was the problem. Emma noticed a live update appearing and read it out to Dan.

'Technical have triangulated Dorinne's phone to within one kilometre of the mast on top of Loughrigg Fell. The date is the same as her being spotted in the Heaven club, but the time is afterwards. Then it's switched off. This is massive.'

'Where's Loughrigg Fell?' Dan asked.

'It's south of Grasmere and Rydal Water, close to where DI Porter has been working on the case.'

'So Dorinne left Ambleside after the Heaven club?'

Their food arrived and they tucked in. Emma smiled at Dan's face when he bit into his pie.

'This will put the boss in a good mood. Good for you,' Dan said.

After they'd finished, Emma said she needed the bathroom and Dan said he'd call DI Porter. He went outside, after paying the bill and wrapping up in his coat. The air was a shock after the warmth of the café.

'DI Porter,' Kelly said.

'Boss, it's Dan.'

'Ah, Dan? How's it going? Are you with Emma? I noticed you've made some interesting updates. It looked as though Lucinda was working hard to break away from this life.'

'Yes, guv. Great news about Dorinne's phone.'

'I know. Loughrigg Fell is deserted and so it's our strongest lead yet. It points at her leaving Ambleside with somebody.'

'We've had a slight problem at Lucinda's house,' Dan began vaguely.

'Really?' Kelly asked.

'It seems that somebody was watching DC Hide and followed her inside.'

'Oh my God, is she all right?'

'Yes, yes, she's fine, she was unharmed, and she can identify the man: it sounded to me like Yus Ali, and he made off with some of the cash.'

'As long as Emma is unhurt. It's frustrating and it'll be tricky to write up and account for. We'll get him if it's Yus Ali. That explains why he has disappeared from his digs. I'll put a note on the PNC to alert all constabularies. He's an easy spot. He doesn't look the sort to own a car, so my guess is train and bus stations. Thanks, Dan. Where's Emma now?'

'Yes, guv. We've just had a quick bite to eat in Glenridding, it's lovely isn't it? Jake's Café did the trick.'

'Ah, Jake's. You should try the ice cream place for dessert, it's off the car park by the tourist information centre. So I think you should head back to the office and Emma go through that diary and you trace the PO box address given for Kian Delaney. We've contacted Royal Mail but they need chasing.'

'We once caught a murderer in Glasgow who hid behind a PO box address, by sending a letter containing a tracking device,' Dan said.

'Well, it's worth a go. Clever,' Kelly said.

Emma re-joined him and they walked back to Dan's car. He gave her the welcome news that, for now, she was off the hook.

'I owe you,' Emma said.

'So you do. She said the ice cream shop over there is excellent.'

'Maybe next time.'

Chapter 44

'The two payphones were within a hundred metres of one another, guv. We're searching for CCTV now. We ran the 999 calls through voice recognition software and they're from the same person. It's a male, and the voice expert we spoke to put him between thirty and fifty years old.' Kate spoke rapidly to Kelly on the phone. She'd grafted all day and Kelly swelled with pride for her team. She wished she could be at Eden House, in the thick of all of the notifications coming in, but she'd be there soon enough. Her team was more than capable of taking orders from her by phone.

'Not likely to be Kevin Flint then,' she said.

'Boss?' Kate asked.

'Ah you know, Maureen Johnson is hell-bent on us pinning all of this on the nineteen-year-old. I think there's more to it.'

From what she'd seen in her short chat with Kevin Flint, he didn't satisfy any of the three golden tenets of murder: motive, means and opportunity. She'd met plenty of killers in her time and he just didn't strike her as spurred by destruction. He had other demons. But that didn't mean she was right. She'd been wrong before, caught out by a whiff of innocence only for it to turn into the stench of guilt.

'What are the locations of the payphones?' Kelly continued. 'I'm in the centre of Ambleside now, I can walk there and take a look around.' Kate gave them to her and Kelly jotted them down.

'It looks like Yus Ali has gone AWOL. I've notified all mainland units. Same with Kian Delaney. Dan's coming back to the office to work on that PO box address. They were our best hope of getting a good artist's impression of fat bald man.'

No artist, no matter how experienced and well trained, could draw without eyewitness input a convincing and singular image of a portly, well-dressed, balding bloke, slightly chunky and short, and perhaps in his fifties. Their description fitted most male punters in pubs the length and breadth of the country. It would be like asking the public to look out for a black Labrador. She thanked Kate, and told Craig about the payphones. She pulled her woolly hat further down over her auburn hair as they walked through Market Cross, and thrust her hands into her pockets, imagining that her Jack Wolfskin thermal was becoming tight around the middle. Tiny flakes of snow fluttered in the sky and the hills surrounding the town looked broody and dormant.

They took the turning down to the marketplace and carried on to Lake Road, where they found two payphones, about a hundred metres apart. They were relics of a bygone era when no one owned a mobile phone. Kelly and Craig stopped outside the first and peered inside. The smell of piss permeated the glass and the inside was neglected and bleak. A few cards were pushed behind old plastic advertising boards and, through the door, Kelly noticed one that advertised personal services. It was entirely normal for phone boxes to be used in such a way, but when one is connected to a murder inquiry, they become upgraded from detritus to evidence. A man had been inside this very box, and called in false information to the police, and then he'd done it a second time, from the box down the road. Anything inside might be something that he'd seen and taken an interest in. Kelly opened the door and gathered the cards. Then they looked at the line of sight in all directions. Down the road to the south were houses on each side, with the odd shop and café. Up the road, to the north, from where they'd come, was the same. A bus stopped at a drop-off on the other side of the road and Kelly looked at Craig.

'It's worth a shot,' she said. All buses were fitted with CCTV and maybe, just maybe, on the nights those phone calls had been made, a passing bus might have caught someone entering the boxes. It would take hours to gather the footage and then trawl through it. Dozens of hours of footage from the hostel where Dorinne Callaghan stayed had already been scoured, added to the man hours spent on the case back in October. Officers at Eden House were also working on the footage from the YHA where Lisa Lau had stayed, hoping to discover who'd emptied her room.

'Let's pay a visit to the Scrag End. There was a man in there yesterday who went by the name of Old Bobby, and he said his main pastime was sitting and watching people. He was a sweet man and he told me he wasn't giving up his local just because of a few people looking for trouble,' she said.

The sky showed signs of darkening already and it was barely three o'clock. The Scrag End offered warmth from the fire, if not from the customers, who eyed them suspiciously when they walked in. Like last time, people got up to leave, but Craig told them to sit back down. Kelly watched as they did so. Yesterday, she'd played the bad cop. Craig commanded attention and the few people who were in there stopped sipping their drinks. The bartender (the same as last time) paid attention and the TV was turned down. Old Bobby sipped a pint, in the corner.

It was Craig who delivered the speech on fat bald man. They had little to go on, and patchy details from people who had vanished and remained uncontactable: Kian was one, Mandy was another, and Yus another. Whatever it was about this investigation, people simply didn't want to talk to them.

'It seems a simplistic way to describe somebody: short, fifties, smartly dressed and slightly overweight or rotund, as we are led to believe. You might all be thinking that describes every drinker in Ambleside except the students,' Craig announced.

He acknowledged the nods and the odd knowing smile. In fact several of the men in the Scrag End now could have fitted that description. But the bartender had used the phrase 'peeping Tom' and seemed pretty certain of the appearance of the man who'd caused such friction between Lucinda and Yus Ali. Kelly stared at him and approached the bar as Craig talked.

'This is a murder inquiry, folks, and we need your help. I'm going to show you some cards, and if you recognise any of them, please make yourself known.'

Craig took the cards they'd collected from the phone boxes and spread them out, inviting the punters to come and glance at them. Meanwhile, Kelly spoke to the barman.

'Has he been in here since?'

'Who?'

'Peeping Tom,' she said.

'No. You were only in here yesterday. He doesn't come in that often.'

'Now you seem sure that you remember him.'

'I do, I just don't go round asking names, that's all.'

'Could you help an artist draw him?'

'Sure.'

By the time Kelly had managed to find an artist who was willing to drive from Kendal to Ambleside to meet them, via her team at Eden House, Craig had managed to get two positive IDs for one card in particular. It simply advertised 'The Agency'.

As they waited for the artist to arrive, which might take an hour, they called the number on the card and allowed the customers to leave.

Chapter 45

Marvin was allowed to leave Windermere police station at a quarter past three in the afternoon. He was released with a caution and informed that HMRC Fraud Investigations would contact him in due course, to speak at a prearranged location. He was told not to leave the county. Maureen drove from Grasmere to pick him up. He was given his personal belongings back and when he went to call his wife, he saw that his phone was out of charge. Even the gloomy sky hurt his eyes after being cooped up in artificial light for twenty-four hours. A quick enquiry at the front desk told him that his wife had not tried to contact him. He knew that an unmarked car would follow them, for he'd agreed to it, in case Lorna should get in touch.

Maureen parked on the opposite side of the street and waited inside the car so she didn't get a ticket. Traffic wardens inside the National Park were notorious for being ruthlessly efficient. Her face was wrought with sympathy and she ushered Marvin into the seat next to her. They didn't speak as she pulled away. She stole continual glances at him, like a worried parent checking on their child. They left the town and soon saw Grasmere in the distance, and the calmness of the lake in the fading light made Marvin exhale.

'I don't know what to do, Maureen.'

'I know, love. I'm lost for words. I feel as though it's all my fault. I wish I'd never mentioned that damn address,' she said.

'Not at all, you've exposed something I knew nothing about, and I need to face up to it.' He peered at his hands and Maureen reckoned he'd aged ten years overnight. In that moment she hated Lorna with a passion. It took her by surprise, because she didn't hate anyone – truly hate, as in the visceral desire to see someone harmed – apart from the monster who'd killed Dorinne. Her fingers closed round the steering wheel.

'The shop's been shut up. The deliveries are stacking up. I've been in the back and I was making arrangements to open today, but the police turned up and they've confiscated all your records, your computer, and they've taken over the office.'

'Dear God. What has she done?'

'What did the police say?'

'She used my name on all the businesses, I'm liable for 50 per cent of everything and so I'm being done for tax fraud.'

'Oh my Lord! Marvin! That's shocking. Surely they can't do that to you if you didn't know about it? It's all her doing; she should be the one going down for all of this.'

'I don't know. On paper, I'm guilty as charged, if I knew about the businesses or not. The law doesn't take into account if you're dumb.'

'Marvin, you're not dumb. You've been tricked. Did they give you a lawyer?'

'No. I didn't want one, I haven't done anything wrong.'

'Maybe you are dumb. Why would you do that? They're the only ones who can protect you. They speak the language. Did you say much?'

'Thank you, Maureen. I told you I was dumb. I went round and round in circles, and I think I made myself look even worse. But the damage has been done. It looks like I might spend the rest of my life behind bars.'

'Oh, don't be melodramatic, that's my job. I'll get you home to my place, then I'll go over to the post office and get you some clothes. You aren't going there to see what they've done to the shop. I'll demand a set of clothes and you can have a bath, and we'll call a lawyer. Don't worry, all will be well.'

'Have you seen Lorna?'

'No, but there was a police appeal on the radio. They said she was needed in relation to ongoing inquiries. Have you any idea at all where she could be?'

'Only that place on Derwentwater. I told the police the same. They took an interest. That Chinese guy I saw her with is her business partner – *my* business partner. He owns 49 per cent of the business.'

'Who is he? I thought you said you own 50 per cent.'

'I meant 50 per cent of what Lorna is responsible for, and that's 51 per cent, so I'm liable for half of that. He's called Zhang Wei and they're on to him, in the hope they'll find her, I guess. They're hoping she'll contact me too and I have to lead them to her. They have these new-fangled cameras and tracking devices, don't they? Not like *Starsky and Hutch* in our day, when it was all bullying and deals down back alleys.'

Maureen smiled at the analogy. 'The mind boggles with what the government can monitor. I heard they can listen to your conversations through your mobile phone.'

They both looked at their phones, which were in the compartment between them.

'It won't be long before they catch her, you'll see. Then she'll have to cough up all her dirty secrets,' Maureen said.

Marvin looked out of the window at the beauty of the lake. Its grace and serenity had beguiled him since he was a lad, going out on a wooden boat hoping to find a perch or even a monster like Nessie. He smiled but it was a half-smile, weak with worry and betrayal.

'Sorry, I didn't mean to speak about her like that.'

'Yes you did, Maureen. And I don't blame you. She's had me hoodwinked all these years. But, brothels? I never would've guessed it.'

'It explains the boob job, Marvin.'

'You noticed?'

'Noticed? Dear God, they're like torpedoes.'

Finally Marvin managed a chuckle. 'I don't like them that much. She changed from being natural to some kind of hard-cased shell.'

'I suppose it makes sense in that industry. It's a risky business, and enough to make anyone turn tough as old boots. Come on, we're here.'

She parked and they heard a horn. It was Harry. They waved. The delivery driver was parked down the street and seemed to be making notes. He got out of his van when he saw them, and walked towards them.

'What's going on? I can't pick up my load.'

'I'm sorry, Harry. I've...'

'He's had some bad news in the family, Harry. The post office will reopen in due course.'

'What are the police doing here again? It looks like a heist.' Harry had grown suspicious when he found cops at Marvin's removing boxes and equipment, when they'd only been here yesterday. Something was definitely going on.

'It's out of our hands,' Maureen said.

'But I need to get some of those parcels,' Harry persisted.

'Take it up with the police,' Maureen said. 'Come on inside,' she said to Marvin. They left Harry standing on the pavement without answers. He walked away.

'Was that terribly rude?' Marvin asked.

'Did you notice how he didn't even ask about your bad news? He just asked about his bloody parcels?' Maureen replied.

'But I haven't had any bad family news.'

'That's not the point, Marvin.'

Chapter 46

At Eden House, as well as working on the onion router used by Lorna Burns, Rob Shawcross turned his attention to arranging the raids on the properties registered to Sunshine Holidays for dawn the next day, with the help of Kate and Emma, who busied herself with Lucinda Dockie's diary. What was jokingly referred to as WPC Dawn Raid, or the 'six o'clock knock', had been deployed by police forces for as long as they existed. Apart from the obvious reason – to catch inhabitants at their most vulnerable, and when they are most likely to be at their home addresses, it also gives the police a distinct and very powerful psychological advantage. Rudely awakening somebody in the delicate last hours of sleep disorientates them and immediately gives the police the upper hand. Rob was trying to coordinate raids on each of the twenty-two addresses at the same time, and it was proving a logistical headache. Each raid should really have two squad cars and a response unit, with tough equipment to break down doors should the folk inside not cooperate. That meant at least eighty staff. It wasn't going to happen and so, after liaising with DI Porter and Kate Umshaw, Rob was prioritising. A remote group of cottages up Birkhouse Moor had made the list, not least because Craig Lockwood's witness, David Martin, had also mentioned them as a place where he had met Lisa Lau. They were stretching all the resources available to them, and Rob felt the strain of an elastic band teetering on the verge of overextending itself. He felt the tightness.

All he could do now was wait, and work on trying to discover the route from legitimate IP addresses, via Lorna

Burns' computer, to some less so. Occasionally he'd nervously swing his chair over to Emma's desk, where she was reading the diary. He couldn't concentrate.

The diary had been an unexpected find, with Lucinda's handwritten updates on her life providing a clear narrative of her behaviour, emotional state and who she interacted with. It could turn out to be a crucial piece of evidence.

Emma was also looking for anything that linked Lucinda to any of the addresses on Rob's list. She read an entry about Yus Ali.

Emma familiarised herself with Lucinda's style, which was fairly erratic. She'd write a lucid entry, which was neat and orderly, about her day, but then on the next page, she'd daub scrawls of desperately emotional outpourings. They ranged from the rantings of a depressive, to the promises of a woman crazed by guilt and wanting to get away.

The entry about Yus was a tirade. It was extremely derogatory, and Emma saw that, when it came to the man's failings, Lucinda didn't hold her tongue (or pen). Lucinda wrote of him falling under a bus or drowning in the lake drunk. The paragraphs (if the piece could be described as being divided into something as sophisticated as paragraphs) attacking Yus were etched deeply into the paper, as if written by a crazed woman, full of anger and hate. Then the writing became clearer and gentler, and more decipherable, as she calmed a little and contradicted herself, and referred to Yus as caring and watching her back, 'when the creepy man hangs about the Grill'.

Emma read it again. She took a snapshot of the entry with her camera phone and sent it to DI Porter. The entry was dated two weeks ago, which was the same time when Yus said there'd been an argument after he spotted Lucinda with fat bald man. It matched the date when Yus had made a fool of himself in the Scrag End pub, calling Lucinda out and embarrassing her.

On the next page was another irate entry, taking back all the good-natured terms she'd used about her boyfriend. She spoke about escaping. *Even the creepy guy would be better than him.* That entry wasn't dated. Underneath she'd written:

> I told Mandy and she told me not to do it. She said he's not right. She almost got into his van one night and he said something weird about his sister that made her freak. Well, I think he can be nice, even though he is fat and sweaty when he pants all over the place. Mandy said anyone who likes it in graveyards is a whacko.

The word 'graveyard' immediately leapt out and Emma felt the excitement that comes when a small detail suddenly seems like it could lead to a big development. She took her phone and snapshotted the extra phrases, sending them to DI Porter. Emma continued to look for anything referencing 'weird guy' or 'creep' or 'freak'. At the back, there was a list of names, and one of them was simply 'whacko'. There was a phone number and a note next to it giving a number for 'The Agency', and an address. It was one of the cottages at Birkhouse Moor. Emma knew that DI Porter had collected a card for the same business, advertising the company of women, from one of the payphones in Ambleside. This time she entered it directly onto HOLMES, getting an instant hit and nodding when the link displayed on her screen: sure enough, it was one of the cards from the telephone box uploaded by DI Porter, as she sat waiting for an artist from Kendal to turn up at the Scrag End pub.

As expected, her phone buzzed and she saw that it was her boss.

'Ma'am.' Her previous nerves returned over her blunder earlier.

'Well, well. Good work, Emma, keep going. Start a profile for this "whacko". The mention of Mandy going to a van, the argument at the Scrag End, the timings, the graveyards – that's a bit unsettling – anything else on that? So, Mandy lied to me about this too; she was close to Lucinda as well as Lisa. Her phone is dead, and so is Kian Delaney's.'

'You've been keeping busy waiting at the pub, boss?'

'You know me, Emma, I don't do waiting very well.'

'I can just imagine. I'll make a list of all the graveyards in a twenty-mile radius of Ambleside.'

'Can you also chase the CCTV for Heaven in Ambleside? We should have heard back from them by now and we need to look for vans in the area.'

'Yes, boss. And Kate has chased the lab for the results on the wheelie bin, they should be in by close of play today.'

'Fantastic. We really need some developments on that crime scene. While I'm still here I'll call Communications Data Capture to run the number for The Agency. If they can trace a number, they could possibly find an International Mobile Equipment Identity to go with it and find an owner, or at least a location. Tell Rob if they give you an IP address so he can add it to the work he's doing on anonymous web activity.'

'Will do. How's the weather down there in Ambleside?'

'Actually pretty mild. I don't want to get stuck tonight, so I'll be leaving shortly after I set up the artist. Maybe even before, if they don't turn up soon.'

'Roads are clear from Kendal so there shouldn't be a huge delay,' Emma told her boss.

'I think they're here,' Kelly said. 'Speak later.'

After passing the number for The Agency to technical support, Emma carried on reading. She'd learned to speed-read on her detective courses. It was a handy tool when 80 per cent of any investigation was reading endless passages of witness statements, lab reports, case files and HOLMES updates. One had to look out for discrepancies, connections and oddities, but at speed, else it would take years to crack one case. There were no dates on these entries.

I did it. I feel like crap and it hurt when he put his hands round my neck, but I let him do it. I've checked. My bruises are not really bad, and Mandy was wrong. He wasn't as rough as some of the others, and he got a real kick out of it. I don't know how I feel about it but it means that I've almost got enough money for the rent in Lancaster so I can start my course. One more time, he said.

Chapter 47

Kelly watched as the sketch came together. It was disappointing but not unexpected. Often, in the early days of her career, she'd got excited about artist's impressions, but she'd learned to measure her response when they came out looking like a lot of people walking down any street in Britain. There was one distinguishing feature though, and that was what Old Bobby had told them. When fat bald man wore his baseball cap, he looked a lot younger. So the artist had drawn two versions: one without the cap, resulting in a much older and smarter-looking image; and the other with the cap, resulting in the man looking at least ten years younger, and more casual. The difference was striking. The artist said she'd like to add a few finishing touches but she should have the finished drawings ready to email over tonight. The customers in the Scrag End pub, especially the bartender, had been impressively helpful, and Kelly reckoned that Craig's stature and presence had helped. They thanked everyone who'd stayed behind and made notes of names and phone numbers.

'Anyone heard of The Agency?' Kelly had thrown in as most of the customers started to leave. Bobby stopped and turned round. The bartender cleaned tables.

'Bobby?' Kelly asked him.

'Mandy, the nice girl who was in here yesterday. You know, she said she'd check on me today to make sure I was all right. I have frequent bouts of asthma and the latest round left me in hospital with pneumonia. She was always concerned. She's a caring girl. Do you think she's all right?'

Kelly felt a cold prickle down her neck. 'Did she always check in on you when she said she would?'

'Yes. And I remember her telling me of an agency she worked for. She wanted to know if I was interested in their... services. It made me chuckle so much I had a coughing fit. She felt guilty afterwards. I told her that at my age, anything like that would finish me off for sure. She was terribly embarrassed. I suppose me hanging about spots like this made her see me a certain way.'

He twisted his flat cap between his fingers around in circles and closed his jacket awkwardly.

'So what was the agency?' Kelly asked.

'I think it was how these fellas hooked up with these girls who came in here, desperate for money. She gave me a card. I threw it away, but now you mention it, I think it might be the same, yes?'

'Could be, Bobby. Look, I have one.' She showed it to him.

'Yes that's it,' he said.

'Thank you for your help. Let us know if you see Mandy. We want to speak with her too,' Kelly said.

They saw him out and thanked the bartender, who nodded.

Kelly packed away the artist's impressions ready to take back to Eden House, but first she uploaded them as files on her iPad and sent them to Eden House to be added to HOLMES. She left with Craig, and they said goodbye in the street. They'd made a lot of progress, but Kelly doubted she'd see him anytime soon. They had so many leads to pursue now, it'd keep them both where they should be: with their teams, working their arses off.

—

It was fully dark and Kelly longed for summer. The drive home wouldn't take that long, but she decided to hold a brief from her car. Though it was frustrating to be away from the team, she knew that in the last couple of days, it had paid off to be out on the road and not stuck behind a desk. She looked forward to collapsing on the sofa and listening to what Josie and Johnny had got up to, and if Josie's room was taking shape. She could think of nothing more comforting than being seated in front of her fire tonight, with them, chatting about decorating rooms and buying new wardrobes, while sipping a large glass of red wine. That was, if she was drinking red wine. It might have to be a pot of herbal tea.

Her phone buzzed as she neared her car. It was Kate.

'Boss, the lab called with a few preliminary results. The metal embedded in Dorinne's hand was hard-wire pre-welded galvanised steel, commonly used for animal enclosures. Our fragment is hex-twisted steel wire, which is very distinctive under an electron microscope. I've seen the photos and at that magnification the surface looks like a crystal forest, it's quite beautiful. There are a handful of factories that ship it, direct in rolls, and I've run it through the registered companies, and two are based here in Cumbria. I called both of them and one had a significant purchase online for forty metres of the stuff last August.'

'Do we have a delivery address?' Kelly's heart pounded.

'Oh, yes. It's to an address on the shore of Windermere. It's the exclusive Lake Road where mansions go for millions.' Kate read it out and Kelly hung up, hoping to catch Craig before he passed through Windermere, so he could check out the address. She caught him just as he was pulling out of Ambleside, and he agreed he should visit the property on his way back to Barrow.

Once on the road, she virtually gathered her team together for a briefing, before they dispersed for the evening. Forensics had been to Lucinda Dockie's house, the CCTV footage from the Heaven club was in, and Kate had some more lab results to share. Kelly invited each of her team to talk through what they'd been working on that day. She neared Kirkstone Pass and wondered if she'd ever be able to appreciate its beauty again after travelling this way six times in two days.

Rob told everybody about the timings and details of the raids, set for five a.m. on seven of the properties tomorrow.

'Windermere and Ambleside police are taking the Scrag End and properties in the South Lakes. Barrow have loaned us twenty more officers, and we'll take the north, including Birkhouse Moor near Glenridding.'

'Thanks Rob. Can you tell us about the graveyard reference, Emma?'

There was a palpable silence as Emma detailed what she'd read in Lucinda's diary. Meanwhile, Kelly remembered something that Maureen Johnson had said in her original statement. It seemed an age ago since she'd read it, but it was only yesterday that she'd had it confirmed by Dorinne's great-aunt.

'How many churches around the Ambleside and Grasmere area?' Kelly asked.

'Seven.'

'Maureen Johnson said Kevin Flint had been caught masturbating in St Oswald's graveyard and given a caution. Might be relevant. Focus on the more secluded ones and report back. Lucinda and Mandy both mention somebody who likes having sex in graveyards, though I'm not convinced it's Kevin. St Oswald's is pretty public and I can't imagine it happening there for people like Maureen Johnson to catch them,' Kelly said. She turned her attention to the physical evidence and addressed her colleague. 'Kate? Forensics.'

'So the traces on the bottom of the wheelie bin are from soil residue indigenous to Loughrigg Fell. It's a thick, gelatinous peat-rich soil that is unique to the area due to the position of the fell. Most soils in Cumbria are thin, and sparsely protected by vegetation because of the steep slopes of the fells, but the area around Loughrigg is damp and boggy, thus preserving a deep layer of soil, even withstanding weather erosion. It's an area protected by numerous becks and rivers and a protective covering of coarse grasses.'

'Cross-contamination?' Kelly asked.

'None, indicating that the bin was moved cleanly from its origins to Patterdale.'

'In a vehicle, we have to assume without any CCTV in that area.' Kelly added, 'Lucinda's diary mentions a client with a van, who she nicknamed Whacko. Also the triangulation on Dorinne's last phone movements gave Loughrigg Fell to within one kilometre. The phone number for that name in her diary was run through technical support, but it no longer exists. Get me a list of properties in the Loughrigg area, Kate, there can't be many.' Maybe dinner cooked by Josie tonight would be off the cards. She felt a pang of guilt, but also the sheer excitement of feeling they were getting somewhere.

'Anything else?' Kelly asked.

'The fibres of white plastic in Dorinne's hair have been traced to a factory producing woven cord polyester strapping, used on parcels. It's sold by a thousand and one outlets, including Amazon and eBay. It'll take some time to work through orders to addresses in Cumbria. One piece of luck is that it can't be bought in shops, only online, so it had to have been shipped to the address.'

Kate also repeated what she'd found about the wire mesh and Kelly confirmed that DI Lockwood was visiting the property on his way home to Barrow tonight.

–

Kelly saw the bright lights of a village in the distance and knew it to be Patterdale; she was nearly home. 'Right, thank you, all. It's been a long day. I'm about to have a lengthy conversation with a civil servant at the FCO, about why no one has been transparent about Minister Qiang snooping around in the same areas of our inquiry – though we haven't come across him, apart from spotting him driving to Sellafield. Did we pick up his vehicle again?'

Automatic Number Plate Recognition was how Craig had discovered Minister Li Qiang visiting Sellafield in the first place, but no activity after that had been logged. Kate did a quick check and got two hits: one from the M6 and another from Heathrow Airport.

'I've been checking frequently, boss, this is the first time they've popped up,' Kate said.

'Is it possible to interrupt ANPR data, Rob?' Kelly asked. As their computer nerd, Rob was always the go-to for such queries.

'Anything's possible,' he replied.

'What about the warrant for the address on Derwentwater linked to Lorna and her business partner, Zhang Wei?' Kelly asked.

'A response team has been dispatched over there, boss,' Kate informed the team.

'Right, I'm almost at Troutbeck, so I'll head to Keswick and have a nosy myself,' Kelly said.

'Good luck, boss.'

Kelly rang off and dialled the number she'd been given by HQ. Finally, they'd done some legwork for her and found a contact at the FCO who might be able to help.

'DI Porter, thank you for waiting,' said a clipped voice on the end of a phone in Whitehall. 'I've been authorised to let you know that the Chinese government have now closed their inquiry into the disappearance of their citizen, Lisa Lau, and they have extracted and repatriated Mr Zhang Wei in relation to their investigation.'

'Excuse me?' Kelly couldn't believe what she was hearing.

'I hope that satisfies your query.'

'Woah, hold on a minute. What the hell is going on? Mr Wei is wanted for questioning on serious charges of tax fraud and alleged organisation of working brothels in the Lake District.'

'I'm sorry, DI Porter, further information on the nature of Mr Wei's repatriation is classified and you'd need top-level clearance to access the files.'

'So I was right. He's an undeclared agent, after all, spying at Sellafield for the Chinese government, and you knew it. And now he's been caught being a naughty boy flogging some prostitutes, one of whom was Lisa Lau with powerful parents back home, he's been flown home, first class no doubt.'

'I couldn't possibly comment.'

'What about the diplomat, Minister Li Qiang, who rescued him and threw Lisa under the bus at the same time?'

'The full list of registered diplomats working on behalf of the Chinese government here in the UK is published on our website, and the website of the Chinese embassy.'

'So, I guess he got a first-class ticket home too, then?'

'Goodnight, DI Porter.'

Chapter 48

Kelly liaised with the squad cars heading for the address on Derwentwater and arrived before them. She waited a mile or so down the road, in a lay-by. Meanwhile, she called Johnny and told him she'd be pushed to make it in under an hour. She listened as he told her how they'd been playing house all day, with Josie moving stuff around and them ordering about five hundred pounds' worth of kit off Amazon. He'd ordered a mirror for her wall, a Sonos system, a new dressing table and a vintage coat stand. Kelly smiled at the thought of Johnny and Josie settling in. He said the chilli would wait for her.

Her thoughts turned back to Marvin's post office and she felt sympathy for the man who'd been duped by his wife. That was the reason she'd come to the property: to look into the eyes of Lorna Burns and get the measure of her for herself. If indeed this was where she was hiding. Her back ached and she rubbed her neck. If Lorna wasn't here then they'd all go home and start again tomorrow.

Every instinct she had railed against the concept of diplomatic immunity. She knew that it was necessary for some things, but overall it was desperately abused. Zhang Wei had a part to play in this mess, and Li Qiang had worked under her very nose, no doubt stripping Lisa's room and getting to the bottom of the whole thing before she did. It galled her. She tried to figure out what was the Chinese government's priority, but realised with a heavy heart that she'd never know for sure. She reckoned, with her cynic's head on, and her knowledge of seeing what power does to people, that their main concern would have been protecting the national interest; that's why she was sure that Zhang Wei was a plant. He simply got bored, so far away from home, and thought he'd make a bit of extra cash on the side by going into business with Lorna Burns. They would also have wanted to save embarrassment; and so they had to extract him as a matter of urgency.

She had to let it go. Her priority was finding the killer of Dorinne Callaghan and finding Lisa and Lucinda alive. The response vehicles pulled up behind her and she got out to greet them. It wasn't her role to get involved in the raid; the response team were specially trained for that. She would merely be a spectator, and if they found anything, she'd go in when it was safe to do so.

They drove in convoy to the private road leading to the property and Kelly hung back. They parked and the officers got out of the vehicles. They knew their roles inside out and got to work quickly; two went to the rear of the property and two to the front. Kelly heard shouts and commands, and a few banged doors. She sat in her car, with the heating on, and waited with her window open, watching for any signs of life inside the great mansion. Her eyes had grown accustomed to the night blackness and she could make out the shape of the house. It had three floors, and turrets marked the four corners. It was a handsome property.

Her phone buzzed. It was Craig.

'Hi, Kelly. You home yet?'

'No, I'm sat outside the Derwent pad, waiting for response to clear the place.'

'Fair enough, I'd be doing the same. Nice place?'

'Gorgeous. She must be making a mint.'

'So I visited the property on Lake Road in Windermere; they have no recollection of an order for cage wire. They're decent people, I got a good vibe from them. They willingly showed me bank accounts and credit card statements from last year and I saw no purchase matching the date. The only explanation I can give is that whoever ordered it used this address, having some kind of access to it.'

Kelly was distracted by her radio announcing that a female had been apprehended inside the property. The woman had put up a fight, so she'd been cuffed.

'Sorry, Craig, I need to go. Female inside. I think I might be about to meet Lorna Burns.'

'Good luck.'

She quickly read a text from Kate Umshaw as she headed to the house. It read: *PO Box, Lancaster, registered to Zhang Wei, Derwent address*. She closed her eyes, took a deep breath and entered the front door of the property, as two officers came out to escort her. Wei might have escaped, but they still had an apprehended female inside the property who could perhaps shed some light on why they'd given Kian Delaney a new address.

'Property clear, ma'am. The suspect is apprehended in an upstairs bedroom; let me take you.'

'Thank you,' Kelly said, and followed the officer upstairs.

The house was richly decorated with ornate mirrors, ostentatious wallpaper and vast sparkling chandeliers hanging from the high ceilings. Lights burned where they hadn't before; the police had flicked on switches as they cleared rooms. The job of searching the property forensically would be onerous and time-consuming. It would likely start in earnest tomorrow and would take much of the local resources. The processing of evidence would run into the thousands in a place like this. The sheer luxury of the place might be what had attracted her to share the hideaway with her lover, but it would take time to get a definitive answer. They'd never know the motives of Zhang Wei. Having such a sideline, when he was supposed to be fulfilling a specific mission, was brazen and internationally illegal, but try telling that to the Chinese. That boat had sailed. Some civil servant in Beijing might lobby the government to expatriate Mr Wei, but they'd never get anywhere.

She was shown into a room, where she found a woman sitting on a nicely made bed. The room, like the rest of the house, was beautifully decorated and could have come straight out of *Country & Home*. Kelly studied the woman. She sat with her hands behind her back and a pink mark was developing on the side of her face, which was surprisingly lacking in make-up. From what Maureen Johnson had told her, Kelly had expected her to be caked in it. She wore casual trousers and a jumper, and looked as though she'd been napping. What she didn't give a hint of was being in any way fearful of what was to come. In fact, she looked belligerent.

'Mrs Lorna Burns?' Kelly asked.

The woman nodded.

'Mrs Burns. I'm Detective Inspector Porter. I'm in charge of the cases of the murder of Dorinne Callaghan and the disappearances of Lisa Lau and Lucinda Dockie, and we have reason to believe that all three women worked as prostitutes in your properties across the Lake District.'

'Am I under arrest?'

Her voice was gravelly, but she tried to cover her working-class roots with a plummy accent. Kelly knew that Lorna had grown up in an unhappy household in Liverpool. Her father was a ship hand and her mother worked in a fish and chip shop. Times were probably tough during Lorna's childhood and finding Marvin Burns had been a stroke of luck.

'Yes. I'm arresting you for evading arrest, perverting the course of justice, controlling prostitution for gain, breaking the Sexual Offences Act 2003, inciting prostitution for gain...'

'All right, I get the fucking picture. You've been busy.'

'No busier than you and Mr Wei. How do you feel now that he's left you hung out to dry?'

'No comment.'

'Good, you do not have to say anything...' Kelly read the woman her rights and she was led out of the room. It would have been inappropriate – and illegal even – for Kelly to conduct an interview there and then, but that's why she'd come: to see what kind of suspect she was facing. Often, suspects cannot contain themselves and let all sorts of nuggets go at the moment of arrest. Here, they had a pro. Lorna Burns was giving nothing away. One thing was for certain: Mrs Burns wouldn't be released any time soon; she'd already avoided police detention and questioning, and couldn't be trusted.

Kelly arranged for the forensics team to attend in the morning, and for a perimeter to be set up around the property. Before she set off for home, she received a call from Rob Shawcross.

'Boss, I traced the number for The Agency from its International Mobile Equipment Identity number on all mobile devices. I traced it to a disused IP, but after contacting the server, they put me on to one in Amsterdam, where I was redirected to a live server registered to the Derwent address. It's a third IP for Lorna Burns and I was able to track the live files of Sunshine Holidays.'

'Wait a minute, I thought you said The Agency?'

'Sunshine Holidays *is* The Agency,' he said.

Chapter 49

Kelly threw her keys on the side and was met with Johnny's broad smile.

'Come on,' he said. 'You've got a visitor.'

'I'm really sorry, but I can't stop for long. We've had a major breakthrough in the case, so I have to leave again after dinner.'

'It's okay, come on. Relax for a bit.' He took her bag and unzipped her coat, sliding the woolly hat off her long hair, kissing her at the same time. She enjoyed the attention but pulled herself away to go into the lounge, where Ted and Josie made a fuss of her. She sat down and asked Josie what she'd been up to.

'Wait till you see my room,' she gushed. Kelly smiled.

'I can't wait,' she said. 'I do need to go back to Eden House tonight, though, we've had a serious development.'

Ted and Josie looked at one another, and Josie shrugged. 'You can eat my chilli, though?' she asked. Kelly nodded and accepted a small glass of red wine from Johnny. She smelled it and closed her eyes, wishing she could stay.

'I've got a surprise for you,' Ted said. 'It's a belated house-warming present and I've been waiting for it to be delivered, but then you told me your baby news and I had to celebrate that too.'

'What have you been up to, Dad? You need to save your money for your wonderful extension, have you told Johnny and Josie?'

'Yes, Josie's been showing me how I need the table under the lantern.'

'Lantern?' Kelly asked.

'It's the ceiling window, it lets in an incredible amount of light. We've also been debating a breakfast bar.'

'That's so eighties,' Kelly said, sipping her wine and yawning. Johnny got her a blanket and she took it gratefully.

'Not any more! It's retro now, isn't it, Josie?' Ted said. 'Right, you stay there because you look exhausted, and I'll show you your first present.' He got up and went to the double doors leading to the terrace. He threw them open and a gust of wind caught the curtains, making them fly like superheroes into the room. In the dark, in the middle of her terrace, she could make out, with the aid of the light from the lounge, a brand new Big Green Egg BBQ.

'Oh Dad, I love it. You shouldn't have, I know how much those things cost.'

'I thought it quite appropriate, actually, you know: fertility.'

Kelly laughed and nodded her head. 'I hope I don't give birth to an egg,' she said. Josie laughed too.

'Let's get this door closed. You know you can cook rain or shine, or even in the snow if you want,' he said. 'I think I'll get one myself. Your other present is upstairs so you can have a look before you go to bed, there's no rush,' he went on. The cold bite from having the doors open subsided and was once more taken over by the fire.

'You know I can't leave it like that.' Kelly got up and wrapped the blanket around her and shuffled to the stairs.

'The little room,' Ted said, getting up to follow her. She reached the top of the stairs and opened the door to what she called her dump room: it was the smallest bedroom and used mainly as a laundry. When she went in and flicked the switch on it was perfectly tidy, with everything put away in new wardrobes, and in the middle of the room, made up with blankets and pillows, was an oak cot. Kelly stopped and stared at it, the reality of it hitting her. She went to it and put her hand on the wood.

'It belonged to Amber and June,' Ted said. 'It took me a while to find, and Johnny helped. They've worked all day long to get it like this.'

'I don't know what to say.' She went to him and he opened his arms. 'Thank you, I love it,' she said. 'There's no going back now.' She laughed.

'I should hope not, I nearly put my back out screwing that together,' he said.

They went back downstairs and Kelly kissed Johnny, then gave Josie a hug.

'I love it, it's gorgeous. Thank you, it's really special.' She sat down on the sofa next to Johnny and leant back into him.

'What else have you been up to, Josie? Although, by the look of upstairs, that's taken all day. Thank you.' She watched the girl become animated and her eyes shone with mischief. Her long blonde hair was braided and she wore make-up. For the first time since Kelly had known her, she looked like a young woman. She'd always thought Josie pretty, but now, in the light, with her sitting casually on the floor looking up at Kelly, about to tell her something really important, she looked more than that; she looked womanly. She smiled widely and Kelly wanted to hug her.

'Watching *Crime Investigation*.'

'Ah, of course! Was it a good one? Come on then, run it by me,' Kelly said, bracing herself for questions. Josie began talking and Kelly closed her eyes. Usually at this point, Josie would give her a snapshot of the crime, then describe the scene, and then the possible suspects. Kelly would have to run through the investigative steps and then choose a suspect. This time was different: it was a special programme on a boy who was incarcerated for life when he was just thirteen years old, for killing his sister and three other women, in his home town of Morecambe in the seventies.

'He hated his sister because she was pretty, how can that even be a thing?' Josie asked.

'Jealousy? Did she get more attention?' Kelly asked.

'Yes, his mother was a right bitch to him but doted on the girl. Anyway, the girl went missing and was eventually found hidden in the bath panel because she started to smell the house out. But the post-mortem was still able to show that she'd been strangled. But still no one suspected the brother. But then women in the town began to go missing and when they were found, they'd been strangled too.'

'So, how did they eventually work out it was the brother? And *was* it the brother?' Kelly asked, fully engaged now.

'Oh definitely, he confessed in the end, and said he enjoyed looking into his sister's eyes as she struggled for breath. He'd let her breathe again and then strangle her again, until finally she never regained consciousness.'

Kelly's eyes shot open and found Ted's.

'Did life mean life?' she asked.

'What?' Josie asked.

'The brother, you said he got life imprisonment. In this country, "life" doesn't necessarily mean a life sentence.'

'Oh, yes, I know. No, he was let out last year and given a new identity. He'd served forty-two years.'

Chapter 50

A dull ache sat under Kelly's ribcage. The boy who'd killed his sister in 1977, along with three other women, when he was thirteen years old, had been awarded lifelong anonymity, but had once been called Jason Walker. Anonymity was extremely rare in the UK, and usually the preserve of child killers. She tapped the steering wheel as she drove to Penrith. It was a glorious day and she hummed along to the music in the car. But her rapping on the steering wheel wasn't in time to the music; it was a release of nervous energy.

Last night, she and Rob had pored over the decrypted files discovered in the bowels of a remote router so sophisticated that the only reason Rob could give for them managing to uncover it was that it was the creation of the man who'd left in a hurry, not having time to close it down: Zhang Wei. They'd given up at eleven o'clock, having found what they were looking for: Dorinne Callaghan, Lucinda Dockie and Lisa Lau had all at some point been registered for The Agency; in fact they were still on the books. They'd also traced their final clients. Kelly's experience with the Tombday organisation three years ago had trained her in the advanced methods employed by far-reaching web activity involving prostitution rings. Lorna Burns was fucked, but they still had to find Dorinne's killer. The clients on her books ranged as far as high-ranking bankers in Manchester and businessmen from Liverpool, no doubt known to Lorna during her time there before she'd met the unsuspecting Marvin Burns.

Jason Walker had been released from HMP Altcourse last June, and had then disappeared as someone else, with the blessing of the state. There was no trace of him anywhere on the PNC, the prison service records, the parole service records, or the witness protection programme, and she'd need a high court judge to give permission to find out. Of course she had good reason, but it would still take time. She'd put her request in through HQ and now she had to wait. It was excruciating.

The two artist's impressions had been released to the press via the media department and many of the newspapers had included the images, alongside the appeal for public help, in this morning's print runs. She intended to throw herself into the loose ends all morning, tightening her grip.

She'd slept well and gone out onto her terrace this morning, first thing, to see her Big Green Egg up close. It was a thing of beauty and she imagined throwing a butterflied leg of lamb on it. Once parked at Eden House, she gathered her things and went up to the office to make notes on this morning's brief, due at nine a.m. They were making progress and it felt good to have some positive steps forward to share with her team. A few officers were already sitting at their desks and she expected the others in soon. She greeted Rob, who'd done such an amazing job this morning, coordinating the raids and blowing open the onion router responsible for the cover afforded Lorna Burns and Zhang Wei. Emma and Dan were also at their desks and the mood was buoyant. Kate would be in as soon as she'd dropped her daughters at school.

'Morning, all,' Kelly said breezily.

'Guv, we got a call back from Amazon. The seller of the white woven cord polyester strapping was an independent and they tracked them down, giving us an address for the order: it's the same one in Windermere, on Lake Road, where DI Lockwood visited last night,' Dan told her.

'Is there any way you can get hold of them and find out who the courier was? I know it's probably a needle in a haystack, but delivery drivers need sizeable vans.'

'Yes, boss. We've also located an abandoned church with a graveyard, on the Ambleside road; in fact it was the priest at St Oswald's who told me when I called to ask him about Kevin Flint. He was more than happy to talk, said the lad is troubled. He said he prays for him.'

Kelly raised her eyebrows. 'Right. And?'

'It's called St Brigid's. It's way off the beaten path but I've put a request in to the nearest road traffic control camera operator, which is on the stretch between Rydal Water and Ambleside because it's a notorious speed trap, for footage they may have. It's a perfect place for bikes to race when it's not busy, and Highways England installed a camera two years ago. I've requested sightings of Transit vans.'

'Add bikes to that list. Apparently Kevin cycles a lot; he gets picked up with no lights occasionally, and he's well known to the local squad cars, who are used to giving him, and his bike, a lift when it's dark. They warn him but it's all very amicable,' she said.

'That's a major route for delivery vans isn't it though?' Emma said. 'Good luck with that one,' she added.

'Good point,' Kelly said. 'It's the *only* one. Well, all you can do is sift through it when you get it, Dan, and well done.'

'The CCTV from the Heaven club is in, guv, I've sent it to you,' Emma added. 'I've made a start on the interior of the club, at ten p.m. The sighting of Dorinne was eleven, or thereabouts.'

'Great. Briefing in the incident room at nine. I'll see you all then. Keep updating HOLMES please. I know it's a pain in the arse to write everything out in triplicate but it's how we save time in the end.'

'Yes, guv.'

She walked to her office and sat down in her chair, leaving her door open. She switched on her computer and found Emma's email attaching the CCTV footage of the nightclub, but Kelly opened the file from outside the club first. She checked HOLMES on her iPad and kept it running alongside her office computer to watch updates as they came in. Interviews were beginning in police stations all over the county, including Barrow-in-Furness, where Craig had freed up cells for the deluge of arrests. The seven people arrested with Marvin had been formally charged with various offences linked to prostitution, but it was Lorna she wanted now, and she had her cornered. They still needed to find fat bald man from the artist's impressions. He didn't necessarily use The Agency to pick up women; that would perhaps be too obvious.

She called Dan into her office and tasked him with trawling the footage from outside the nightclub, starting at nine p.m., and told him to find her if and when he found something. Meanwhile she turned her concentration to the interview scheduled for Lorna Burns. She had to make sure that her questioning was watertight to catch her out and build a solid case. Mrs Burns had been interviewed several times during the night, but Kelly had ordered them to wear her out and gather new information. Her interview would be the one they used for the CPS. She read the recordings carefully, looking for ways to trip her up. Kelly cared little for the woman's arrogance and she wanted her shine tarnished a little before she spent any energy on her. She'd already spoken to the CPS about her, and they'd agreed in principle, due to the weight of evidence against her, that she could be kept in a cell for forty-eight hours. No one had told Lorna Burns this yet.

Twenty minutes passed and then Dan appeared at her door.

'Guv, you need to come and see this.' She got up and followed him to his desk, where he'd been working on the file. She fixed her vision on his screen, and followed his commentary. He began the footage on a street corner, on which proudly sat a large building, straddling both ways. She could also see a view of both streets for about twenty yards. Plenty of vehicles drove past the site, up and down, some stopping, some dropping off. It was a Saturday night, last October, and Ambleside was in party mood, at the end of the summer season before the winter kicked in for real. Simultaneously, she'd tasked Emma to arrange for at least five other officers to trawl through the various files of CCTV they had collated since Monday. It wasn't just the Heaven club data they had to plough through: they had the footage from the buses on duty on the night that Yus Ali said he saw Lucinda with fat bald man; they had the Ambleside club records, inside and out, as well as the buses passing the phone boxes in Ambleside on the dates they were used to report false sightings of Dorinne and Lisa; archives from Sunday night – the likely date when the wheelie bin was transported to Patterdale; and the archive from Highways England, which logged vehicle activity between Rydal Water and Ambleside, perhaps heading for St Brigid's church. It was an enormous task and required large amounts of concentration. Now Kelly watched as Dan talked her through what he had. She was waiting to hear back from the CPS with regards to the lifelong anonymity that was granted to the boy who killed his sister. He'd be fifty-six now.

'Here,' Dan said, pointing to his screen.

A Transit-sized van flashed on the monitor and he rewound it. He paused the shot as Kelly watched, and zoomed in, but they couldn't make out the driver; they could though make out the VRN and Dan had made a note of it, as well as the time. In the next half an hour of footage, he'd made a note of three more.

Kelly felt a moment of pride because this was the shitty part of the job: staring at computer screens looking at pixelated images designed to make any sane human demented. Across the office, she knew that a dozen officers were spotting vans large enough to transport a wheelie bin, and making notes of their details to collate later. The sheer weight of delivery and trade traffic alone could have them here for weeks.

Kelly watched Dan open a new file; this time it was footage of an empty lane. It was a clip from the Highways England camera set up between Rydal Water and Ambleside. It was placed where most boy racers were likely to speed: the stretch

301

just after Pelter Bridge. A vehicle's headlights came into view and they watched the lone car pass.

'This is from Sunday night, when we assume the wheelie was transported, and the soil samples suggested it came from the south. To get from the Loughrigg area to Patterdale, one would have to use the A591 at some point, and that point might be Pelter Bridge.' Kelly continued to stare at the screen. Dan fast-forwarded, and she saw another car pass, twenty-five minutes after the first. Dan stopped the footage just as Kelly thought she saw a branch flying across the road. She looked at him questioningly.

He rewound it and paused the frame and she looked again. It was a bike travelling south, with no lights. He zoomed in and, from the shape of the person on the bike, and the large, muscular legs, she'd swear on her life that it was Kevin Flint.

'I'll be damned. What are you doing, Kevin?' she asked. Dan smiled.

'Watch,' he said. He fast-forwarded again and froze on a large Transit-sized van, and zoomed in.

'Look at the VRN,' he said. The same van had been outside the Heaven club the last time Dorinne had been seen alive.

'Did you check it out?' she asked. Dan nodded. He pressed a few keys and an ANPR report came up on the screen with a name and address, registered to the vehicle.

Kelly blinked and stared at it for a few seconds. She couldn't believe what she was seeing. Her heart pounded. 'Have you got it on a return journey?' she asked.

'Oh, yes.' He returned to the footage and found what he was looking for. It showed the vehicle leaving Pelter Bridge later that evening, as well as Kevin on his bike cycling back north, minutes after the van.

Mandy said anyone who liked it in a graveyard is a whacko...

Kevin wasn't a killer; he was a watcher, a voyeur. Now she understood why Kevin fell silent when she showed him the photos of the women: he'd seen them at the graveyard, but he'd been too scared to tell her. What had he seen Whacko do?

One thing was for sure by that time on Sunday evening, Dorinne was already rotting in plastic bags.

Chapter 51

The morning shift busied itself with cleaning the rooms set for changeover today. Most of the room-maids found tips when they cleared the smart rooms of trays of food and detritus hinting at long luxurious baths and endless bottles of champagne. This one was no different. It was an adjoining room, and the cleaner went to unlock the room next door. She rarely saw guests and she had no idea who'd stayed here last night, but it was unusually clean. She went through to the other room and entered the living area first. Again, it was very clean and she thanked the Lord for small mercies: it was one less room to spend ages on. A quick tidy and a wipe of the bathroom would do. A spritz of bleach around the bathroom would give the impression it had been deep cleaned by housekeeping.

There was literally nothing to tidy and she stood in the middle of the room with her hands on her hips, staring at the TV remotes, which were side by side on the TV stand. The magazines were untouched, the chair neatly pushed under the desk, the curtains drawn open in symmetrical satisfaction – just how she would do it – and the net curtains were straight.

She opened the complimentary drinks fridge. It was fully stocked. Now she understood: the room had been empty. It was a mistake. The room next door had been booked and she thought this one had too, simply because it was joined. She called housekeeping.

'No, it was definitely occupied,' the head of housekeeping told her. 'Check the bedroom, just in case, because it could have been a quick stopover.'

'Right, I will do.'

She went to the suite, where she expected to find an unmade bed and some evidence of human activity, but what greeted her made her knees go weak and she screamed, falling backwards and jarring her hip on the table behind her.

Instinct took over and, later on, she'd have no recollection of screaming so loudly or for such long duration.

The maid cleaning along the corridor was the first to get to her, then a guest from the other direction. Both reacted the same way and stepped backwards, knocking into things as they did so. The woman remained on the floor, but was pulled back by the guest and out of the sleeping area. Her throat was too sore to scream any longer and the room fell eerily quiet. The guest made a call on his mobile phone and the two women listened as he spoke to the emergency services.

'Two people... dead... hung from the ceiling... I don't know!'

Finally he hung up and the three of them sat on the floor in the lounge area, breathing deeply, in shock, not knowing what to do next.

Somebody else came in the room. 'Don't go in there!' the guest said.

'He's the manager,' the cleaners said in unison.

'I still wouldn't. There are two dead people in there,' the male guest advised.

'I heard a commotion, are you serious?' the manager asked.

'What do you think? Did you hear her scream?'

'Yes. It's my hotel, and I'm responsible for the guests and staff.'

'It's not your hotel. You're the manager but you're not responsible for this! Let the police deal with it. Beside, you could be contaminating a crime scene.'

'Don't be ridiculous, I'll have to prepare for the police coming, if you say they're on their way.'

'Of course they're on their way, there are two dead people next door!'

'How do you know they're dead?' the manager asked.

The guest hung his head and threw up his hands in despair. The manager went into the sleeping area, regardless, and they waited for the inevitable reaction.

They heard a puking sound. One of the maids began to cry and shake. The guest held her and soothed her, putting his arms round her and rubbing her shoulder. 'It's a huge shock. You'll be all right. I know it's horrible.'

The police were at the hotel in under twenty minutes, and an ambulance arrived seconds behind. They were ushered upstairs to the room by a receptionist who'd been called by the manager, after he'd recovered from his nausea. It was no surprise when a medic pronounced life extinct for both of the victims. What took a little longer was the police gathering witness statements and guest lists. Requests for CCTV followed but the manager informed them that, regrettably, a power surge affecting several hotels in the area last night had erased all the footage. It sounded a likely story, and one that must be looked into further.

Forensics would spend most of the day at the scene and the investigation was sent to DI Lockwood at Barrow-in-Furness, as the hotel, in Windermere, was under his jurisdiction for serious crime.

Chapter 52

'For the tape, can you confirm your name and date of birth, please?'

'I've been over all of this.' Lorna Burns was irritable, and well might she be; she faced hefty charges, and they hadn't even got to the bottom of it all yet. 'Lorna Burns, twelfth of the second, 1963.'

'When was the last time you saw Zhang Wei?'

'Yesterday, when I turned up at his house.'

'Did he tell you he was flying back to China?'

'No.'

'What was his role in your business affairs?'

'Forty-nine per cent stake in everything. He bankrolled me at first, then, when we became more successful, we set up a company to make things legitimate.'

'Didn't he mind being named as the director of a company when he was an undercover agent?'

'Obviously not. His getaway plan was always in place wasn't it?'

Lorna didn't mince her words.

'Why did you waive your right to a lawyer?'

'Because I know I'm screwed. If he's fucked off back to China, like you say, then clearly I'll take the rap myself.'

'We have Paul Knight in custody, who is telling us that you employed him and encouraged him to support the business, even when girls were hurt.'

'He said that? He must have a fragile ego. He knew what he was doing.'

'When did you move into the sex trade?'

'Soon after I met Zhang. He said his diplomatic immunity would protect us, no matter what. He said he could buy police departments and governments.'

'Are you expecting me to be impressed? I've seen it all before. It's a bold statement, which seems to have been true – for him, at least. But not you.'

'Losing him like that must have been a big blow to your investigation.' Lorna sat back and folded her arms. Kelly had to give it to her: she had balls. No wonder she'd been so successful.

'With these charges, you're looking at six years and the repayment of all of your profit from criminal activity. What say you blow the whistle on him?'

'Are you kidding? I'd be dead tomorrow. I don't care what you want. Do your worst. By the way, Marvin knows nothing. So I'll be out in two years for good behaviour. That's not so bad. You gotta love the English criminal justice system. Don't you get tired of it?'

Kelly moved on. 'So, these three women.' She spread out the photos of Dorinne, Lisa and Lucinda. 'They worked for you?'

'They look familiar.'

'And Zhang panicked when this one went missing?' Kelly pointed to the photo of Lisa Lau.

Lorna nodded.

'And?' Kelly waited.

'The embassy sent a diplomat up here to find out what happened, but also to question Zhang: it looked bad on them. And it compromised Zhang's cover work as a scientist. He argued that he could carry on, but they said they were transferring him to London. I didn't know they intended to take him back. He should have listened to me and taken off.'

'You told him to do that?'

'Yes, you never would have made the link to Zhang if it wasn't for Lisa.'

'That's not exactly true; we were on to Zhang when the diplomat was traced visiting him at Sellafield.'

Lorna rolled her eyes.

'Do you know what happened to Lisa?'

'I wasn't told. That's not why the diplomat was here. His job was to avoid a diplomatic incident. They'll make something up for the family but they won't tell them she was a prostitute. They can't cope with the shame. That's why Zhang had to go. And I guess now you haven't got him, he can't be charged. There's no point pursuing it, is there?' Lorna asked. 'And you've got what on me? Six years of soliciting women, big deal.'

Kelly knew she was right. The CPS would want to concentrate on Lorna Burns. Going after a foreign national, from a country where extradition was zero, was a waste of time and money. Her phone buzzed and she read a text: Yus Ali had been apprehended at Gretna Green, changing buses. He was in custody.

Kelly put the photofits of fat bald man on the table, face down. First she turned over the one without the cap.

'Recognise this man?'

'It's a pretty crap drawing.'

'Think. A man in his fifties, smartly dressed, pokey features, we've been told, like a "peeping Tom", portly, overweight even, short and friendly.'

Lorna sat back and then took the picture in her hands. She stared at it.

'He's been seen with Dorinne and Lucinda, and Lisa picked men up in the pub where he was a regular.'

Kelly waited and watched as dawning realisation hit Lorna.

'This is the same man but with a baseball cap on, giving him a more casual demeanour. Imagine him in a uniform, coming and going, having access to all of your holiday lets, delivering necessities, like plastic sheets, lube and baby oil.'

'Oh my God.' Lorna looked at Kelly and back again to the artist's impressions. 'Harry?'

Chapter 53

Kevin cycled furiously and his lungs screamed. But he didn't care; it made him feel alive and curbed his nerves too. They were to meet at St Brigid's. Despite his hard efforts, he could still feel his heart pounding in his chest, like a chugging train, working hard to climb a steep gradient. The freezing morning air kept him alert and he rotated the pedals fiercely. Leaving the beauty of Rydal Water, he headed south to the turning before Ambleside to the small road leading to the hidden church. He felt hot, and considered stopping to take off his coat and tie it round his waist, but knew he'd need the extra heat when he reached his destination. His back wheel skidded on black ice and he almost lost control, but regained it quickly and straightened up. Adrenalin spurred him on and he pedalled faster. He saw oncoming traffic and braked carefully, not wanting to be seen. He slipped inside a great bush on the side of the road as the car screamed past him. Remounting, he took off, shortly coming to the turning. He slowed down when he got off the main road, as the tarmac wasn't of the same quality and the last thing he needed was a flat tyre. The track went uphill and he stood up off his seat, exerting himself further, until he came to the opening in the trees. He turned off and got off his bike, thankful to be out of the saddle. His breath billowed out in clouds before him and he looked around, hoping he hadn't missed him. He didn't even know his name.

He placed the bike carefully against a wall behind some bushes, safely away from prying eyes, and carried on to the iron gate. He remembered the women coming through the gate, laughing and joyful, safe in the knowledge that they were going to be treated to what they wanted by the man who knew exactly what to do. His appetite was insatiable and Kevin admired his confidence. To command a woman, and have her do your bidding in such a manner, without complaint or even hesitation, must be something that fantasy was made of, Kevin thought. He knew he'd never be able to do it: not unless he had help.

The vegetation was heavy under snow that hadn't melted, though the weather had turned mild. In remote parts, the dump from a few days ago still lingered on at the sides of roads and in abandoned churchyards. The ruined walls were covered in a pristine blanket of marshmallow and Kevin was reminded of the romantic story of the medieval couple. It distracted him and as he turned the corner, around a grand erect obelisk, he slipped and went down on his knees. He got up and brushed himself off. Now he was thankful that he had his thick coat and his temperature equalised again.

He went to the church building itself, or what was left of it, and leant against a buttress jutting out of a ruined wall. The moon reflected off the crystals of snow, and he held out his hand as a flake fluttered down from the black sky. It settled for a second and then melted away. He watched his hand in the illuminated glow. Then he heard a vehicle. He clenched his fist closed and his heart began to pound.

The engine stopped and he waited, barely able to breathe. Where should he stand? How should he stand? Should he say hello? Should he show himself or hide, in case it wasn't the man? He moved around the buttress a little, into its shadows, and pulled up his hood. On a grey day in the middle of winter, all the colours were muted and shadows were deep. The sky darkened and snowflakes floated gently to the ground, and he watched, mesmerised, as they made tiny wet dents in the drifts already there. He heard the sound of clothing rubbing gently together as a person walks through mud or snow, and he appeared under the iron gate, next to the thick tangles of ivy, laden with white. The archway was framed and the man stood underneath it, as if about to launch into a Shakespearean monologue. It was a scene from Peter Rabbit's *A Winter's Tale*, when the animals get caught by the farmer slipping on a frozen pond. The farmer shoots at them and cracks the ice, sending them falling into the icy water and under the thick sheet of ice. The plight of the animals had always made Kevin feel cornered. He had no idea why the image of the innocent rabbits, being mercilessly hunted by the incensed farmer, popped into his head now.

The man stopped and looked at Kevin. He smiled slowly. He had on a great oilskin overall, which covered everything else he might have on underneath. He wore a baseball cap on his head and Kevin was struck by how different he looked in the daytime. Gone was the well-dressed gentleman, taking the hand of a maiden and leading her to her stone bed, taking off his coat to lay it down on the stone for her. In his place stood an ordinary man, not mysterious at all. Just present, as if he'd lost his dog on a walk and stumbled on the graveyard. Kevin wasn't mistaken, though he did question himself for a moment: no, it was the same man. Kevin could see it in his eyes and his plump cheeks, and the slightly rotund shape of him. Kevin had always thought woman were attracted to fit men, like in the magazines, but this man had proved otherwise and the women he brought here were desperate for him. The trickery beguiled him and he wanted to learn how to do it.

'Your name's Kevin, isn't it, son?'

The man's voice was familiar and comforting somehow. He'd heard it plenty of times, here at the graveyard, telling the women what they wanted, and how he was going to give it to them. He'd heard it elsewhere too. In Marvin's, but there it was not as masterful.

'Yes, I'm Kevin.' His voice broke. He felt suddenly small and out of his depth. The man moved forward and Kevin flinched, trying to disappear into the hard stone behind him.

'It's all right, lad, I'm not going to hurt you. Calm down, relax,' he said. Kevin's shoulders untensed slightly, and he stepped forward.

'So, Kevin, you like watching?'

Kevin nodded.

'I used to like watching. I knew you'd keep coming back the first time I saw you. But now it's all got a bit serious hasn't it? The police been to see you?'

Kevin nodded.

'And what did you tell them, lad?'

'Nothing.' It was blurted out and smacked of fear and desperation. Kevin admonished himself silently.

'All right, no panic, I believe you. Why would you tell them anything and ruin what we've got going here?'

Kevin liked that the man used the term 'we'. It made him feel good inside.

'What's your name?' Kevin's voice shook.

'You can just call me Mr Wade.'

'Mr Wade. The delivery man.'

'Yes, lad. I feel there should still be some kind of respect for your elders, son. Things have gone to pot in our society, haven't they? Does your ma or pa know where you are?'

Kevin shook his head. 'I hate them.' His tone was venomous. It was the first time he'd ever vocalised how he felt towards his kin, and it took him by surprise. He'd said it a thousand, if not a hundred thousand times in his head, but he'd never heard it come out of his mouth, in a sentence that made sense, or that was listened to by someone who cared.

'So, Kevin, you want revenge, right? Is it on your mammy?'

Kevin looked at his feet. He didn't really know what he wanted. He hadn't thought that far ahead.

'I see. You want what I have? The ladies?'

Kevin's cheeks burned but it only manifested itself as a darker shade of grey in the blackness. He looked up at Mr Wade and shrugged his shoulders.

'Come to my house, lad. I'll show you. I'll take care of you. You can tell me what you want. I'll help you. I know how it feels to hate. I can show you how to make it better. I can get your bike in the van now.'

Kevin started to ask how Mr Wade knew he had a bike.

'How else did you get here? I've seen your bike tucked away behind those bushes before. Nearly scared a woman half to death, her thinking we were being watched. I rather liked being watched myself. You learned a lot already, did you, lad?'

Kevin smiled and looked down again. 'I know what to do,' he said.

'Just not got the ladies?' Mr Wade smiled broadly and Kevin felt at ease. He liked him. He almost dared to think he'd made a friend. A real friend: one who understood him and accepted him for what he was.

'No,' Kevin said quietly.

'So, shall I put your bike in the van?' Mr Wade said again.

'Now?'

'Why not? Days and nights all roll into one for me, out all hours, coming and going. Is your pa at home?'

'No. He'll be at the pub. I stay out of the house when I can,' Kevin said.

'That bad?'

Mr Wade turned round and moved off and Kevin followed him. As they retrieved his bike from the bushes, they chatted amicably about the snow, and Kevin realised that Mr Wade loved the local fells as well as he did.

'I've been away for a long time, and when I came back, I ticked all the fells off, one by one.'

'Where did you go?'

'I'll tell you all about it one day,' said Mr Wade.

'I used to live in Lancaster,' Kevin said. 'But when I came here, I just started walking, and reading, and I found all these places that no one knew about, and I could walk for miles without seeing anyone.' He was babbling, but once he'd started he couldn't stop. He continued talking as Mr Wade loaded his bike into the back of his large van. He chattered on as he climbed into the cabin, he prattled on as Mr Wade started the engine, and he still hadn't stopped by the time they pulled onto the main road.

'Where do you live, Kevin?'

Kevin stopped talking abruptly and gave his address.

'Why?'

'Isn't it obvious, lad? We need to get your mother.'

Chapter 54

'Where are we going?' Patty Flint asked. She clutched a half bottle of cheap whisky. It was all she could find in the kitchen as she was being rushed by her son to grab a coat.

'To Mr Wade's house.' Kevin's voice had changed. She looked at him and then to the stranger who her son called Mr Wade.

'You deliver all those parcels at Marvin's post office, I've seen you,' Patty said to Mr Wade.

'Clever woman, Patty.' Mr Wade was familiar in his tone. Patty was crouching in the back of the van among boxes and various wrappings. Her son sat up front with the delivery man she'd seen at her local shop.

'Is that how you know each other?' Patty asked, keen to understand the relationship between the older man and her young son. Maybe he was the reason that Kevin had become so aggressive towards her lately. Her grip on him had disintegrated but, if she found the source, then maybe she could reverse it. She hadn't wanted to get in the van, but she knew enough about her son not to antagonise him lately. He'd changed so much in the last forty-eight hours that when he took her arm and squeezed so hard she thought it might break, she knew he meant it. She'd done as she was told.

She watched her son, who kept glancing sideways at his new friend. She hoped to God he wasn't gay. Tommy would kill him – if he ever sobered up. Mr Wade looked like a dandy all right. He had a weak wrist and his face was witless, set in a stupid grin.

Her mother would have called him the village idiot. Maybe he and Kevin were the perfect match after all.

'What you chuckling at, Patty?' Mr Wade asked from the driver's seat. Kevin turned round and scowled at her.

'Nothing.'

He turned down a bumpy road and she realised that they must be in the middle of nowhere. From the back she couldn't really see anything, but she could hear no other traffic, and she knew that, in the Lake District, bumpy roads were off the beaten track.

'Where are we, Kevin?' she asked.

'I don't know, Mam. We'll find out soon.'

'So you've never been here before?' Even with her senses dulled Patty knew this wasn't right.

'You'll see soon enough,' interrupted Mr Wade. 'Here we are. Come on, let's go inside.' He turned off the engine. Patty strained her neck through to the front seats to see what was outside. She got a glimpse of a fairly large house but it looked run-down, a bit like a ruin. Her guard went up and she knew that she didn't want to go inside. Mr Wade got out of the van and came to the back, opening the doors for her. She struggled to get out, there were so many objects in the back, but he helped her, holding his hand out and clearing the boxes in her way. She took his hand.

'Call me Harry,' he said. He was the picture of charm, and Patty held on to his arm as she climbed out into the light and looked around. But she didn't trust him. Kevin did the same, studying the house and the surrounding trees and fields. It was truly isolated.

'What a place to live!' said Kevin. 'It's huge!'

'Where are we?' Patty asked nervously.

'This is my home, and you are my guests.'

Kevin looked at his mother and followed Mr Wade to the front door, which was unlocked. He didn't think of him as Harry; it seemed disrespectful somehow.

'I'm not going in.' Patty lingered outside, watching for an opportunity to run, anywhere, just not inside that house. Kevin strode over to her and took hold of her arm.

'You're embarrassing me,' he hissed. She didn't recognise his voice. It pained her to see him changed.

'Go on, Kevin, show her that she needs to obey,' Harry said. Kevin's grip on his mother tightened even more and she gasped.

'Kevin, you're hurting me.'

'Get inside!' he snapped at her and forcefully marched her inside the house, almost throwing her before him. He let go of her and Harry closed the door.

Kevin was like an excited puppy. His eyes darted about as he took everything in, as Harry locked the bolt and popped the key into his trouser pocket. He smiled at Patty and she didn't like it. The alcohol in her system was beginning to wear off and she moved closer to her son.

'Are you ready to begin, Kevin?' Harry asked.

Patty backed away slightly. 'What do you mean? What are you wanting him to do? I'll not have you hurting him. What are you up to?'

'Shut up, Patty.' The order was spat by Harry and she saw that Kevin was smiling at her. She looked at the delivery man. The weakness she'd spotted on the journey had vanished. He'd turned into something else, and Kevin was taking it all in. His eyes were wide and alert, and his grin taunted her. It was like the other night when Kevin had made her feel scared and she'd appreciated his true size and capability. For the first time ever, she saw him as able to fight back, but more than that too: she'd created a weapon that could go off at any moment. She felt fully sober now, and the need to get out of this place hit her. Why had she agreed to come in the first place?

'You're going to open that door and take me home, or...'

'Or, what, Patty?' Harry waited for her to reply, and all the while, Kevin saw, he was flexing and extending his fingers. Patty saw it too. She didn't reply.

'This is where it begins, Kevin. This is what you've been waiting for. I'm going to give you a gift. My present to you is standing right in front of you. It's the deliverance you want. You want to smash her head in, don't you? You hate her.'

Patty flinched. She stepped back further, until her back was against the door.

Kevin watched and his mother stared at his fingers, which were also flexing and extending now. She watched them. Her throat constricted and she began shaking her head.

'Kevin... Don't listen.' Her voice was a whisper. She recognised the emotion showing all over his face and identified it as plainly as Harry Wade had spelled it out. With every second, she saw him become more worked up. He ached to hurt her. Every moment that she'd spent taunting him, shouting at him, calling him names and ridiculing him came back to her, and she realised that she'd shaped a monster.

'They all know what she does to you, Kevin. In Marvin's everyone talks about it. They all know she fiddles with you, they talk about it all the time.' Harry spoke deliberately, not taking his eyes off Patty the whole time. Kevin's knuckles were turning white.

'Kevin. You dirty little disgusting Water Boy!' Her voice was pure venom. No one moved. It was a last attempt to knock Kevin out of his stupor.

'This is the point where you're all in or all out. Do you understand, Kevin?' Harry asked.

Her eyes flickered between the two men and she turned and began banging on the door. Harry went to her and took her by her hair and she squealed in pain. He shook her like a rag doll and she stopped screaming.

'This is when you either become nothing or something.' Harry's face grimaced with intent, as he held Patty still. He ripped her head back and put his other hand round her throat. 'I can show you how to take control, but you need to prove to me that you are worth the risk. See, you know everything now, and she'll tell.' Patty stopped struggling and Kevin saw that her chest was heaving with fear and he liked it.

'What do you want me to do?' he asked.

'Let me show you.'

Harry smiled. Patty couldn't see it, but she felt his body soften a little and thought this could be her chance. She tore herself free and ran in the other direction, but Kevin put out his foot and tripped her. Harry clapped his hand on his thigh.

'Well done, lad! You're a natural. Come on, help me.' Harry strode to where Patty was struggling on the floor, trying to get up, but she'd hurt her leg. She held it and cried.

'Kevin,' she said simply. He ignored her. He only had eyes for the man who was playing him like a puppet, like he was in some kind of trance.

'Kevin!' she shouted. Harry swiped her face with the back of one of his huge hands and she fell over onto her side, banging her head.

'I'll hold her,' Harry said. He held her body from behind as she struggled, but she was no match for the delivery man.

'Get on top of her, and put your hands round her throat. Like this. I'll cover her mouth when she fights back, don't you worry about that; it won't last.'

Kevin knelt in front of his mother and looked at her neck. Harry was strong and was holding her fairly still. He put his hands on her throat, exactly where Harry had shown him, and began to squeeze. His hands fitted neatly and formed a perfect circle as he pushed harder and harder. She began to jerk about and thrash, but Harry controlled her enough to make her still, so Kevin could enjoy what he was doing.

Kevin's grip was loosening and he panted with the exertion.

'Getting tired? It's tougher than you think, isn't it?' Harry said. Kevin nodded and sat back. Harry took over and came around the front, never taking his hands off Patty. She coughed and spluttered but had no time to recover before Harry got her in a vice once more and Kevin massaged his hands. His mother's body convulsed and contorted. Harry squeezed tighter and tighter... His mother's eyes were popping out of her head and full of terror.

'That'll do.' Harry stopped.

Kevin stared at him, confused. His mother slumped to the floor, still breathing, if only very faintly.

'What are you doing?' he asked.

'This is the best bit, Kevin. Look at her: she thinks she's over the worst. She's coming to; she thinks we changed our minds. Oh, this part is amazing. Look at her eyes when she realises that I'm going to do it again.'

Patty's eyes widened. She put her hand to her throat, and her breathing got louder, but her larynx was so badly damaged that she failed to get enough air in. Harry was on her again, but it wasn't long this time before she passed out.

'Is she dead?'

'No. Do you want her to be? Or do you want to do it all again?'

Kevin stared at him.

'Let's go and visit the others while we wait.' Harry picked up Kevin's mother and flung her over his shoulder.

'The others?'

Chapter 55

Kelly stared at the phone. The special order from the magistrate was complete and the prison service was able to release the new identity of the man who'd been let out of prison last year. After forty-two years of being looked after by the taxpayer, having been passed as rehabilitated, and no longer deemed a threat to society, the boy formerly known as Jason Walker had been given a new life under conditions of absolute secrecy – until now.

His new name was Harry Wade, and he worked as a delivery man, often picking up parcels at Marvin's. Kelly had come within feet of him on Tuesday, as he picked up packages and said he didn't recognise the addresses she or Maureen mentioned. Now they knew for sure that it was Harry's vehicle that delivered regularly to the address on Lake Road in Windermere. The family spoke fondly of their friendly driver, who was always prompt and jovial. Little did they know that he used their address to take receipt of hex wire and plastic strapping to detain and torture a woman.

Harry Wade's van now linked the disappearance of Lisa Lau and Lucinda Dockie to the murder of Dorinne Callaghan. They had witness statements confirming he used the services of prostitutes, and now, by tracking his VRN, they had a map of where he'd been and when, and his journeys matched what they knew about the last whereabouts of their victims. Paul Knight had given them a positive ID for several liaisons with Dorinne at the Birkhouse Moor cottages. It was incredible how loose one's mouth got when faced with time inside at Her Majesty's pleasure. But it was also somewhat shocking that

Harry had been so brazen as to join The Agency. He must have done, else Paul said he wouldn't have got access to the cottages, but Rob couldn't find his name on The Agency's files. The obvious answer was that he used a different name. They'd have to trawl through every shred of data from the archives. The only thing they were missing now was Harry's address, because the van was a permanent lease to a company in Kendal. A quick phone call had drawn a dead end as the company couldn't find any records of the vehicle ever belonging to them. But they had the soil sample, which put the wheelie bin in Loughrigg, where Dorinne's phone had gone dead last October, and there was only one road into the area, from the A591. Cars were already dispatched. There were only eleven registered addresses in the remote Loughrigg area, taking into account the perimeter around the mast where Dorinne's phone had pinged its final clues.

There was a final nail in the coffin for the man who should never have been released from prison. There would be questions asked about why he hadn't been forced to wear a tracking device at least for the initial phase of his release. The final piece of watertight evidence that would hang Harry Wade in the dock, though it was a pity it wouldn't be literally, was a phone call from Ted. From the degraded and minute amount of DNA material taken from Dorinne's body, the lab had managed to increase the yield of the sample once it was established that it didn't belong to the victim herself. They'd been able to create a profile, something that was only a recent scientific breakthrough, and they'd got a hit on the DNA database: it belonged to Jason Walker.

–

Kelly and Dan travelled in a car behind the armed response vehicles. They travelled with blues and Kelly reached 70 mph on a tight bend.

'I came here for a break,' Dan quipped.

'Haven't you heard? We chase nutters here too. Hold on.'

'This one's a classic.'

'Even for Glasgow?'

'Aye, even Glesga, the old girl.'

Lights flashed and sirens stung the winter air. Adrenalin coursed through Kelly's veins as she shifted the Audi into manual. She kept up with the vehicles in front and they finally arrived at the only property in the area that, after several reconnaissance missions in the last hour had, by helicopter, shown up as having a delivery van parked outside. A telescopic lens showed the same VRN.

The cars screeched to a halt and armed officers got out, kitted up and bellowing orders. Kelly and Dan would have to wait, but it didn't mean they couldn't get out of the car to listen to the final brief on the mission, before the op order was carried out. Armed response had their own chain of command should anything go wrong, but Kelly believed she still benefited from listening. They'd travelled down a dirt road and seen the house in the distance. She stared at the van, parked outside and took a pair of binoculars out of her glove compartment to confirm the VRN. It had been parked outside Marvin's on Tuesday. What had been going through his head as he toyed with them? She also wondered where he got his money from. A prison inmate for over forty years, no family left who hadn't already disowned him upon conviction, and reliance upon the witness protection service; it didn't add up. The house was fairly large, if admittedly a bit run-down. The only thing she could think of was that the sensitive nature of his case had justified him being given enough funds to live in isolation.

But first and foremost, her priority was whether they'd find Lisa and Lucinda inside; or indeed, as Dr Demi Cramer believed, even more women. Kelly and Dan watched as the officers took ramming equipment up to the house. Whoever was inside was given a warning first; the chopper that had ID'd the van hovered overhead and announced its intentions from a loudspeaker. Kelly felt the gusts of air generated by the blades as they rotated at about eighty knots. Debris and small stones were blown away from the house, but despite the warnings, no movement could be seen. Kelly felt heaviness in the pit of her stomach. A couple of officers went round the back of the property and the others smashed their way in, one by one, through the front door. The noise of wood cracking and the guttural commands of the officers was deafening but still Kelly stood her ground, unflinching, with Dan behind her, ready to run forward when they were given the all-clear.

Three ambulances turned up and Kelly waved them over to a piece of scrubland where they could park. She briefed them. If she was right, then the property they waited to enter was a true house of horrors. It seemed long minutes before the radio crackled and Dan looked at Kelly and back to the house. The medics were fully kitted and expectant as they readied themselves to sprint into the house.

They listened to the Response Commander liaise with his officers who'd gone into the building, as well as those who'd taken the back. Kelly looked around her. The house was about as remote as one could get here in the Lakes. Any sound wouldn't carry and there'd be no deliveries: Harry Wade picked up everything he needed at the post office sorting branch, sometimes with other people's addresses on them, keeping what he wanted and posting what he didn't. She shivered, but it wasn't due to the inclement weather, more about what Harry Wade had done with all that hex wire and polyester strapping.

A cry caught their attention and officers began calling out, declaring rooms clear and affirming orders carried out.

'Get down!' one shouted from inside the house, and Kelly recognised the tone as that used with a perp, not a colleague.

'Last warning, or we will apprehend you, with force.' The words were enunciated clearly and emphatically. Everything would be recorded on bodycam. She heard a scuffle break the airwaves and put her hands together, clasping them in frustration with the wait. It was time to get on their armour.

Some parole board somewhere had decided that the guy inside the house, who had butchered a corpse to get her to fit into a wheelie bin, was a reformed character. The opposite was true: forty-two years in prison had proved a catalytic converter, taking an already highly unstable individual, hell-bent on hurting women as an act of revenge for what a bitch his mother was, and pouring fuel on the fire. Inside prison, he'd have had access to an army of psychologists who would no doubt have perpetuated his victim status, as well as libraries, TV and the one thing positive to make a lunatic more loony: time.

They were back full circle again. She'd read his file. His mother used to lock him up and feed his sister delicious food, with Jason watching in pure misery and his sister feeding off the power as well as the food. When he was sentenced to life, he was suffering with rickets and had injuries to virtually every square inch of his body, fresh and healed. This was what real trauma looked like and the child's response had been absolute. It wasn't evil, or inhuman; in fact it was very typical of any mortal exposed to prolonged, incessant suffering. Not to react would have been questionable. But why murder? There were plenty of abused kids out there who don't murder – but then, she knew a few of her psychology friends out there would say that most of them do go on to abuse, which is a kind of slow assassination akin to murder. Maybe this should be another class of murder?

There was a loud bang. It sounded like furniture tumbling over.

'Medic!'

The ambulance crew rushed inside. No response team would allow a medic inside if it was unsafe, and the notification of 'location secure' came seconds later.

It was their green light. Dan banged his fist on his thigh in exuberance.

'Come on,' Kelly said. She took a deep breath and hoped what they found inside didn't stay with her for too long. In

London, when she'd worked for the Met, she'd been plagued with bad dreams during and after cases like this. She'd find herself locked in a remote warehouse, hunted by a maniac. She figured it was her empathising with the victims. It sucked.

They went inside and the first thing she noticed was the smell. It was more than stale; it was rotten. But then, if this was where he'd chopped up Dorinne, it really was no wonder. The house was dark and, straight away, one had the distinct feeling of entering a place of torment. She remembered back to Tuesday when she'd come face to face with Harry, thinking that he, Maureen and Marvin obviously enjoyed a kind of friendship. It was clear that they shared banter when Harry collected his bundles.

An officer came down the stairs and nodded to them.

'It's all in the cellar, ma'am.'

Dan looked at her and she glanced around.

'Through the kitchen, there's a door at the end. We heard screaming and rammed the door.'

'A woman screaming?'

'No, it's a young man, ma'am.'

Dan followed her towards the kitchen and another officer passed them. He had his hand up to his mouth. Kelly had seen that look before: he'd seen something that he'd never be able to erase as long as he lived. She swallowed and steeled herself. They reached the opening where the door had once been: it was now broken and propped up by the filthy cooker. Greasy water covered unwashed pots in the sink and a stench leaked silently from below.

'DI Porter, coming down now,' she shouted. Stench wafted from the bowels of the house.

'Right you are, ma'am,' was heard from below.

The light was an orange glow and Kelly saw beams of blue torchlight piercing the gloom. Officers crammed on the stairs.

'There's very little room in there, ma'am, we're letting the medics work. There's room for one of you.'

Kelly went down the staircase and Dan followed behind, but just to the bottom of the stairs, where he'd wait for Kelly's command. The response officer nodded to them both. 'I'll organise stretchers. There are five women down there,' he said.

'Alive?' Kelly asked.

'I think so, just about. They're in cages.'

Kelly and Dan exchanged a look that was a mixture of disbelief and devastation too. 'What about Wade?' Kelly asked.

'No one of his description in there. There's a teenage boy, were you expecting that?' he asked.

'No,' Kelly replied, but she had her suspicions about who it might be. 'Dan, will you go back up and see how the land search out the back is going?'

'Aye.'

Kelly turned to the dungeon-like room underneath the house and held her breath, knowing that the odour of maltreatment would hit her soon. It was difficult to see and she was met with a scene of chaos. Medics worked on three women, demanding more vehicles, and two officers helped them. Kelly saw Kevin Flint, who cowered in the corner, un-cuffed. She went to him and knelt down.

'Kevin, look at me, it's DI Porter.' He turned his eyes upwards and held her gaze. He looked scared.

'What happened? What are you doing here?'

'He tried to kill Mam.'

'Is your mother here?'

He looked as though he'd been in a fight and had what appeared to be blood on his face, hands and jumper.

He nodded.

'Where?'

Her radio burst into life again. It was Dan, calling her outside.

'Boss, there's a deceased female and a deceased male in the barn behind the property. I can't ID either of them. I don't recognise the woman and the male has his head bashed in. She's been almost dismembered by blows with something sharp.'

'What did you do?' she asked Kevin in a whispered voice. He stared at her.

The first stretcher left the cellar, carrying a woman, and Kelly saw that it was Lisa Lau. She stared blankly, without any sign of cognition, and was utterly silent. Kelly guessed that, down here, one learned not to scream. She looked across to another woman being given an injection; Kelly didn't recognise her. She desperately searched the faces of the other three and finally, on the fifth, saw Lucinda Dockie, who also stared blankly, like an empty vessel. And she'd only been in here for three days. The deterioration was rapid. The women were in various stages of dehumanisation: they were dirty, weak, cramped, incarcerated and terrorised. Kelly turned to where they'd been held, and her eyes adjusted to the gloom, enabling her to look upon the cages covered in hex wire. In the corner she spotted a blue light and realised that it came from a camera. She hoped he'd filmed the whole thing, but equally recoiled at the thought of watching it.

'Kevin, come with me.' He stayed where he was.

'Kevin!' Kelly shouted. He jumped and stared up at her.

'Get up.' He did so, slowly. Kelly led him upstairs. She'd seen enough of the dungeon. When she was back out in the sunlight, she squinted her eyes and gave Kevin to an officer to guard. She cuffed him and read him his rights, though it still wasn't clear what he'd done. She called Kate back at Eden House to arrange forensics. It would take days to sift through this crap. In time, they'd find out who the other women were. This is where Dorinne survived three months, she thought, and it made her feel nauseous.

She walked round the back of the property and entered the barn, to where Dan stood over mashed-up bodies. Kelly approached. She looked at the woman first.

'I think that's Patty Flint. Kevin, her son, was in the cellar.' Dan looked confused.

'Have you got a print kit?' she asked.

'Yep.' He went to her car to locate it and saw Kevin sitting in the back, with an officer. The lad didn't catch his eye. He retrieved the finger-printing kit out of a bag in the back and took it to Kelly.

'If this is Wade, it'll take half an hour to ID him from his record. I'll call the coroner.'

Chapter 56

One Hour Earlier

Patty began to revive and Kevin watched as her head lolled over Harry's shoulder. She looked frail and almost dead. The door at the back of the kitchen led to a corridor and a narrow staircase. It smelled bad down there and Kevin's pulse quickened.

When he'd first started to watch Mr Wade, who he only knew then as the stranger, all those months ago, he was attracted to the rough sex and the hint of violence to control the women in his grasp. But now Kevin suspected there was more to it than kinky outdoor thrills. And he was about to find out. He knew those women in the papers had been with him. He knew they disappeared, but still he said nothing. He told no one, not wanting to lose the bond he had with his idol. And now, he was sure that he was about to witness what he really did with them. His palms were sweaty. His mother made choking noises, then her eyes flickered open and caught his gaze.

In that moment he knew that he hated her totally. Even the dampness in her eyes as she tried to manipulate him into getting Harry to let her go. He knew that it was all about saving herself and had never been about loving her son. If he could have reached, and stayed still long enough over Harry's shoulder, he would have beaten her skull to pulp right there. She must have read his thoughts because her sniffling stopped and a look of sheer terror replaced the one of surety that her son would save her.

Harry expertly manoeuvred his mother through the narrow doorway and flicked on a tiny light, which glowed orange in the murk. Kevin heard groans and murmurs and guessed what was coming. He was the man's apprentice now. His position was solidified in trust and camaraderie. He felt himself go hard.

As Harry laid his mother down on the floor, Kevin made out faces and bodies, covered in sweat, writhing. They were begging; though he heard no voices, he could just tell they were by the way they looked at him.

'Kevin, please.' It was his mother's voice. He turned to her. Harry sat beside her, watching them both and kicking the cages occasionally if their residents made a noise. Kevin noticed that Harry's face had changed. He no longer looked like the man in control from the graveyard, but like a maniacal character, almost a puppet. Kevin stared into his eyes but they'd gone blank. He looked around him in horror but at the same time fascination. He wanted to please Harry, his new friend, but he was also repulsed by what he saw. Up until now he'd thought of Harry as some kind of romantic protagonist, the champion of the male kind, dominating women and making them do his bidding. But this was something else.

Suddenly, he couldn't breathe.

'I have to get out.' He didn't recognise his own voice.

'Kevin,' Harry said when Kevin was almost at the door. 'Don't you want to finish her off?' he asked.

Kevin looked at his mother on the floor. Some of the occupants of the cages whimpered.

'Watch,' Harry said. He undid his trousers and straddled Patty, ripping at her skirt; all the while, Kevin stood mesmerised but appalled at the same time. Patty tried to speak but Harry's hands were round her throat in a moment and she began to gurgle. Harry banged her head against the stone floor and kept a grip with one hand as he pulled his trousers fully down and kicked off one leg to free himself to do what he wished to Kevin's mother.

Kevin couldn't move. He was about to witness his mother's rape but he felt nothing. As his eyes grew more and more used to the gloom, he saw more evidence of the real Harry Wade. Kevin had fantasised about him as a charmer, a big brother, a winner of women, a champion – a lover, even? He pushed the thought away shamefully. As his senses came to, he was aware that Harry was now fully penetrating his mother but with his hands firmly round her neck so she couldn't do anything about it, apart from stare blankly as her eyes became engorged.

He watched, spellbound but sickened too. The images before him merged into one: the rotten skin of the women, his mother's eyes, Harry's lust, the orange glow, and the lack of air.

Suddenly he launched at Harry and knocked him off his mother's body with such force that Harry fell back and cracked his head. Kevin picked up his mother, who was light as a doll, and swung her over his shoulder as Harry had done. He left the chamber of horrors behind and took her upstairs, finding a back door leading to a yard. He hurriedly ran into an outbuilding and laid his mother down gently. She tried to cough but it turned into a coughing fit, and she couldn't stop. He heard movement behind him and swung round, still kneeling over his mother.

Harry stood behind him, blood running down his face.

'What do you think you're doing, lad?' he asked. Kevin stood up slowly.

'Not like that. I thought you said I could do it?' Kevin said. Harry smiled.

'I'll hold her for you,' Harry said.

Kevin turned back to his mother and saw the fresh horror dawn on her. She began shaking her head. Kevin realised that his mother actually believed that he'd taken her from the basement to save her.

Harry moved swiftly and held Patty down. She was still struggling for breath but Kevin felt nothing. He sat on her chest and heard the wind being forced out of her lungs. He splayed his hands round her neck and squeezed. It felt good.

He let go all the pain, all the anguish, all the abuse and long years wondering why he was different and so hated and

333

ridiculed. All of that pain was propelled into this moment of perfect revenge.

Yet, it wasn't enough. He wanted to obliterate her. He got off her sweaty body and Harry stared at him.

'Where are you going?' he asked, puzzled.

Kevin had spotted a pitchfork. He went to pick it up. Harry smiled and looked back at Patty, who still had a bit of life in her.

Kevin walked back to them and held the weapon firmly in his hands. Harry looked at Patty and smiled. Patty turned her head to Kevin and closed her eyes.

Kevin raised the fork above his head.

They heard a chopper overhead.

Chapter 57

Ted Wallis was on the scene in half an hour. He'd seen first-hand what Dorinne Callaghan had been subjected to, and now he had the chance to match history to location. Kelly and Dan waited outside the barn for him. The bodies were left untouched. A lone fly buzzed around her head, and Kelly batted it away.

'You looking for a meal?' she said to the tiny insect. It didn't take long for the critters to smell a banquet, even in winter, and all it took was one. But time of death using entomology wouldn't be required on this scene. The bodies were still warm and the blood freely dripping and pooling.

Ted, and Kelly, would be looking for patterns to show how what they'd found on Dorinne matched the conditions and items in the house, or, more specifically, in the cellar.

Ted pulled a coat out of the boot of his car and wrapped it around him. Kelly walked towards him, after explaining to Dan that the coroner happened to be her father. They didn't embrace on the job but they exchanged a look, of familiarity and reluctance at the same time: their bond was forged over death but nurtured elsewhere, and that's where they saved their affection for. This was work.

Ted strode to Dan and shook his hand. They entered the barn. Kelly had already given Dan an idea of how the coroner liked to work and no one spoke. All three put on gloves, masks and shoe covers. When the forensics team arrived, Ted wanted to have the measure of the place, so he could direct the gathering of evidence. It was a complicated and sizeable scene, like the house itself.

'The database came back already and confirmed it's Wade,' Kelly said. Nowadays, the police could upload a fingerprint to their phone and get it checked within half an hour. Harry Wade's print record was classified but the court order she'd obtained gave her clearance, and the prints were matched to Jason Walker. They stood over his body as Ted mumbled to himself.

'I presume that's the offending weapon?' Ted asked, pointing to a pitchfork.

'Reckon so,' Kelly said. 'It's got a fragment of bone on it and judging by the amount of blood… We couldn't find a secondary armament used or one to defend. What do you think?' she asked.

'Judging by the state of his face, I'd say, looking around, it's pretty likely,' Ted said. 'Is that Patty Flint?'

'Yes. I met her only yesterday, with Kevin, at their home in Grasmere.'

'Apart from the obvious trauma to her torso, she's been viciously strangled and her undergarments rearranged. Her eyes are haemorrhaged and the bruises are already beginning to develop.'

Ted referred to Patty's body, which had been cut up pretty badly. Unlike Wade, with his battered face, it was Patty's body that was erased. Dan had wandered over to a disused metal bath and now shouted to them both.

'In here. It's like a scythe. It's covered in blood and other stuff,' he said, with disgust. Ted went to him and peered inside the bath.

'Yes, look, there's a tiny trail of droplets. Mind where you walk, it leads from her body.'

Ted and Kelly looked at one another.

'One smashed face and one smashed body. Two or more weapons. Strangulation,' said Kelly.

'Messy,' said Ted.

Kelly took a call from Eden House. Kate informed her of the discovery of the bodies of Kian Delaney and Mandy Williams. 'Looks like a sex game gone wrong,' Kate said.

'Get me the APNR for the diplomatic plates of Minister Li Qiang and see if he was in the area.' She hung up and turned back to Ted and Dan. Two more needless deaths. She didn't buy the sex game one bit. A shiver ran down her spine: why such callousness? She'd have to open a new case. The hotel where they'd been found was an exclusive boutique place deep in the Lakes, near Keswick. A forensics team had been sent and she'd get around to reading the preliminary report later. It was so senseless.

She looked back at the bodies in the barn. 'I think I need to ask Kevin his version. It wasn't in Wade's MO to kill in rage.'

'What are you thinking?' Dan asked.

'Apart from what a week to start working for me?' she asked. He smiled. 'I think he's been watching Harry Wade do whatever he does to prostitutes in graveyards and finally he got to know him. His hero. Wade was a regular at Marvin's and he would have known the gossip surrounding the family. Maybe he used it to manipulate Kevin. Maybe Patty was the next victim and it all went wrong. What are you up to, Ted?' Kelly asked her father.

He bent over the body of Harry Wade. 'He wears a ring. There's an unusual lesion on Patty's throat, where the bruises are forming, and it matches Harry's ring hand, if she was strangled like this.' He went to Patty and put his hands close to where the bruises were. Sure enough, on the right-hand side, where Harry's ring was, was a thin curved mark. 'It matches Dorinne's.'

'Why do that to her body though?' Dan asked, pointing to the massacre before them.

'It's my job to find out how long it was between when she was strangled and when she was slaughtered, and then see which of them killed her,' Kelly said.

'If it was Wade, then it will scar Kevin for life, seeing that done to his mother. If it was Kevin, given the state of the scene

337

it'll be difficult proving the timeline of who did what to who, beyond reasonable doubt,' Ted said.

'Patty could have killed Wade first,' Kelly said. 'Let's allow forensics to do their job and make sure those women are looked after. Christ, what a week.'

Chapter 58

Ted Wallis watered the newly planted roses, which he'd bought to trail up the back south-facing wall in his garden. They were an array of pinks, yellows and peaches when in bloom. It was a mild February, and daffodils were already starting to poke through on the verges and fields around Keswick. Building work was due to begin on his kitchen extension and conversion next week and it would all be finished by the time his grandchild was born.

He stood up and placed the watering can next to the outdoor tap. He went in and washed his hands. He was due at Kelly's at five o'clock. He'd decided to semi-retire and was training a junior pathologist to take over from him three days a week. She was a talented woman who'd worked in the university hospital in Liverpool. She was fairly abrupt and had reminded him of Kelly when they'd first met. There'd be fireworks there, he thought.

He went to straighten his tie and put on a jacket, checking his hair and spritzing some cologne on his hands and dabbing his face. Once he'd picked up a bouquet of flowers and a bottle of fizz, he'd head over to Pooley Bridge to see Josie's new room.

The trees had begun to bud and some even bore blossom. Snowdrops lined the main road between Keswick and the turn-off to Pooley Bridge. The days were slightly longer and life was emerging in the Lake District. It was Ted's favourite time of year and with Kelly and Johnny's baby on the way, it seemed apt that he drove past a field of lambs running round their mothers.

The radio played tunes from the charts and he fiddled with the dial in an attempt to find something he recognised. The news came on and the first piece was about Harry Wade. No matter which station he listened to, the story wasn't showing any signs of going away any time soon. He listened intently, having as he did a personal stake in the story. There were some bodies that he found difficult to forget: Dorinne Callaghan's was one of them. Her great-aunt was speaking to the presenter. It was a pre-recorded piece and he'd heard it before. Maureen Johnson was telling the interviewer that she had regarded Harry Wade as a friend for many months as she got to know him through Marvin's post office in Grasmere. It gave the story a macabre and disturbing twist that was, sadly, journalistic prime material.

The pain we have experienced as a family is indescribable and I would urge anyone to give Dorinne's mother the privacy she needs. Dorinne was a lovely daughter and no one deserves to die like that. Harry Wade was a monster and he lived among us like one of us. I'll never get over it.

Ted remembered Kelly telling him that Dorinne's mother wouldn't share that rose-tinted version of her daughter, but it was one of those necessities of the grieving process: the deceased is always pleasant. He pondered the plight of the women found in cages inside Harry Wade's cellar. Lucinda recovered fairly quickly after a short stay in hospital. That was, physically; her mental state was another matter entirely. The other women weren't so lucky. They were identified as having gone missing from various locations just outside Cumbria. Wade was clever: he spread them out. The police reckoned he'd begun reoffending as soon as he left prison. Picking them up, or using The Agency and choosing a few non-local women, frustrated the investigation and meant police couldn't link them. All four of them had passed away in hospital, including Lisa Lau, whose body Ted had released for repatriation that week, only to hear that it would be delayed due to an outbreak of a virus in China.

He took a deep breath. They'd never know how many deaths Wade was responsible for on his eight-month rampage. Questions were asked in the House of Commons about the failings that led to his release from prison. Heads rolled.

He'd autopsied the bodies of Mandy Williams and Kian Delaney and ruled death by misadventure. Kelly hadn't been pleased with him but if there had been foul play, he couldn't find it, and science didn't lie. It might be tricked sometimes, but Ted was a medical doctor not a magician. It was one of the most frustrating outcomes of the whole case. Kelly had even tried to go to the FCO with her theories but had been told to back off. Her only other alternative was the media, but that never ended well. She regretfully dropped it. The two youngsters were buried and all but forgotten, but not by Kelly or Ted.

–

Ted emptied his mind of death as he parked outside Kelly's house and he smiled, expectant for the evening ahead. They had more positive things to focus on and their mini-celebration was not only for the conclusion of the case but also for the fact that they had moved in the final piece of furniture from Johnny's before he rented his house to the holiday let business. He gathered the flowers and got out of his car. A cyclist whizzed past him and Ted almost dropped the bottle onto the pavement. He shook his head. His nerves weren't what they used to be. He'd watched the tape from inside the cellar with Kelly and struggled to keep one eye open as the events inside the chamber of horrors unfolded. They now knew that Kevin had saved his mother, and Harry had chased after them, outside.

Kelly opened the door with a broad smile and accepted the flowers. 'Come in!'

Josie sat in the lounge on her phone. Johnny sat on the terrace with a beer. 'Dinner's in the oven,' he shouted.

'Well trained already?' Ted said to Kelly. 'So, it all went well?' He asked Josie about her mock A level exams. 'You're beginning to show, when's your first scan?' he asked Kelly.

'Is that a trick question?' she said. He knew full well that her twelve-week scan was this weekend but what he didn't know was that she felt strangely nervous.

Johnny came inside and Josie went to give Ted a hug. 'I can't wait, I'm going with them,' she said.

'I think we'll see a pair of flip-flops down there, Ted,' Johnny said, referencing his own preference for the footwear and tenderly holding Kelly's belly.

Kelly checked on dinner and went to sit on the terrace, letting Ted and Josie catch up. Ted had helped her with her psychology revision; she was toying with criminal forensics.

Kelly had told her news to her team at work. HQ was preparing her maternity leave.

Occasionally, in the middle of the night, between three and four a.m. when Wendy, her mother, used to say the devil was looking for soldiers, she'd think about Kevin and wonder if she'd be a good mother.

Kelly had interviewed Kevin seventeen times. He would only talk to her. He admitted to killing Harry Wade, in self-defence, he said, to protect his mother. He was looking at a manslaughter sentence. If a judge took pity on him, and what Kelly had unearthed certainly qualified as extenuating circumstances, he could be looking at five years, out in two. What was uncertain, and neither Ted nor extensive forensic analysis had been able to give a definitive answer to, was who killed Patty Flint.

It was a matter of perspective. Like Harry's mother, Patty Flint was a twisted bitch who'd tortured Kevin for nineteen miserable years. Kelly had seen the patches of his skin that had healed and those which had not. Every time he undressed he must be reminded of her and what she did to him. Kelly had written to the CPS explaining the context of the crimes, but no one was interested. Kevin would be sentenced for what he'd done, not for what Kelly thought he might be capable of in the future. That kind of crime wasn't recognised: the type that is inevitable. She'd be keeping a close eye on him, that much was sure.

She felt her belly and asked herself how anyone could harm a child. The question was always answered in the same way: with a resigned acceptance that, as long as she was a police officer, people did fucked-up shit to kids.

She spoke softly to her unborn baby. 'Not you,' she said. 'Not you.'

Acknowledgements

I would like to thank the following people for their continued support of the Kelly Porter series. To my agent, Peter Buckman, for your constant advice, inspiration and commitment. At Canelo: Louise, Fran, Siân and the whole team for your passion and faith in the series, the amazing book covers and your editorial skill.

Thank you to Rob Scahill, our local publican turned shopkeeper, who inspired me with the original photograph on the front cover: an evening stroll cutting through the graveyard at St Mary's motivated me to come up with this entire plotline.

Thanks to Woose Ali for the name (though you're nothing like Yus!)

I'm lucky to have three special people in my life; Mike, Tilly and Freddie, who never fail to encourage and believe.

And, finally, to the fruit bowl, which props me up when I'm flagging.

CANELO CRIME

Do you love crime fiction and are always on the lookout for brilliant authors?

Canelo Crime is home to some of the most exciting novels around. Thousands of readers are already enjoying our compulsive stories. Are you ready to find your new favourite writer?

Find out more and sign up to our newsletter at canelocrime.com

Lost Cause
Rachel Lynch

DI Kelly Porter has solved some of the Lake District's most gruesome murders but nothing has prepared her for the monster she's about to meet. The answers may lie with a local oddball – is he a victim, or a killer?

Lies to Tell
Marion Todd

Since she joined the St Andrews force, DI Clare Mackay has uncovered many secrets lurking in the picturesque Scottish town. When there is a critical security breach inside Police Scotland, she realises she may have put her faith in the wrong person – will it be a deadly mistake?

The Body Under the Bridge
Nick Louth

DCI Craig Gillard has spent his career hunting criminals. When a missing person case reveals itself to be far more than a routine disappearance, it isn't long before the perpetrator has another target: DCI Gillard himself. Suddenly the detective isn't just running the case – he's part of it.

A Front Page Affair
Radha Vastal

Capability 'Kitty' Weeks is determined to prove her worth as a journalist. Headlines about the Great War are splashed across the front pages, but Kitty is stuck writing about society gossip – until a man is murdered on her beat and she is plunged into a story that threatens the life she has always known.

When the Past Kills
M J Lee

The Beast of Manchester was the case that defined DI Thomas Ridpath's career, but the wrong person was convicted and only later was the true culprit put away. Now, those connected to the case are being targeted. Someone is desperate for revenge, and Ridpath risks losing more than he can stand.

Small Mercies
Alex Walters

DI Annie Delamere is off duty and enjoying a walk in the Peak District when she comes across a mutilated corpse. As the body count increases, Annie is under intense pressure to solve the case. But are the crimes the work of a deranged mind – or a cover for something even more chilling?

Home Fires Burn
Lisa Hartley

DS Catherine Bishop is dealing with the aftermath of the most brutal case of her career. Her small team is overwhelmed by an arsonist, and a new murder case provides far more questions than answers. The pieces finally fall into place, but have Catherine's demons already won?

When the Dead Speak
Sheila Bugler

Eastbourne journalist Dee Doran is investigating a woman's disappearance when the body of another is found. There are startling similarities between the dead woman and one who was killed sixty years previously. Dee is determined to uncover the connection, but sometimes the only thing more dangerous than secrets is the truth...